Willard Meachen
66. Walter Road.
Swansea.
27.8.42.

The Doctor and his Patients

THE DOCTOR
AND HIS PATIENTS

by

ARTHUR E. HERTZLER
M.D.

author of

THE HORSE AND BUGGY DOCTOR

LONDON
JOHN LANE THE BODLEY HEAD

First published in England 1941

Printed in Great Britain by
LOWE & BRYDONE PRINTERS LIMITED,
LONDON, N.W.10,
for JOHN LANE THE BODLEY HEAD LIMITED
8 Bury Place, London, W.C.1.

To my daughter Agnes
Who has been my guiding star
In death as in life
Shining with a clear and
yet clearer light.

CONTENTS

PREFACE

This book may well be regarded as a sequel to the eleventh chapter of The Horse and Buggy Doctor published two years ago. I had numerous requests for greater detail than was given in that chapter, things but hinted at in the book, it was complained. I asked one of my correspondents how much she wanted me to tell. The reply I got was: "Tell everything. We will read more than you have the courage to write."

I have not told everything, but not from lack of courage. I would have been delighted to tell much more. I have been guided in part by expediency. We doctors are still fettered by civil and ecclesiastical laws to such a degree that to tell all of the truth at this time would serve no useful purpose. True, we as a profession are almost free to do as science directs us in the saving of human life. Please note I said *"almost,"* because now and then we are halted in our duty by the uplifted hand of those who know less than nothing about our problems but who do have authority. I have pointed out in a timid sort of way when and why we must stand aside and watch our patients die.

But when it comes to the elimination of those things which cause suffering, slow suffering even unto death, we doctors are still seriously handicapped. These are things we meet every day. Astronomers and geologists after a long struggle now follow the great laws of truth unhindered, but biologists, to which group we doctors belong, are still restrained, restrained in thought and deed. The "beliefs" that have drenched the earth with blood countless centuries still dominate the doctor. But the handwriting is on the wall. The same God who wrote the laws of astronomy and of geology also wrote the laws of biology. The moving finger writes and having writ moves on!

Only the public can compel the changes in the laws which will permit us doctors to follow the dictates of our science and our own conscience in the alleviation of human suffering.

B

PREFACE

We doctors have pleaded in vain. Only the people can release us from our fetters. Therefore I have emphasized the influences now at work in society which replace hate with the common fellowship of man. These things must begin in the family. I remember well the hard lot of the child near seventy years ago, and I see the children today. Hate is going out of the world, and I have pointed out as clearly as I dared the influences at work as I have seen them. Of course no prudent doctor would tell it all, now. Indeed I need not be more specific because the mother and her child are painting a picture on the walls of time, which sooner or later must dominate the world. The old doctor may well sit back and complacently say: "Well, you licked us doctors for centuries but forces greater than we have taken up our battles."

In a word, civilization has progressed so far that all now clearly can see the fundamental differences between love and sex, and Christianity and religion. It is only through the universal observance of the fundamental altruistic law of life: "Life of self for the life of others," that civilization will come, if it will come. Love never has killed nor has Christianity, though both have suffered terribly by misrepresentation as sex and salvation. Those who refuse to recognize the avalanche these two united forces have started are hypnotizing themselves to their ultimate inundation.

If I have contributed anything to the clearer understanding of these obvious facts which any doctor may see, I shall feel that my years of labor have not been spent in vain.

It has been said that in the deepest grief there is no weeping. It is equally true that the greatest tragedies of life are expressed without words. I have tried to interpret these speechless tragedies in the language of an old doctor. God does not punish. We punish ourselves by transgressing the laws of biology.

A. E. H.

THE DOCTOR AND HIS PATIENTS

I

The Prelude to Paradise (The Child's Place in Christianity)

NEAR fifty years ago when I was a young doctor I was called to see a very sick child. My patient was a little girl two years and nine months old. As I entered the room she lay on a cot unconscious, just relaxed from a convulsion, a victim of the summer complaint, the dreadful scourge of those early years. The surroundings cried out of poverty. On one side kneeled the young mother; on the other side the grandmother stood. Both were silent, paralyzed by fear. Neither uttered a word as I entered the room. The soft sound of the rapid breathing of the child seemed startlingly loud. Even my unpracticed eyes told me that the end was near.

My attention was at once arrested by the fact that the child clutched in her convulsing left arm a doll. It wasn't much of a doll, just the unskilled handiwork of a loving mother. The head was triangle-shaped, and for eyes shoe buttons had been fastened on. The legs and arms were tubes of cloth stuffed with cotton. It had no clothes. When the grandmother sought to remove the doll, as I pretended to make an examination which I knew was futile, the unconscious child cried out and clutched it tighter. In the final quiver, as the spark of life flickered away, she hugged this doll to her breast.

Had I the gift of the brush I could even today reproduce that scene in all its detail, so deeply did it impress me. That picture has haunted me all of my professional life. What did that mean? What was the germ of the sense of motherhood in that dying child that caused her to clutch that miserable simulacrum of a baby? In all these years I have never seen a child with a doll but what I think of that dying child and that doll. One's heart can cry out, "What does it mean?" and the echo comes back, "What does it mean?" All one can know is that it is an unconscious sense of future motherhood, pure and undefiled. I have tried all my life to trace this beam of light from childhood to old age and I believe it can be traced. Despite the fact that this delicate something has been buffeted about through the ages it today shows forth in a clear and yet clearer light.

I am told that a girl playing with a doll does so just as a matter of imitation. Of course the pioneer mother first got the idea that her little girl needed a doll and proceeded to make one. The child did not say, "Mother, get some rags and make me a doll," but the fact remains that she grasped the significance of the doll when it was presented to her. Clasping it in her arms as she died was not an act of imitation or of instruction. It was something inherent in the child which we cannot explain. Perhaps some children do play with dolls in imitation of other children playing with dolls or of a mother nursing a newer baby. However, that is not the whole story nor the most important point. This child of whom I speak was born and lived out on the prairies, had never seen other children playing with dolls, and she was an only child; therefore there was no chance for imitation. There is here something deeper than mere imitation. Boy babies are not interested in dolls. Instinct, or whatever it may be, does not tell boys that they will some day be directly concerned with babies. Boy babies do sometimes play with dolls, that is, they can be taught to play with dolls, but they take to it with the same enthusiasm that their fathers show for washing dishes. If they do so, it is under duress. I have never yet seen a boy undress a doll and put it to bed. We might as well admit we do not understand the difference between girl and boy babies in their relation to dolls.

We adults are but grown up children. If we ask ourselves what of all things in the world touches us most deeply the answer must be: a child. When does this sentiment begin? It begins when we first see a child, even when we first dream of the child we hope for. When does this sentiment end? The answer is indubitably—with death. We go forth and boldly fight the problems of the world, but no matter how we fare, in old age our minds return to the baby we once

had, now dead, or grown up, or only a memory. This sentiment is the one thing that is coextensive with life itself. It
must seem, therefore, that the child, and what it represents,
parenthood, is the fundamental problem of life in its deepest
sense. It is the common denominator of the whole human
race. True enough, we see in the mammalia a regard for
offspring but, in most instances, it is the mother only that
fights for her young. The male parent is not concerned. He
will fight to protect his female at the breeding season, but
the offspring does not concern him.

Protection of offspring is the one thing that appeals to all
mothers, whatever their belief about other things may be. It
is the only sentiment that conquers all things, even hate and
lust. The child represents parenthood in its noblest aspect,
parenthood based on a spiritual quality only remotely connected with the pagan idea of sex. The ancient history of
both war and religion does not mention children, save in
purely selfish relations. The child in the deepest sense rises
above all religion; it is in itself a symbol of life everlasting.

The general position of the child in the family we must
accept as the gage of civilization. If we are ever to have world
peace we must find a common denominator that appeals to
all classes and all peoples of the world. The child is that
common denominator. Only when we understand collectively
that when our commanders order a charge they are going to
kill some mother's own boy, be he friend or enemy, will
there be universal peace. The failure to recognize this demon-
strates the shallowness of our civilization and shows us that
our concept of Christianity is still overshadowed by greed
and hate. That sentiment exists now in parents' breasts but
as a mass concept it has not yet become vocal because war is
the male's game, or perhaps better said, the game of dominant males, in which sons of other parents are to die. But
the politicians keep this sentiment locked up in the hearts of
the individual boys' parents, particularly of the mothers, by
their unending, skillfully laid propaganda. The result is mass
hysteria. Liars all. It makes me mad when the mothers are
offered pap in the form of a gold star in return for a lost

son. Blare of horns and beating of drums loosen the voices of fools but do not fool the doctor. The gold star heals nothing. The war mother who comes to her doctor dry-eyed and pleading for something to give her sleep has not reached the eye of the world. Only we doctors who have been confronted by these silent mothers can realize the infinite depth of their love or the endurance of their grief. Mothers have only one verdict: He died needlessly! To end wars? To save democracy? She hates those who promulgated those idiotic lies. Second to her in a hatred of war is the doctor.

Just a concrete example. When I was a young doctor the care of a baby boy was entrusted to my all too inexperienced hands by his parents, who were among the best friends I have ever had. The baby grew to be a young man, volunteered to save democracy, and remained in Flanders field, choked to death by the most nefarious invention of man, poison gas. I met his parents many times after. Never a word was uttered by either of us about the loss we all felt. We knew we were thinking of the same thing. That boy was closer to me than any other of the casualties of the war. Why should I also not hate the accursed so-called civilized nations?

Remember that doctors, in time of mass murder, called war, are the only group of men who offer their helping hand to friend and foe alike. During the Civil War, ministers of both North and South frantically thumbed the Bible hunting for evidence to bolster their cause. Always, they pour forth prayers that God may scatter the guts of the opposing soldiers over the landscape. The doctors carefully put those self-same viscera back and sew up the wounds their own fellow citizens have made, and, believe it or not, send out a voiceless prayer—for what is prayer but an intense wish to do the right thing—as all doctors do for their patients, that their efforts may be successful. Which voice do you believe God will hear? Doctors strive to prevent suffering and they hate no man except those who would deliberately increase it. It is this fundamental attitude that makes it possible for doctors to understand the sorrow of mothers bereaved by war. They realize that every soldier who dies of wounds represents not only a doctor's failure but a mother's grief.

The public see companies of stalwart men marching to war, and yell their fool heads off, but the mother sees her son going forth no one knows where nor for what purpose. If we could just get into our heads the fact that our alleged Christian civilization is a mockery, never so eloquently proclaimed as it is today! Selfishness and hate are the spirit of war. After two thousand years of prayers—see where we are at. All Christians, sure. It reminds me of a medical student who was sent to vaccinate a patient against smallpox. He knew the theory of the technic but after he had applied the vaccine he added a touch of his own. He carefully disinfected the little wound with alcohol, applied an aseptic dressing powder and bandaged the arm. Theoretically our civilization is like that. We inoculate ourselves with a little of the spirit of Christ and then promptly destroy it by the age-old greed and hate which lie at the foundations of religion.

If we scan the history of other religions, we see there has been in several instances an attempt to elevate the child to a position something like that held by our child in the manger, but without success. Christian, agnostic or atheist must acknowledge that with the advent of the child in the manger a new era dawned for the human race. It was this concept that caused the child really to become an influence in civilization. "Suffer the little children to come unto me" is the clearest line in all history, yet it has fallen on unhearing ears because the child has been needed to receive the bayonet of some other mother's son. The modern version of the Christ idea is: "Come here, kids, you must eat a lot of spinach so you can grow strong enough to put a bayonet clear through a Heinie, or a J. B. or a poilu." That doesn't look good written out, but acted out it is all right with the world. It is war.

What is the essence of the grief of mothers for sons who never return? It is a thing we call love, in its highest form. It gives me pain to listen to those who maintain that sex gratification is the highest form of love. If so, Christ missed it. "Bring on the kids;" nothing said about "Bring on a few concubines." "Suffer the children to come to me" has fallen on unhearing ears because we have been trying for twenty

centuries to make it fit in with our pagan sense of sex which
is, in its exercise, nothing more beautiful than greed led by
plain lust. Selfishness, sex, lust, murder, when exercised in
mass, have written the history of the human race up to date.
Children do not fit in with any of those things.

Yet throughout all the centuries the nations of earth have
fought each other because some one "believed" this or that
and children were raised, as they are even today, to be a sacrifice on the altar of our unending beliefs. It would be far
more consistent to admit that we believe that might makes
right. Belief has nothing to do with truth. Somebody has
something we want: greed. To have war, hate must be developed to a degree which will cause a people to give the lives
of their sons for the acquisition of the thing desired by those
safe at home. It would be far more consistent if alleged civilized nations, instead of calling to Christ for the brotherhood
of man, would be frank and say: "To hell with Christ, let's
fight it out, and get what we want—that Christ idea can wait
until then." It would have the merit of truth, and truth is
sometimes the forerunner of enlightenment.

Where was the child during all those years, all the years to
date, in fact? Of course now war has become our international
poker game, frankly played for gain rather than hate, but
in order to secure the necessary cannon fodder it is necessary
to excite hate in the common herd, euphoniously called by
us "The great American peepul." It is no doubt the sign of
advancing civilization that the leaders now know they are
betraying their trust. The old warriors did not trouble to lie
about their motives. Even that represents some advancement.
"He kept us out of war"—even Kansans believed that once.

Just how stupid our leaders are is obvious at the present
time. Now they are tearing out their hair in a frenzy to vote
money to build armaments. During the past few years politicians have been hard put to find ways of spending money in
order to employ men. They languidly built overpasses over
cowpaths. Even an old doctor could see that the pot was
boiling in Europe during the past twenty years. Why did

they not build armaments then in anticipation of what must certainly come? Will little Johnnie in the front seat please answer?

Only when we fully recognize how unreliable are the men who chart our course do we realize how far we are from a solid foundation of amity and peace. Only if or when we realize that he who died on the cross came to replace hate, will we be able to understand that our child was sent to save the world, to save the world through love. Love doesn't fight. How dumb we are is evidenced by the fact that while we pretend to be Christian we yet repudiate all the teachings of Christ. Our civilization is still utterly unchristian in fact, at least after propaganda has made us mad. We do not allow it to interfere with what we want to do.

Millions of people the world over, particularly mothers, are running around in circles praying for peace. Prayers did not control diphtheria and they will be just as futile in controlling war. These things must be rooted out at their source. The courageous use of what little brains God gave us would solve the problem. The problem of child murder, called war, must be approached in the same spirit with which the doctor attacks the control of a disease. It must be clear, of course, that when a doctor attacks a disease problem he is without hate. He deals only with facts, facts which are the great unchanging laws of nature. These he must shape for the benefit of the human race. He asks no selfish reward.

Everybody must admit we doctors are pretty smart. After two thousand years of wailing we got busy and studied the laws of nature and did something, such as finding a remedy for diphtheria. Compare this with the recent events of history. The civilized world wailed that war must be prevented. The idea did not work to any noticeable extent. War came. The logical thing to do is obviously to wail louder; at least that is the remedy now being tried. To date that plan hasn't worked and it will not work until one side or the other gets thoroughly licked, which will, as usual, not decide anything, except of course that one side was overwhelmed by the might of the other. Hate will remain.

The only thing that will change this is a mass appreciation that whenever there is a casualty some one's son has died. And only when the world at large comes to regard war as doctors do disease—diphtheria, for instance—will it realize that after all both have much the same result: the death of our children. The child is no longer menaced by diphtheria, but war still threatens him. We already know the causes of war, but we cannot so far forget our own selfishness as to apply the remedy.

Moments of excitement—they need not be attended by bloodshed—may cause us to forget the child. Let me relate an instance. A great revival was gripping the village. So fervent were the labors of one man and wife that they failed to note that a child of their own, aged four, was seriously sick with a chest full of pus. They had been so busy praying that the souls of the crooks and drunkards of the neighborhood be "saved" that they overlooked the serious state of their own child. When they noted his impending death they forgot all about the future life, not only of the drunks but also of their child. When they saw how seriously ill he was they prayed that his life might be spared, but they were deaf to my pleadings that I be allowed to drain the chest. Nothing was said about his soul. That puzzled me. Despite the prayers of the parents, now directed toward the child, he died. As the last quiver of life passed over him the mother extended her arms and cried: "Oh God, put life back into my boy!" As a doctor at the bedside I have often marvelled at this fact: it is life the parents want preserved. At such times this transcends the idea of salvation in their minds. Did any one ever see a parent at the bedside of a dying child who would not sacrifice his own soul to save the life of his child? Subconsciously they then realize that the most eloquent prayer is a parent's effort to do the best by his children. There is a vast difference between the point of view one gets at the bedside and at the revival meeting: sense rules one, the emotions the other.

Many years later, when this mother saw a neighbor's boy recovering after an operation such as her boy had needed, she said to me: "I have wished so many times we had allowed you to operate on our boy. We forgot God sends you doctors as well as the preachers." No one can fail to wonder what it is that cries out when a parent envisages a child lying in his grave. All is there but life, life—what is it and where has it gone? That is one situation where parents and doctors are engaged with the same thoughts, and they have the same thoughts when they see a dead soldier.

As a young doctor I was often puzzled when the minister at the funeral of a child intoned that the child was better off with its maker. No parents ever fell in with this idea. "Doctor, save our baby" is the cry of the parents. Parents do not want their children to go where the minister says they will be better off. Let the reader figure out the meaning for himself. I gave it up decades ago, but there is something wrong somewhere.

Envisaging such scenes, one wonders why the development of the human race has been so slow and has made such a sordid history. (I need not go into details. Suffice it to say that much has been written about the relation of sex and religion—all terrible, too terrible to mention. We cannot ignore the fact that religious persecutions have been the most cruel and atrocious in history. While war killed, religious frenzy tortured. The only thing comparable to religious hate is frustrated sex. If a cow flashes a bull the willing sign he at once becomes frenzied and defies all restraint, and for a brief moment becomes as cruel as the old makers of history. When sex becomes lust, hate is its handmaiden. To kill is not enough; tortures as extreme as human ingenuity can invent alone satisfy. Not nice history to read but it is being made according to the good old formula. But this is the significant thing: religious persecutions have gone out. This shows that the human race is giving ear to the child in the manger. Greed and hate are the things that need to be subdued.)

Faith and belief have been written large in the history of the race. Faith, like love, is made to cover a multitude of things. Faith in its noblest state may be the expression of the highest sentiment but when expressive only of belief it has often been the handmaiden of hate. One cannot will to believe; he can only say he believes and history teaches that he automatically hates those who believe otherwise. Galileo had *faith* in his interpretation of the laws of nature; those who *believed* the world was flat persecuted him. Though he had to recant on his knees to escape the wheel, when he got up he murmured to himself, "But the world does move."

Let us keep clearly in mind that Christ welcomed children. Countless millions of children have lived since then who have never seen a welcoming smile. Even in my childhood, many grew up without knowing the meaning of a parental caress. Many so live today. I see children all about me who are starved physically, starved spiritually, because parents are dumb and society is too busy saving its soul—in response to some belief fostered by religion—to give heed. It is because those who formulated the creeds that Christians were asked to believe were not through living the lustful ages of the past. Confusion arose because there was no distinction between the religion taught and paganism. Religion as taught bore no relation to the Christ idea; today we have the curious hybrid called Christian religion. After twenty centuries of prayer some children are just beginning to receive their birthright, a right to see what Christ taught. They are just pushing their way through the mist of religion.

Yet even in the early days there was the same tender concern at the bedside of a dying child that is illustrated today by the case previously mentioned. That meant there was something in the human heart far nobler than the teachings of the times. The common people are morally superior to their leaders. They desire only peace and their children. Let me repeat what I have said before. Nobody, so far as my experience goes, ever dragged the "inspired" teachings of the past to the bedside of the dying child. There all people think alike, although at other times they are divided by this and that. I can gather but one fundamental fact from it: the dying child goes back to the Child in the Manger, an all pervading concept. Religion, on the other hand, is some one's opinion. The greatest mistake, I believe, is to confuse the two. Christianity and religion just do not mix.

Often, as a young doctor, I felt a desire to kick parents in the face for wailing to the doctor, and to an unhearing God, to rescue a dying child which had been neglected. Perhaps the patient was one of a brood of ill nourished, substandard children. One child had had to leave the mother's breast to make room for the next. It was God's will that the mother produce as many children as possible. That was religion, some one's opinion, and I know enough history to know who first got that idea. It is just as sacred as the AAA. I have lived it all, as child and many times as a doctor beating the weary country roads. When death came this sordid picture gave way to something else. Perhaps there was a little memento carefully treasured. The mother might show it to her doctor when she would not dare to show it to any one else, even the child's father. I have heard ministers berate mothers for this act of mourning as a willful flying in the face of God. That was religion pursuing the woman even to the grave of her child where of all places the Christ idea should prevail. The doctor was the one person in the world who would understand. In all my professional experience I look upon nothing with greater satisfaction than those confidences reposed in me by grieving mothers.

I cannot recall without emotion the time a mother showed me a small soiled shoe and said simply: "If I only had not had to bear more children than I could care for this might not have happened." Weaned too soon, to make room for the next. Summer complaint was the answer. That was the Christ idea in the mother's heart, crying out against the religious teachings of the time. That was more than forty years ago and I did not recognize its meaning but I did instinctively feel that it was a voice in the wilderness.

Certainly there was a crying in the wilderness, though unrecorded in history, which said plainly: "Sisters, we must unite and subdue these whiskers about us for the rights of our babies." But the mother feared she would be reprimanded by her ecclesiastic advisor for flying in the face of God if she gave expression to her belief that there was something wrong about the teaching that she must bear all the children possible. God willed that the child should die? She knew better. She believed in her doctor. Why is it that, when preachers want to explain something, they say: "God willed it." That sounds to me like the wife who shoots her husband in the back because she loves him so. If any one will take the trouble to read history he may be surprised to find how nearly the two situations are alike—saving the face to excuse an act of hate.

I am glad that I have been privileged to live the life of a doctor close to his people. I can look at facts as I see them. I know grief in all its forms. Grief points upwards always to the cross, a symbol of that fact. Here I believe one can get a clearer notion of the difference between religion and Christianity than in any other way.

Twenty centuries failed to cure diphtheria, but science did. Why? Doctors did not want to see the children die. Here is the foundation of civilization—using one's brains for the common good of mankind. The world is sick. Is there not some common cause for its sickness which, if identified, might yield to a common remedy? What is wrong with the world is that it is motivated by hate, and back of hate, lie sex, lust, greed. Back of all these religion has shown its hand at some time both before Christ and after.

The right of the child to be well born and to be loved is ignored. "Let the little children come unto me" means that no more are to be born than can be well born and well cared for. Excess population is the result of ignoring children's rights. Excess breeding is the response to religion and ignores the very foundation of Christianity. When man was deprived of his concubines—yes, deprived of his concubines—some excuse had to be invented. Sounds ugly. Hate, sex, lust, greed—only the child, common to all races and nations, negates all these things, once it gains its true place. Is it not possible that the child is to be to civilization what the Klebs-Loeffler bacillus is to diphtheria?

The first impressions of childhood have a way of lingering throughout life. As a child, aged nine, I saw the first ray of light though I did not know it. Most of my playmates were children of Catholic parents. I used to go with them to church. At one side was a lady holding a child in her arms. No one told me whom it represented yet something was awakened within me, a sense of worship, while the rest of the proceedings produced only awe, as I remember it now. If anyone was ever really inspired, I vote for the person who first thought of presenting an image of a woman holding a baby in her arms in a house of worship. I have tried to picture it as allegorical but it is something more than that.

The image of the virgin and child was forbidden by our church. To worship it was to worship a man-made image, to break a commandment. To me it has never been so, any more than to adore the image of a living mother and child. Does a photograph or painting really differ in principle from a marble bust? What the race needs more than anything else, I believe, is to be able to look at such scenes, scenes which excite love without thought of sex. My room is lined with pictures of children, and all of them awaken in me the noblest sentiments of which I am capable.

After I entered professional life I came to see madonnas and their children in real life. The real far surpassed in magnificence the best efforts of the great painters and sculptors of all time. One could make the real child smile, but not the painting or marble image.

To see patients going about the clinic—mother and son, father and daughter—the expressions on their faces indicating a joyous perambulation among the clouds, is an unending fascination to me. This relationship is subconscious. Tell a father that he has greater affection for his daughter than for his son, and he will strenuously deny it, and he would be right so far as conscious feeling is concerned. The same thing applies of course to the mother and her son. Here is something that is really inspired. Here lies the force that may some time bring peace among men. It is not sex, that much is sure. It is nameless, and so delicate a thing that only by a careful study of it will one be convinced of its presence.

Although this relationship between mother and son, father and daughter, is unexplainable, when death takes a child it

C

stands out most prominently. Nobody tells you about it. You must through personal contact learn to feel the differences in degrees of grief. If one could just fathom the meaning of this relationship one could write a new philosophy. Every bereaved parent knows this is true. If one overlooks it he is missing the finest thing in life. Against this all pervading feeling the voice of religion cries in vain. It emanates from the manger and shows how sex may be completely submerged by love.

In order to understand a hoped for civilization we must have a new vocabulary. A fine civilization we have when the same word must cover the gentle affection of a child for his parents and the "rights" our marriage ceremony implies; when one word includes everything from the mother's look at a nursing child to the wailing of the tomcat on the alley fence. The word is love, but the use of that term seems a desecration when it is also used to cover the more sordid things of life.

We need, perhaps, first of all to develop a vocabulary which will put the facts in a new light. Yet words without understanding go for naught. If understanding comes, words will come. Perhaps we may think of the love of a child as a spiritual love. Let them have the unqualified term "love" as a synonym of the aberrant psychology that leads to the marriage altar. After that sex has charge and it would serve clarity to call that sex love.

Every child wants love and appeals for it in his smile at an age when the sounds he makes are not yet understandable as words. The first "dada" he utters is the most eloquent speech ever made. It says, "Do you know where I came from? To you a personal Christ is born."

The love of a child is enduring yet one dare not trifle with that love too long. Often parents wake·up to the fact that they have been neglectful so long that the love of their child has gone elsewhere. This is emphasized in old age when they realize that the proffered love has long been withdrawn and that they are alone. From the dawn of memory I can recall with bitterness how the religious teachings prevented manifestations of love between parent and child. When parents see the sunset they throw away religion and cry out to their children and the children hear. Where does that still small voice come from if not from the cross? You cannot fool an old doctor who has seen that picture many times.

The old scenes have changed. We are in danger nowadays of making an equally grievous error. A child's affection is something that cannot be "farmed out." A child's love, it seems, can stand abuse, even neglect, but it cannot be ignored, at least not indefinitely. It may not show a fissure for years, even decades, but a fissure will come as sure as death itself. I believe it can be said in the end that a parent gets all he deserves, usually more. Let me see the deathbed scene of an aged person with his children about him and I can write the story of the measure of love he has bestowed on them in their childhood.

There is only one way to stay with our children—and that is to stay with them. They accept companionship of their parents if it is never refused. If we would just never forget for a single moment the message the newborn babe brings us.

Though this chapter has to do chiefly with an attempt to find the place of the child in the picture of Christianity there are some other pictures also that lead us to a new vision. Though they will be subjects of discussion in future chapters I might mention here the two groups of people who fit into the general scheme of lustless love. I have in mind the unmarried women and the aged.

The first class, the unmarried women, divide themselves into two groups. There are those who at an early age enter, voluntarily, some sisterhood with the purpose of devoting themselves to a cause. These not only excite our admiration but our profound veneration. But they are beyond the realm of the doctor.

The second group are not attached to any unending obligation, yet devote their lives unselfishly to a cause or a person. These come under the ken of the doctor sometimes as patients but more often as we come into contact with the objects of their devotion. They give their lives, decades upon decades, to the care of some ailing relative, or perhaps they live vicariously caring for children left dependent through some disaster. In all the world there is no example of unselfish devotion equal to this. To say that they bear a cross is hardly a figure of speech.

The end of life also may show a beautiful picture. It is the old couple who have lived through the tumultuous period when sex was dominant, and who finally settle down with a quiet more enduring love. The beautiful part of life remains when or after sex has flown. Nothing shows more clearly than these scenes that there is something more lofty than sex, something that cries out before sex is born and lives again after the endocrines have undergone their final atrophy. Nothing could be clearer than this. If one has an unknown something and is able to remove something and have something left, there must have been two things to begin with.

We have these examples of life at its noblest: the child with its infinite affection, the single person ignoring sex in order to perform a noble purpose, and the aged who cling to each other after the stress and strain of life has ended. In these things we must seek the basis of a Christian civilization.

Leave me a picture of the mother and her child, a picture without lust, one which reveals the humanizing effect of suffering and of love, and I can construct for myself a real Christian civilization. As far as I am concerned, the ecclesiastics may wipe off the map everything they have contributed to history. What have they to show for twenty centuries of tenure in the faith of the world? True, hate is rapidly decreasing, but that is the result of the closer relationship of mother and child, not primarily the teaching of the ecclesiastics. I believe it is of fundamental importance to study love in its uncomplicated form, as we see it in the child, and in some adults devoted to an unselfish cause. Only by so doing can we understand that love and sex are fundamentally separate phenomena though they must needs, for the perpetuation of the race, become fused. Such a study helps to distinguish between Christianity and religion. A person may have a religion and still be a Christian. Also a Christian may have a religion provided the religion is not allowed to harbor an expression of hate. Herein lies the difficulty of our civilization. Religionists have persecuted each other because of variations in belief and have done so in the name of Christ. The most hopeful sign of the times lies in the fact that the hate between the various denominations is largely a thing of the past. The demand of a Christian civilization is that they cease to hold the curtain of creed between themselves and the love of their fellow man. When this is achieved the human race will be united in a spiritual sense and selfish conflicts will be no more.

II

Paradise Illustrated (The Child in the Home)

FEBRUARY 10, 1895, a girl was born. Wondering blue eyes, which in after years turned black, and a wonderful mop of black hair supplied the landscape. Even the little pug nose was wonderful. Kansas was putting on a blizzard that night. The only means of heating the poorly built house was a coal stove. The little mite was restless until her soft nose found a position in my left ear. Here, she seemed to say, is a comfortable position. Then she lay quietly breathing throughout the night. I sat sleepless, transfixed, immovable, fearing to break the quiet spell. She was named Agnes after the lovable character in David Copperfield; the selection was prophetic for she grew into a sympathetic, kind, understanding girl with unquenchable fire, unfailing love, surpassing understanding. Holding that baby I had no doubt that a new world was born for me that night, and my racing mind tried in vain throughout the night to fathom it. That mysterious something is still a mystery. Nearing morning she changed the scene with the very mundane cry, "Breakfast!" Then I realized that she was a human being.

Only personal experience can tell one how completely a mite of a human being can take hold of him and change his whole outlook of life and give him an unending desire to shape his whole universe about that little child. There are no words which will express the relationship, and no one would write them if he could.

From that night to the present I have been thinking about what a child means to a parent. As a doctor I have had constantly in mind how greatly we could lessen its suffering if we could write a chart for its entire life. It is fairly easy to picture the life of the child in the abstract as a basic factor in civilization, as I attempted to do in the previous chapter. But when we get down to concrete cases the problem is more difficult, because each child presents a different problem. We are still too confused and hesitant to deal surely with his spiritual welfare. What to do, how to conduct ourselves in order that each child may achieve its highest place in life, is a problem no one, I dare say, has ever solved to his complete satisfaction. Mixtures of orneriness and love in the child (we can never be sure which is which) in ever varying proportion, keep the parents mystified.

Late in life when a parent reviews the years he remembers incidents which give him pain. What we regarded at the time as meanness on the part of the child becomes in after years obviously only temper on our part. If one could but live those moments over again, fortified with the knowledge of a lifetime, one feels he could have done better. For instance, once one of my little daughters was suddenly seized with a desire to take a razor to school. Horrified, naturally, I took the implement from her. It hurt her feelings. I have thought a thousand times that if I could only go back and explain to her that such an implement might inflict damage I could send her away happy. If we would stop and criticize ourselves before we start on our child much pain would be spared the child at the time and ourselves in retrospect. In after years she used to recall the incident with a merry laugh, speculate on why she was suddenly seized with such a desire. It apparently left no scar on her but it did on me. Her fleeting hurt look at the criticism remains with me still.

Such speculations are as futile as a surgeon's review of a case which has turned out disastrously. In agony of spirit he wishes he had done something differently, or had done nothing at all. He cannot recall the past and if he could there is no assurance that any other procedure would have been followed by a more favorable result. Yet such tense reviews make for better surgeons. And perhaps living over again the lifetime of our children might convince us that a more heart-searching inquiry would lead to a more careful study of the relation of child and parent.

It is evident that society, which one cannot control, is still woefully indifferent to the welfare of children: it lacks a sense of personal responsibility. The pains children suffer are poignant things but they are generally ignored. We are too indifferent; they are but children, we say. We do not try hard enough because our interest in them is not intense enough to make us give the situation our best efforts. This brings to mind an occasion when I was engaged in some studies that just would not come out right although the premise seemed to be sound. "Stick to it. He who has not shed tears over his work does not know what it is to try" was Professor Virchow's admonition. Though unhappily even such intense effort does not insure success, if we shed tears of intense desire we might learn to understand what it is a child is trying to say to us.

When the scientist is confronted by a problem he tries first of all to separate it as much as possible into its various elements, the combination of which constitutes the subject to be analyzed. We may perhaps understand children better if we look at various phases of their lives as separate phenomena.

After babyhood and the purely protoplasm stage of eat and squall is past, we find many factors which we do not recognize when we look at them as a continuous process. These changes may be divided into, first, the physical or *biological*. Under this heading may be considered the natural relationship between parent and child: the young animal must be fed and kept from physical injury. It grows up in the same pen with older ones and shares the general environment. The influences surrounding the child vary as greatly as the character of the parents because the parents furnish nearly all its contacts.

Next are the *environmental* influences on the child. While in the early years the parents can and do create the atmosphere in which the child lives, later the child when away from home becomes a part of the community and the parent exerts his influence only as a part of the community. The influence surrounding the child when away from home may be better or worse than it is at home. It depends on the home.

Then finally there is the *spiritual*, or whatever one wishes

to call the intangible influences that surround us all but do
not admit of definite comprehension. Parents may or may not
feel that something when the child is well. Full understanding comes when the child is seriously sick or dies. That
something should be appreciated by the parents before the
dark hour comes.

Even this simple classification leaves in each group many
inexplicable factors which are as mysterious as the forces of
gravitation, the laws of chemical attraction, or the nature of
electricity. All are factors which we recognize in a general
way but do not understand. They are just names we use to
indicate forces we perceive but do not comprehend. So why
should any one, even a trained scientist, hesitate to use the
word "spiritual" when he is confronted by the greatest mystery of all?

No one sees the influence of the home on the very young
child as does the family doctor. We may conveniently think of
childhood as made up of two periods: the first six years,
when there is little contact outside of the home except when
in company with the parents, and a second period extending
from the beginning of school to the time of puberty.

I regard as the chief reward for a long, hard experience in
the practice of medicine the opportunity it has given me to
see so many children developing in an endless variety of
environments. I find an unending fascination in watching
the children who visit the clinic, not as patients but merely
as visitors who have come along with their parents, the
patients. After one reaches a certain age he no longer is afraid
to act silly in the presence of a child. Even a very small child,
thought to be sensible only to hunger or pain, will reward a
request for a smile. Any youngster, three, four or eight, will
accept a proffered candidate as a spare grandpa. Even young
ladies showing the first widening line of the hips regard his
antics with toleration, and accord him the respect which cul-
tured ladies give the aging. One can study them thus from a
somewhat impersonal point of view. As I recall the love
unfailingly proffered by every child, not suppressed by cru-
elty, I am convinced that we have overlooked our chief oppor-

tunity of life. No one, I am sure, not even a mother, has sounded the depth of a child's infinite capacity for love.

How often do we view each child and its problems with doubt, uncertainty, even indifference, as a part of a parade? One gets the impression that many parents look on their children in a very impersonal way, parents who pursue their own pleasures and regard the child as a poor relation who has thrust himself into their home. Yet the child's whole future is in their hands in those early years. Much could be done if parents had the vision or took the time to understand these young teachers. Children use the Platonic system in teaching their parents: they ask them questions. For instance one of my little folks asked if God made mosquitoes, and receiving a positive answer, asked: "Well, why did he?" To neglect to answer questions leaves an unfavorable impression. To ignore them is a mistake even though one knows that he will hardly make a passing grade.

Though child abuse has lessened greatly in the last half century it is still today by no means rare. Even before memory for specific events develops the impression of neglect remains with the child. Constant abuse makes a normally loving child an apprehensive wild animal ready to avoid a slap. I have had as patients a few first class bandits who were startled at every sound. Even after they had paid their debt to society that apprehension remained. I have seen a young child who has been abused start with apprehension at every move and every sound, afraid it was going to be whipped. Those who have had to do with children's homes still see such instances. I once spent a year teaching a little boy to smile. If parents so whip a child that the marks last long enough for the prosecuting attorney to see them the public learns of it. Such indiscretions may lead to a fine or even a jail sentence. The law tells the parents in effect to be more careful in beating up their children so as not to annoy the neighbors. And that is as far as the law goes.

The welfare of the child does not come within the arm of the law. Starve it. Abuse it as you like, and it will be all right in the eye of the civil and ecclesiastic law. It is but an expression of the right of dominance of the parent over the child. Parents who ignore the welfare of the children should by such acts forfeit the right of the child from then on. Society should see to it that they produce no more children.

Even though a child is not subjected to physical punishment it recoils in horror at a combat between the parents. The child is the adhesive the fates sent to hold the parents together and subconsciously it feels that it has failed. It vainly tries to cling to both parents. Who gets a new hat or who goes fishing are simple things in the parents' minds but to the child the disagreement indicates a fissure. More pronounced differences make deeper impressions, yet the parents look with indifference on the influence of their quarrels on the child. Only after love for the child has come to transcend all of the passions of the parents can we hope to see a new society. There is everywhere evidence of a new awakening but it is an individual thing. The public as a whole is not concerned in the child beyond the threshold or even the front gate.

Of course when the public hears that children were penned up at home while the parents were out enjoying themselves and that the house burned, together with the children, it is properly shocked. We do not stop to think that perhaps when we go away, gaily leaving children in what we believe to be competent care, we may be committing the same negligence though it be only in a spiritual sense. The parents have taken their sense of love out for an airing while the child at home is burned up for lack of understanding care. Who in his declining years does not wonder why he was so blind as to leave the children alone for even a single moment? It is this memory which causes grandparents to spoil the grandchildren. Conversely of course undue restriction of liberty, no matter how well intended, may bring about a reaction against all restraint. Reward comes from good judgment; good intentions lead but to regrets.

Like most trite sayings, the statement that a child's character is formed in the first six years of its life is true—but to only a limited extent. There remains much to be done in the years to come. In those first years memory is just budding and concrete things are in a measure blotted out. The problem is complicated by the fact that the environment which surrounds the child during the first six years usually continues after that time. It is still influenced by the love or the personal selfishness of the parent. In the early years the child is always at hand but once it becomes a part of the community the parent to some extent must run along with the child, or lose it.

Even if we, as parents, are wholly unselfish, if one can imagine such a state, many things happen in the second six years, despite our best efforts, that we may wish our children might forget. Shall we teach them things that are not true, which they will most certainly find out are not true, but which we hope they will remember as beautiful? Or, if we do, will they recall them and reflect on how we lied to them? It depends on the child and on how such things were presented. I do not agree with those who believe that a child should not be told fairy tales until they are old enough to understand that they are fairy tales. If the child understands that they are but fairy tales, they cease to be fairy tales. The story of Santa Claus is of course our most beautiful fairy tale. I have never known a child resentful in after years of being told this tale, because in spirit it is not a fairy tale. I recall with great glee that a young miss once confided to me that she knew there was no Santa Claus—"but don't tell mother" was the admonition. She was engaged in writing down a list of her needs which was of course really intended for home consumption.

One has often heard it said that the boy is father to the man. Obviously what is meant is that, despite all that can be done to prevent it, some time in the future the boy will sit in judgment on the things that were done to him when he was a child. I can still remember some of the things I had in mind as a child to do to some of my elders after I achieved my maturity. Of course intellectually, at least in a measure, I have grown up with the times but that still small voice still lingers. I still remember the shape of the noses I had a desire to flatten. This is mentioned only to show the permanency of childish impressions.

I hasten to say here that my father was some centuries ahead of his time and I never experienced the literal interpretation of the biblical admonitions. Yet he was orthodox, and in that day no one ever disputed the word spewed out by those who had been "called." But I know now it did prevent him from showing the affection he otherwise would have shown. Only much later, when as a young doctor it fell to me to lessen his suffering during his last days, did he reveal the depths of his love. That old teaching was all a mistake, he declared; the only thing that matters on one's deathbed are one's children. Fortunately there had always been a bond of understanding between us that no theologians could dim. I had learned in my childhood to shun the men who gave voice to those pious sentiments; it is an aversion I have never fully conquered. Nothing in my experience shows more clearly how little our intellect can do in our maturity to blot out the impressions received in childhood.

As I have observed the child in the home in the past fifty years, two paralleled factors have impressed me. As the ecclesiastic authority lessened, the status of the child improved; or perhaps it was the other way around. Which is cause, which effect, is none of my business. I have only to record my observations. Every one realizes that our theology is having trouble to keep up with the advance of civilization. Most ministers realize it and are doing their best to keep pace.

That the girl is the mother of the woman should have been equally obvious long ago. However, no one thought of that in the old days because as a woman she had little part in directing the course of events, or perhaps better said, of beliefs. Woman was generally regarded as synonymous with female; it was her job to produce the future generation. Nevertheless it is the woman's rise to a position of influence in the world which is the primary cause of the child's emergence from the darkness of simple servitude to the light of recognition as the parent of the future. Some wise person said years ago that the hand that rocks the cradle will rule the world, or something to that effect. That noble sentiment was uttered far ahead of its time. Most likely the person who first made the observation had little idea of the importance of the truth he had enunciated. However, it has come to pass, and she now rocks many other things besides the cradle. It is futile for any housebroke man to attempt further elucidation. Of course, woman held a much higher position in Greek civilization than during the twenty centuries following it. There is one occurrence in ancient history that I cannot think of without amusement. It was a custom of the time of Alexander the Great to honor particularly eminent persons by declaring that they had been immaculately conceived. In harmony with this, Alexander himself was said to have been sired by Jupiter. Alexander's mother protested; she said she feared that such an idea might get her in bad with Mrs. Jupiter. This is the first instance I can find in history where a woman called the hand of the wise men.

I have searched history in vain to find out just why and how woman achieved the place she occupies today; how she escaped from a state of male dominance. Oh sure, we men gave her the ballot, but we did it for the same reason that we do a great many other things, such as buying a new car. I have a suspicion that some baby got to working on papa's sympathies and he came, unconsciously of course, to think that mama was pretty nice and had some brains.

Then of course there is the Sampson story. Perhaps male dominance went out with the beard. Just how women brought about the regular use of the scissors and the Gillette the books do not say. If, before she was married, the girl ever got close enough to the object of her affections to complain that his whiskers tickled her face he might have been induced to remove them. The mental processes of Delilah previous to the shearing of Sampson are withheld from us. At any rate postnuptial pleadings never brought about any such submission. These are purely speculative ideas we doctors sometimes engage in when we are confronted by a nebulous situation and yet must act as if we know. Even now this much may be said: that in many families in which papa wears whiskers there is still male dominance in the family.

Yet somehow mothers began to rebel against the situation when they came to realize that there was a limit to their capacity to produce, and a like limit to the range of their moral influence in the guidance of the children. It was my privilege in my boyhood to live for four years in a Congregational neighborhood in which the children were given their rights much as they are today. Why there was this difference was a mystery to me. It is the old problem of which came first, the hen or the egg, the form of religion or the exalted place of the child in the home. Why these changes came about, why the pattern has spread, no prudent person would attempt to tell, even if he knew. Of course we doctors would like to take the credit but the truth is, these influences were operative in the days of my childhood when infectious diseases still were rampant and the science of medicine had not yet become operative.

But I may say with due modesty that doctors played a large part in helping mothers to bring about these changes. Speaking in general terms, in those years a mother could figure that she would not be able to raise all of the children she bore. If she decided she wanted to raise six, she would need to bear ten. Of course she never did so calculate because her wishes, if she formulated them, were ignored by the forces that dominated her physically and spiritually, or rather, theologically. It was her job to bear as many as possible; how many of them she could rear gave anyone little concern. I have figured out that the reason the tomcat was given so few brains is because a greater intelligence would curb his potency. What he lacks in intelligence he makes up in voice. A tomcat is not a figure of speech, he is a prototype. One must say for him that he is frank and asks for no crown of glory. I regard this as a very brilliant observation.

Things have changed, however, and papa has risen to a plane above the level of the feline. The realization of the importance of bearing fewer children in order that they may be better cared for I regard as one of the major spiritual

achievements of the race, comparable in importance to the
invention of the wheel in industry. Woman had to work out
this problem in spite of opposition and she still labors under
the handicap of tradition. Men always have been and still are
woman's greatest enemy. We are, I hope, beginning to exhibit
our capacity for education.

Perhaps the most important factor in bringing this about
is that parents have discovered that the child, in order to
achieve its highest estate, must be wanted. Young people
have learned what causes children and are no longer surprised at their arrival. In fact, many even send the unborn
child an invitation, written in a language that knows no
words. It is interesting to note the changes this has brought
with it. Because it is wanted, the child's welfare is considered
before it is born. Matters of diet, rest, exercise and mental
tranquillity on the part of the prospective mother are considered. Mothers go to their family doctors to inquire about
these matters. Many inform themselves by reading some of
the numerous books written for the purpose of enlightening
them. The interchange of ideas between the woman and her
doctor as to the reception to be accorded the newcomer
reacts to the advantage of both mother and child. In the
larger centers there are special clinics maintained for the
purpose of meeting the needs of those too poor to employ
private doctors. It is sad to note that those who produce the
most children often do not avail themselves of these sources
of information. They are guided by other considerations
than the need of the unborn child. Doctors get funny ideas.
I have often wondered why there was only one child born in
the manger. Some one must have slipped something into the
picture at a later date.

In days gone by the child had itself born in the home and
hence was a rather cheap acquisition. The doctor was called
to the residence and a woman neighbor or two were invited;
not uncommonly several came who were not invited, all ready
to offer a young doctor advice. This retinue could be accumulated at no expense whatever. The women donated
their services and paying the doctor was entirely optional

with the head of the family. I figured out once that my attendance at "blessed events" brought me something less than a dollar an hour, gross. Any old doctor will recognize at once that I achieved these figures only by ignoring those cases in which I received nothing; these amounted possibly to about half the total number. It is interesting to remember that I sometimes occupied my time while waiting by counting the number of youngsters scattered around in the various rooms of the house, if the house had more than one room. I learned to compute the chances of receiving a fee as inversely proportional to the number of previous arrivals.

That the economic factor is not a thing of the past is revealed by the fact that the birth rate of those on relief rapidly mounts. Kids included in the More Abundant Life are less carefully counted, particularly if hospital expenses are included in the public beneficence. Hence papa's sleep is not disturbed even for a night, so why buy an adding machine?

In the cities nowadays, if the child has any pride of ancestry it is born in a hospital where adequate medical care is mandatory, under the guidance of specialists capable of meeting any emergency. Theoretically, this should rebound to the advantage of both mother and child. Yet the child lacking this auspicious start may console itself with the fact that the safest place to be born is in the home under the guidance of a capable family doctor. Of course this statement annoys the specialists but facts are facts. I did not compile the statistics.

The disturbing fact is that when the child is being born in hospital surroundings, with every facility for meeting emergencies, there are many emergencies to meet. I trust no layman will attempt to analyze the problem further because we common doctors cannot and the specialists will not. They start with the premise that being specialists their work must be superior. They sometimes overlook the fact that the capacity for watchful waiting used to be regarded as the chief virtue of a doctor conducting a case of labor. In other words, the fact that childbirth is a physiological process, like digestion, is frequently disregarded. Food grabbed off a bare table may be surer of digestion than that served in courses preceded

D

by an appetizer and followed by a digestant. It depends on the digestion—and on the food.

A child born under modern conditions bears a very large price tag. The sight of such a bill, as a young father once told me, was enough to make any one sterile henceforth from fright. Of course, since we are heading toward socialized medicine, the day may come when the baby costs nothing, even in well to do families, as it does now in the underprivileged families. The pain the mother suffers, with modern anesthesia, is nothing compared to the pain suffered by the taxpayer, who pays the bill, whenever he thinks of the taxes he must pay daily.

Of course the child has responsibilities which he may not at first appreciate. The chief dereliction on the part of the child is the carelessness with which he selects his parents. This causes the doctor more trouble than any other one thing. Look over the case-book of any doctor and this fact will stand out. The magnitude of the consequences of this lack of foresight may not appear for twenty years. An inspired writer recently has said that ninety five per cent of the idiots are the product of normal parents and that many outstanding persons are the offspring of relatively dumb parents— but not so dumb as to write misleading statistics such as those just quoted. Only an I.Q. expert could achieve such conclusions. Any stock breeder of course knows that blood counts, and no two-quart cow ever produced a four-gallon daughter, and vice versa no four-gallon mother ever had a two-quart daughter.

I sometimes wonder what the child thinks about before he escapes from the maze of adequate medical care which, as conceived by those unacquainted with what constitutes such care and wholly devoid of a sense of humor, includes some funny ideas. What, for instance, does a baby think about while lying in its bassinet with an identification disc attached to its toes, just like a cadaver in a morgue? But this tag may have a far reaching effect. If the child grows up resembling another person, even another race, the hospital can be blamed and no scandal ensue, at least for papa; he can always sue the hospital. One can with care salvage something out of any disaster.

The only excuse for this screed is that any old fashioned person who prefers a baby financially unencumbered may achieve this by staying at home with safety, even though it may upset a well regulated household. These papas who have their babies born in hospitals miss a lot of fun. The comments on alleged family resemblances ventured by the voluntary assistants give him a good reflection of himself which could otherwise only be acquired by becoming a candidate for some office.

By having his baby born in a hospital papa may postpone responsibility for a time but sooner or later the child finds itself in the custody of its mother, thanks to the identification disc. In this environment it can secure the proper diet. Preferably of course the child is nourished as nature intended. I sometimes also wonder what a baby thinks after it gets home, accustomed as it has been to a tip-toeing nurse with her face encased in a mask. A mask may be needed, but not all mothers smoke, even today. Cigarette smokers as a class usually take care not to become mothers. The wearing of masks, I may explain for the benefit of the uninformed, was ordered by higher ups who were ignorant of the bacteriology of respiration. Either that or they feared the nurse might get mad at the baby and spit in its face.

In the absence of nature's diet, the science of nutrition has been perfected to such a degree that most efficient substitutes are available. Nowadays a baby dependent on artificial feeding has an excellent chance of surviving. This is in marked contrast to conditions existing fifty years ago. Then, the infant, condemned to artificial feeding, had less than half a chance of surviving. No branch of medicine has made greater advances than the science of child feeding.

In the old days the doctor's worries came in the dreaded "second summer." During the first summer the baby had its own private supply of milk; the second summer this privilege was denied it and it had to risk contaminated food. The result was a frightful mortality rate. Many a weary night have I spent bathing a child whose convulsions were due to unsuitable diet, only to lose the battle in the end.

Nowadays the child's food is as sterile as the canneries and dairies can make it, and unless the mother's hand slips and the can opener or her finger is poked into the contents the food reaches the child in a sterile condition. Thus the child is protected until it is old enough to visit grandma or to toddle to the corner drug store. After that it is in the hands of the fates.

When he contemplates these improvements the doctor must stand aside and introduce the sanitary engineer. Quite aside from the achievements of the pediatricians, two very important factors have entered to protect the baby in this day. These are the screen and the refrigerator. It is difficult now to imagine anyone living in a house which lacks these conveniences. Yet fifty years ago screens were almost unknown and the number of flies all over the house, and on the baby's face, was limited only by the available standing room. Everything was contaminated in spite of every care. Milk, particularly, was and is a convenient breeding place for bacteria as are all other articles of food for children. Lack of refrigeration made it impossible to preserve the cow's milk, then the chief mainstay in infant feeding.

These things all have changed for the good of everyone concerned. For all save the "underprivileged," meaning those who prefer to continue to live in the dark ages, enlightenment has come. Even the underprivileged are forced to accept the guiding hand of the school nurse. Some schools even supply warm soup. In the old days, I cannot help but observe, a birch rod was used to transmit warmth.

The physical welfare of the child, as noted above, is more or less in the hands of the parents. Such a statement looks fine but it is subject to some very obvious modifications. Parents who are not able to provide sufficient food in a measure are not responsible. Society in general is responsible, whenever the number of children is greater than the parents are able to feed. This number is at present beyond their control, and low earnings cannot be augmented by an exertion of the will because of the wage-hour law. Society must see that all hungry children are fed, or else change the laws. The most important thing is that the child should have within its reach an adequate amount of food. We as a nation are afflicted with overproduction. Not so much the overproduction of food and children as the overproduction of highbrows who know nothing about the fundamental factors of distribution, either of food or children, but who insist on writing the rules which shall govern the raising of children. No intelligence seems to be able to bridge the gap between an overbulging forehead and a child's empty stomach.

Some time ago I overheard one of a bunch of boys say "Bill, he would be a great athlete if he just had enough to eat." Bill lacked sunshine because he literally played in the shadow of a church. There were so many in the family that there was not enough food for any one of them, despite the best efforts of a low-waged father.

I can tell a starved child's walk a block away. I know that usually it is starved because there are too many in the family. The excuse for the excessive number, that it is pleasing to God, is a lie. That is only an after-thought and is purely man-made. Any historian can name the man who first formulated it. It has as a basis nothing less than unbridled lust. And lust is not concerned with the science of nutrition, nor with the problems of food distribution.

Rail if we must for another twenty centuries; in the end the truth will out. The earth is not flat; it was not created in six days; the sun and moon never stood still at the behest of any mortal. Christ was conceived in love and not in lust. I have scanned great paintings for a good many years looking for a rachitic, undernourished moronic child among those gathered about the knees of Christ. Never a one did I find. The artists for once were centuries ahead of their time. There is no use talking. It is impossible to harmonize the teachings of the past with the needs of the child.

Up to this point we have discussed children categorically as persons subject to our will. This period of infancy and early childhood we may arbitrarily end with the beginning of the sixth year, the beginning of school. In the second period the children are no longer "its." They have become boys and girls and as such must be considered separately. They are growing up as best they may and in doing so are becoming a part of the community.

Community influence is largely beyond the control of any particular individual. To control the environment of the child the parents of a community must act in unison. In no other way can they insure for their own children the influences they consider desirable. The problem comes back home. Its sphere of influence becomes a community affair, for our superior children are subject to the common level of their environment.

As an example of how soon sex differences become evident, note how early in life the little girl devotes many hours to the care of her doll. It is interesting to observe that children no longer punish their dolls for disobedience. For years I have not seen a child spank her doll. One could learn the technic of their mothers by observing how the children treat their dolls. In fact we see here the whole panorama of life played before us in miniature. The little girls are engaged in warming up practice in anticipation of the real game of which they know nothing. I have only impatience for those who call these activities "play." They are rehearsals for life's drama. If we grown ups would attend to our duties with the same enthusiasm the children manifest in their "play," we would have a different world.

The idea of a doll baby includes subconsciously the idea of paternity in the child's mind, yet it is without any tinge of sex as the adult knows it. When she gives doll parties and doll dinners, in imitation of her elders, she is preparing for a future which she is only subconsciously aware lies ahead. The fates are talking to her. She continues to play with dolls until the beginning of puberty when she puts them away. It is interesting to note the dividing line. Part of the time the girl plays with her doll; part of the time she is a very dignified young lady quite above such childish things. Yet many a young lady, and some older ones, still have hidden away a favored doll of their childhood.

Formerly children were the products of their own immediate neighborhood. With modern means of transportation few children are isolated, much to their advantage. They meet different children and learn to play together, learn to give and take. All this play is a thing that teaches unselfishness and may redound vastly to the advantage of some young male twenty years hence. The girl with her doll is the parent of the young mother and her babe.

. Those of us who are aging note regretfully that much of the time formerly devoted to dolls and their doings is now devoted to automobile rides and pictureshows. One wonders what influence this may have on the future home.

Children now are a part of a running machine wherein each child passes along from stage to stage without effort and even in spite of itself, just an object on an assembly line in an automobile factory. Play is regulated as completely as work. Everybody is put through the same process. The products should be identical. However, already heredity and home environment are beginning to show. Stubbornness, ill temper and selfishness begin to creep out. Happily, bad home influences are modified by the environment of the school and the guiding hand of the teacher. If I declared that the average teacher had more sense than the average mother, some mothers might flare up, say some unkind things, and thereby prove that my assertion is correct. But mothers also are meeting the changing times.

I once sought to set forth in a speech just in what way and why the great need of modern society is better parents. Without going into all the details here, I might suggest that this is a subject the parents might well consider carefully before they criticize the teacher to the child. Whenever there is a row between parents and teacher, one may safely say the teacher's judgment is superior. At least, her judgment is worthy of consideration. School directors, so far as my inquiry has gone, bear me out in the belief that complaining parents are usually not too far removed from the need of police supervision.

The male child represents a somewhat different problem in so far as the doctor is concerned. He is more commonly in need of repairs because of an exaggerated aggressiveness brought out by the leading role he is to have in the future. But in him the change from a bygone age is also obvious. Because he is no longer beaten up himself to forestall his being spoiled, the old habit of boy fights has almost disappeared from our playgrounds. He is under the same benign influence as his sisters, and give and take becomes a habit. Hence he escapes the yokel stage and emerges from boyhood to the state of a young gentleman unconsciously and without effort on his part.

The boy child, unhindered by parental differences, is quite an uncivilized sort of a young animal but is amenable to a certain degree of guidance. His time, too, is devoted to anticipatory activities and not much concerned with the influences of civilization. He has to do with material things. Lucky is he if he can model himself after his father. He is a reflection of his environment much more than the girl.

When I was a boy we made wooden guns and fought imaginary Indians, or we herded cattle, riding on stick horses. We hunted imaginary 'coons and fried a neighbor's chickens, or we "borrowed" fruit from some neighbor even though our home orchard creaked with the same things. It was adventure, not worldly goods we sought. We were grown up before our time.

Just a glance at those hard old days of fifty years ago. Something has been lost. We were ornery young rascals but not criminals. I shudder to think of what would have become of us if we had had to face conditions as they are now. Boys are now sent to the reformatory for things we did as a lark. On Hallowe'en night the town marshal went to bed early or was called to see a sick friend in a neighboring village. Every property owner was the guardian of his own fate. Father might thunder maledictions if his sons or his neighbor's sons did certain things and then go into the house and tell mother about it and they would both have a hearty laugh. Reminiscing, I realize that we learned much. To take a farm wagon apart, carry the sections to the top of a barn and re-assemble them, is some engineering feat requiring general-ship of a high order, as one could readily see when our elders came to lower the parts, in broad daylight too. Likewise, to persuade an unwilling bossie to enter a school house and take her place at the teacher's desk requires remarkable patience and tact, not only in managing bossie but in per-suading teacher that we were all at the revival meeting the night before. Really we meant no disrespect to the teacher, although our selection of an animal might imply it.

The things we had to play with had to be acquired by our own ingenuity, too often by stealth, because so many things were sinful. In fact everything enjoyable was sinful, either by commission or omission. Going fishing, swimming, every-thing that was fun was forbidden. Here is a significant thing. Things that were sinful on Sunday were just boyish mischief when, on other days, our fathers were free from ecclesiastic dictation. We Protestant boys were envious of Catholic boys who had a priest to help them play ball on Sunday after-noons.

In those old days each boy had a dog. But sad to say the boy was not considered when the dog was acquired. A watch dog was secured. The boy just preempted him. My dog cost my father forty cents. He had no pedigree, therefore no pride of ancestry. Yet he received from me all I had of affec-tion because no one else seemed to want it. Where I went he went also. He was always ready in an instant to fight for me; and I for him, when no one else in all the world took heed.

Nowadays policemen are called in in many instances when really paternal understanding is all that is required. When-ever a boy is taken by the law for some minor infraction I believe the father should be taken along and receive double the sentence the boy receives. Not long ago a young boy "borrowed" a car and took a ride. The owner of the car had left the key in it—a tacit invitation to the boy to take a ride.

Which was the guilty party? The boy was arrested and received some sort of sentence. No one raised a protesting hand. But the boy, an underprivileged youngster, had merely wanted a ride, a favor not otherwise obtainable. In this and any similar case, it is the owner and not the boy who should receive the attention of the law. If that is not contributing to juvenile delinquency, what is? In the day time we expect the teachers to look after our children. At night the task is turned over to the police. Few parents trouble to find out how much time the police spend in the effort to keep boys from committing their first crime. The parents—oh yes, bid four spades; doubled. Let the game go on.

What a boy needs above all things is a father; a male parent is not enough. The boy, given a chance, wants a father about whom he can build his idea of what he would like to be when he grows up. It is interesting to see upon what small material a boy can build up his ideal man.

The father is learning that the boy craves his companionship and that what their relationship will be at eighteen depends on his relation to the boy of six or ten. Just today, a Sunday, I addressed a dear young matron: "What's Walt doing?" The cheery reply came back: "He and Bill went fishing." Said William is a male child of some six summers. Father and son gone fishing on Sunday, imagine that! Sixty years ago such an act would certainly have resulted in bringing down the maledictions of the neighbors and would have furnished the text for sermons for Sundays to come. Yet that simple statement shows the birth of something intangible, call it spiritual if you will, since it defies definition. Father and six-year-old son going fishing together—on Sunday!

Yet the whole thing is really very simple except no one seems to know what happened to hell. I have put this question to a number of ministers. Nobody knows. Did the old ministers take it with them or did they go to it? At any rate it seems to have vanished from the great American home, and with it the need of beating up the boys to save them from something that now apparently no longer exists.

When I analyze those old days I conclude that our parents

were not morally, but only ecclesiastically, cruel. They withheld their affection from us for what seemed to them to be our good. It is pleasing to note that no matter how parents lived, many died with an infinite love for their children. And only when old age grips our parents do we come to understand the many things they did which we in our boyhood thought cruel. We discover that they were only the result of their own false teachers. But pampering and sympathetic companionship are as far apart as the day and night. The first can be bought with money, or hired from a menial but companionship can come only from the heart; and it takes time.

The boy's environment has changed with the times. Today he receives ready-made toys and he starts with these. He learns all the makes of automobiles, or he learns all about airships. He learns about the things which occupy the time of his father, or should. He learns to live. Few boys now in their mind's future are policemen or railway engineers as in the old days. But the modern boy is not thoughtless; he is as interested in the future as ever, sometimes at a surprisingly early age. I have before me at this moment a scribbled letter from a very young grandson who declares his intention of being a doctor and learning big words so he can talk like grandpa. His slightly younger sister protests, also in a letter, because she thinks that if brother becomes a doctor she will automatically need to become a nurse, to which she objects. She prefers to be a housewife and have eight children. Precious letters these. Life to them is more serious at ten and twelve than to grandpa at seventy.

Nowadays it sometimes seems that children represent a higher degree of civilization than their parents, that they are far ahead of their parents in civilization. With them all is equality, all is harmony. Parental harmony in any community is nowhere so complete as it is among children, even though the children sometimes take pokes at each other's noses. They are only writing history. The parents are reft by differences in social standing, social practices, politics and religion. While all these differences put together do not furnish a cause for the shedding of blood in these enlightened days, they still supply an excuse for making a division among the children one day a week, except in so far as the children have better sense.

It is the lack of harmonious action among parents which makes rotten politics as we see it possible. Because parents differ in some little insignificant thing they fail to act in harmony in more important matters. Our various beliefs today are but vestiges of the things of the past. One should read history because one still sees the old practices cropping out at the present time. Only by knowing facts can one become sufficiently mad to want to remedy them. Knowing history, one more easily understands many of the present manifestations seen in the clinic today. The doctor cannot ignore facts. Sex, hate, lust still furnish a large part of our problems. The mutilations of the sex fiends of today were a part of some religious rites in another age. How deeply we are still submerged in practices of the past is manifest in much that goes on all about us.

I have spoken of the third sphere of influence as "spiritual." That may seem to be a silly word for an old scientist to use but in doing so I call attention to things we do not understand. I grew up in the hard old days. I never heard the word "love" until I recited *"Amo, amas, amat"* in Latin class and was exceedingly embarrassed when the girls giggled. I never knew a parental caress. Yet when my father went to the mill or hauled something to town I also went to town; there was a bond between us which we both felt.

I have already said that not until my father was on his deathbed did he tell me that he had restrained his expressions of affection in the years when I most needed them, because of ecclesiastic interdiction. "It was wrong, it was all wrong," he exclaimed in bitterness of spirit. Father was never afraid of the truth.

Yet father and I understood each other from the time of my earliest recollections. The relation showed in neither action nor words, but it was something that has never dimmed though he has been dead nearly fifty years. That relation-

ship is what I mean when I use the word "spiritual." Theology is the expression of man's own conceit. Spirituality is
beyond the range of any one to destroy. You don't believe
it, you feel it.

The companionship of even a few children may bring
discord. One child may be favored by one or the other of the
parents. It is natural for father to feel that daughter is the
grandest person who ever lived; so far as he is concerned he
is exactly right since she goes far deeper into his affections
than the child's mother ever did. The boy receives the backing of his mother, and she too is exactly right. Slight touches
of these parental differences are right and beautiful. A parent
may regard the children with equal affection but one child
may lead him to a seat with the gods. Some little thing,
some circumstance of its birth, a serious sickness, may touch
a cord that would not otherwise be reached. Obviously
these fine differences do not divide the parents but unite
them more closely. Yet doctors are called upon to umpire
some very peculiar games or combats.

Very commonly the combats have an economic basis. The
father is pushed to provide things the mother wants for
the children but which he honestly cannot afford. The spirit
of the mother may be laudable. It takes an intelligent
woman to employ without hurt the modern successful home
father provides her. Some one has truly said the larger the
income, the more difficult it is to live within it. The children must be dressed as expensively as any other children,
possibly to lead the pack a little. It is a disputed question,
when a mother dresses her children expensively, whether she
does it out of pride in them or to express her own ego.
Let the women decide, if it is necessary to decide it. All
that is clear is that the attractiveness of the child depends
vastly more on the skill of the mother than on the earning
power of the father.

Sometimes the children are made to feel that they are not
provided for as abundantly as they should be. Of course
they know nothing of the facts, nothing of their father's
earning power, and only reflect the ideas of the mother.

Most often this discontent does not show until they are no longer children but boy and girl, and old enough to compare their state with that of other children. The mother should be observant enough to see when such notions enter their heads and come to the defense of the father. Even more important, the father may be derelict; he may not be doing all that he could to enable his children to meet the prevailing standard of their environment. If this is not possible the parents should acquaint the children with the facts.

There are other things even more potent for bringing to light jars in the family relations. The mother, more often than most persons suspect, becomes uneasy with something akin to jealousy because she feels the daughter has supplanted her in her husband's affections. The mother should realize that her daughter has only spiritually eloped with father. A husband's love may still be hers as much as ever but that something a father feels for his daughter goes beyond the stars. The mother should recognize its nobility.

These women may become irritable and nervous and are worthy of a doctor's fullest sympathy but there is not much one can do about it. Most likely daughter designedly and secretly did purloin her father's affections when her mother was away some place expostulating on the artistic value of Chinese art, the state of civilization in the reign of Rameses III, or something like that. All facetiousness aside, I believe every woman should realize that when she gives her husband a daughter she has in her house a very skillful rival and she had better do all she can to prevent clandestine meetings between father and his little girl. Daughters have stolen the love of many more husbands than all the blonde office girls in the world.

This jealousy of the child is all wrong; the daughter has ascended to a height of love in her father's heart that no wife can ever hope to reach. That is a private paradise. The mother should realize this. But it is a spiritual paradise in which fathers and daughters dwell. This fact cannot be too strongly emphasized. The mother dwells in a very mundane sphere having to do with the quality of the biscuits and the general appearance of her landscape. Mother-son complexes cause trouble much more commonly than father-daughter relationships, but not because of the father's jealousy. The mother sees in her son the perfect male she failed to marry, because there was none such. Her error comes when her love causes her to set the boy against his father.

Behind it all is the mother's fear that sonny will grow up like father. Often this fear may have a very obvious basis. If sonny is thin like father, she comes to the doctor looking for something to make him grow plump; if fat like his father, she wants a diet to thin him down. The doctor stores these observations in his mind and dodges the issue as best he can. An artful doctor will comment on how much like his mother the boy is. Interesting, he goes on to explain to the mother, that when the boy is physically like his father, he is so often spiritually like his mother. And there is some truth in it, sometimes. Besides I do not believe all liars go to hell.

Unless the doctor breaks up the complex he knows what the next step will be. Sonny, in the natural course of events, will find interesting scenery in his environment. One of the most distressing things which the doctor has to contend with is the intense jealousy a mother may develop toward her son's sweetheart and then his wife. I have been interested particularly in those cases in which the mother is jealous when the son begins to look around. It is exasperating to see jealousy in the abstract. One sees exactly the same situation when wives have decided to become jealous of their husbands although they are unable to fix on a definite third party.

There is another source of trouble which will be more fully discussed in a later chapter. The mother, having a male companion of her own creation, may find her spiritual needs fully satisfied. Here the doctor must look for a sex complex, a frigidity, even a hate for the husband which developed before the scent of orange blossoms departed. These are peculiar cases; instead of jealousy there is just lofty contempt.

When in addition, such a mother sets the son against his

father the situation is loaded with dynamite. There is an element of hate in the mother's mind and the son consciously shares it. These are hard problems for the doctor. Mother's face is set. She hates the old skinflint who brings home the bacon. It is impossible to determine the first causes. All the doctor can do is to get behind the ropes and observe the contest.

The sad thing is that the conflict may continue and become a problem for the next generation. She may treat sonny as she would a husband. "Don't do this and don't do that. Where have you been and where are you going? And hurry back!" The result is, sonny becomes antisocial, rebelling not only against his father, as the mother intended he should, but also against her and against society in general. Such cases are found more frequently in the well-to-do home where the mother has abundant leisure. On the other hand, the son may come under the complete domination of his mother. Probably it would be confusing to say he is "henpecked." To say he is "mamapecked" would describe the situation without ambiguity.

There is less trouble between children and parents when the struggle for existence is constant and acute, demanding the undivided energies of both, as was commonly the case with the old pioneers. How to feed the family and clothe them fit for school was the problem of many young mothers as well as fathers. When both are pushing the cart they must stand close together. I have seen many women who could qualify for Secretary of the Treasury in any administration. I have seen so many fine things done by women in adversity that I never cease to marvel. Spirituality, as I mean it, thrives best in honest poverty. The "more abundant life" thrust on families not experienced in the distribution of opulence is a greater menace than poverty.

The saddest cases the doctor sees are those in which the father becomes profligate, wasting the already meager family substance. The mother struggles silently, devoting herself to the children with a self-sacrificing devotion that surpasses understanding. This, I am disposed to think, is the finest picture one sees in life. Yet neighbors wonder how it happens that the children of a profligate father sometimes become such magnificent children. Men and women grow from such environments to move the nation, and statisticians rush into print to show how a worthless father produced a splendid son, thereby thinking to show that the laws of heredity have been upset. The doctor knows better; he knows that the son is also the product of his mother, and in such a case it is her intelligence that enables the boy to make a place in the world. It is a vast, incomprehensible spirit that guides the mother. Here is motherhood, if not at its best, at least at its most heroic.

A sad problem for the doctor and teacher as well as the parent is the moron, although it brings out some of the finest traits of parenthood. To see mothers trying to do the impossible, and making all manner of sacrifices to educate a deficient child is an all too common sight. Instead of facing facts, deficient children are dragged through school when it is apparent to everyone that it is useless. Sure, it is the old story: everybody is entitled to an education—even though it is a hopeless quest.

(The makers of statistics are prone to regard all deficiencies dating from childhood as hereditary. Nothing could be further from the truth. Accidents at birth, incomplete recovery from infectious diseases, which was far more common in days gone by, have nothing to do with heredity. But the results are erroneously charged to the parent by those who wish to reach the conclusion that morons are as apt to have intelligent parents as morons like themselves.)

Frequently parents bring to the clinic children afflicted by inherited conditions. When the child falls behind in his studies, the parents are advised by the teacher or the school nurse to take him to the doctor. The doctor is told that the mentally deficient child became so after a fall, an injury remembered only in retrospect. Perhaps the doctor sees that the patient is no dumber than his parents. But the doctor is not the only one with a problem on his hands. The more intelligent morons reach the schools and become the prob-

E

lem of the teacher. Many pupils graduate from high school who have intellectually never advanced beyond the third grade. I record here the statement of the man who recalled in after life that the seven happiest years of his life were spent in the third grade. Nowadays he would be graduated despite the fact that he had not advanced beyond the third grade. These students are not only a trial to the teacher but a hindrance to the more intelligent children who also should have some rights. I am told the hopeless moron is tolerated in school because he is better off there than on the street.

Happily, the doctor's lot is not always filled with responsibility. He can sit back and observe his young friends develop normally in many cases. There comes a time when the child begins to show evidence of outgrowing childish ways. The girl addresses the old doc as Doctor Doe. The transitional stage comes so gradually that the parents scarcely recognize it or, if recognizing it, do not feel the import of it.

It signalizes the fact that the children are about to leave this chapter and enter the next. But it is a change which must come. The endocrines begin to whisper a faint recognition of sex. Whether the awakening is gradual or sudden, there is a difference between boy and girl. The girl usually awakens at an earlier age. At least it is generally recognized that girls are more intelligent and mature than boys of the same age. As her hips begin to broaden ever so little she unconsciously proclaims to the world that she is, not will be, the queen of the race. She feels at first a sense of pity for her young boy playmates. She cannot understand why they do such silly things, why they are so careless of their clothes —though obviously they are all legs and feet.

The young folks think they are grown up and quite able to chart their own course. Actually at no period of life are they more in need of the love and companionship of their parents. But the confidence must be based on years of association and understanding. If we lose them during the terminal child years they are gone beyond reclaim when they move into the next chapter and sex begins to talk louder than the parental whisper.

As the child grows older, he has today many advantages, in addition to his regular school work. For one thing, there are music lessons for everybody, a fine way to bring children into harmony with their environment. Even so I am forced to add that I believe there should be a law to prevent young males from being compelled to practice on a piano. Wind instruments are of much greater value in preparing him for his subsequent career, for it is well said that "He that tooteth not his own horn, the same shall not be tooted." Possibly this quotation is supposed to be regarded as a figure of speech. At any rate it would not seem right to say that "He that poundeth not his own piano, the same shall not be pounded!"

The doctor looks with apprehension at the athletics of today. Getting bunged up, thoroughly licked, and liking it, all in the spirit of good fellowship, is all right. Rivalry but no hate. It all spells equality in the end. Yet athletics of today must be distinguished from play. In athletics the most physically fit are further developed so that the local team may defeat the team from Punkville. This overdevelopment of the fittest, which finds its full expression in high school and becomes a racket in college, has penetrated even the grammar school.

Play on the other hand, as distinguished from athletics, is the exercise of functions within the normal limit. Observe the pups. They have a fine time rolling in the grass but they never try to determine which can make two miles in the shortest time. Children will play in their own way if they have the chance. Of course in restricted neighborhoods more or less organized play is unavoidable. Hikes are the best of the planned exercises.

But we must detain the children in this chapter a little while longer. This period is contemporary with the establishment of menstruation indicating that the girl has arrived at the period of potential motherhood. This occurs about in the eleventh to the fourteenth year; and one of the greatest mistakes nature ever made was to establish this event in what is yet really childhood. The sensible mother prepares her daughter for this occurrence and explains its meaning. At no other period of life is a girl so greatly in need of an understanding mother. Not all mothers inform their daughters, even at this date and age. Some mothers are so "nasty nice." Formerly it was an exception when the child received advance information, and many a child, stricken with terror at the unanticipated appearance of blood, received a nervous shock that remained with her and formed the foundation for a neurotic future. Let it be repeated: a frank statement from the mother at this early period of the meaning of menstruation contributes much to the development of a stable nervous system. The very lofty-minded mother, who shrinks from any thought of sex, preferring to allow her daughter to blunder through until after the honeymoon, is on the way out. She was noble in her own mind but good intentions were never legal tender in any bank, or in any moral problem.

The wise doctor may discover years later that a nervous ailment dates from severe nervous shocks received at an even earlier age. Not long ago a striking example presented itself in the clinic. Tactful search revealed a fact never mentioned before: that when the patient was six years old the family had all slept in the same room. She had been awakened one night by her father exclaiming to her mother, "I'll kill you." Forty years later she was still a problem for the doctor because of the shock she received as a child. It was only hate she heard her father give expression to. She did not know then, and I doubt if she does now, that back of that hate was sex. Freud's so-called psychoanalysis has as its basis the searching for such things that remain in the subconscious mind but goes quite too far in attempting to find in some sex shock the explanation of all nervous ills.

The girl is dressed from babyhood to anticipate the day when she will have a shape to show. In this day, girls from childhood to maturity, in fair weather or storm, are almost bare-legged. But that there may be a subconscious modesty is suggested by the following occurrence. I, and my granddaughter, aged about seven, were standing on the curb

awaiting a car. She grasped my hand with unusual firmness
and stood nervously as close to me as possible. I said gently,
"What is the matter?" She replied, "Why, Grandpa, I have
on silk pants and it feels as if I did not have any." In spite
of being accustomed to bare legs she was pants conscious;
the unaccustomed silk did not have the security of cotton.
I recall also one day seeing a young girl facing a blustering
breeze, shivering along dressed in a huge neckpiece and
sporting a muff as big as a beer keg—and bare legs. She was
radiantly happy. She was taking a trial flight into adolescence. Most girls like to dress up in their mothers' clothes
and do it with as much gravity as if they were out trying to
decide whether or not to grow up.

Even so, one sees very little in practice to indicate that
such scanty clothing is injurious to health. The thing is to
look fetching. Ideas have changed, and we old folks know
so little of what is going on in the children's minds that we
had better get back of the ropes where we can watch the
parade without danger of being trampled upon. Fifty years
ago a properly trained boy, when he assisted a girl into a
buggy, fixed his gaze on the horses' ears, or on the stars,
real or imaginary, lest he get a peek at her stockings. Yet
the girls had delicate lace on their petticoats and panties. I
reckon this precaution was taken just in case some accident
befall her, as in a swing or climbing a fence. Even so, I have
never known a mother who sewed lace on her boy's shirt-
tail, although some did dress them in velvet, and put lace
onto their white collars, trying to make them into little
Lord Fauntleroys.

Nowadays nothing is left to the imagination of the boy.
He has inspected all the legs in the neighborhood, including
his mother's, since babyhood. He grows up with the pure
mind of an African savage. This leaves him time for more
weighty things, like athletics and music.

This early familiarity with exposure of the extremities
may have the advantage, if it be such, of making the girl
unconscious of her exhibitions when the age arrives during
which she represents real scenery. But is a girl ever uncon-

scious of the shape of her legs? It would be interesting if some one would trace the history of the rise and fall of lace on nether garments.

To the parent, the children's development into little men and women, is a wonderful sight to behold, yet it is filled with painful regrets that it must be so. Their day is past. They have implanted in their child all that they have to give. It is not a matter of what they wished to do, perhaps what they prayed to do. Only what they did do counts. Whether or not these years have been utilized wisely, they must recognize the truth of the words of Omar Khayyam —"The moving finger writes and having writ moves on and all your prayers and tears will not erase one word of it." Neither prayers nor tears change anything. The wise, unremitting companionship which they give in childhood alone counts. Less sleep in years gone by on the part of the parents would have done more than anything else to lessen the need for the doctor's sleeping potions.

What is the final summary? Blessed childhood, crying from the manger to maturity, tries to teach us that love is speechless. There must be demonstration. If this truth could be realized there would be less call for tears from parents in future years, and the children might escape disaster as they grow up, even the third and fourth generation might have more pleasant memories. We are architects of our own hell, and we populate it right here on earth.

What has happened to the relation of parent and child? Just this: The voice in the manger is penetrating the paganism of the dark ages. For centuries people believed God spoke only Hebrew. This able and virile people, I would like to say in passing, were never notable for their modesty, but in claiming such close intimacy with the Eternal they certainly crossed the boundary of credulity. In those days when "facts" spread only by word of mouth they could get by with anything—that they could get by with. Those times are as remotely related to the present as the ass, as a mode of transportation, is to the airplane.

Let us teach our children that the spirit of God or the

vast incomprehensible universe—call it what you will—never talked any language. Just as the real language spoken between parent and child has no words. They commune in the language of love. Words find expression only when sex comes in. One might conclude that the chief use of words was to lie with.

In the infinitely fine contact between parent and child words are meaningless. Eternal demonstration alone has a voice. For the first twelve years or so we hold their hands in ours as we teach them to write. The time comes when they take the pen in their own hands but their script is bound to bear a close resemblance to that which they wrote while their hands were still guided by ours. The heart of a parent cries out to the child as he sees him write. "Don't bear down so hard! look out, too much ink, you'll make a blot; look out, you are writing a crooked line." Perhaps we were guilty of these same faults when we directed the pen. What the written page will show, let me repeat, depends very largely on what we have taught the child the first ten or twelve years of his life. Hope and prayer without works bring us nothing; works and eternal vigilance alone are rewarded.

We doctors must look at the truth as we see it in children in order that we may better understand the more complicated phenomena that we meet in the next chapter.

III

Paradise Visioned (The Child Learns of Love and Sex)

In the early years the children are in the hands of their parents. Their companionship is available whenever the parent wishes it. They believe in their parents. The father is the greatest man there is and mother is the haven to which they fly at the moment of distress. When they reach school age they are subject to the influence of other children but they are still amenable to parental influence, and crave companionship.

Comes a time when goose fuzz appears on the boy's cheek and the changing contour of the girl signals to the parents that their complete dominance is at an end. The development of the endocrine glands puts new ideas into their heads and they become independent human beings and seek new companionships in response to an urge they do not understand. They no longer crave parental companionship but are about to put to a test the soundness of the training they received in the first dozen or fourteen years of their lives.

Ordinarily when people speak of children leaving home they mean they are no longer availing themselves of the protection of the parental roof. It would be better if we realized that when our children go forth hand in hand with their endocrines they have left home, even though they are nominally under parental protection and parental authority. We are fooling ourselves if we believe otherwise. We can only hope that in the formative years we have implanted enough character in them to carry them through the danger period. If I were asked for a definition of prayer I would say it is the crying out, the wordless plea of parents that their children may be protected from evil when they are away from the parental observation in these formative years. No one, be he Christian, agnostic, or atheist, can escape this involuntary cry: "God protect my child." The child is in the hands of a relentless fate; he will act according to the dictates of his early teaching, and, sad to relate, according to something that is hereditary of which he is unconscious and which he may curb but cannot control.

This, the golden age of youth, may be divided into two periods, the high school age and the college age. The first is lofty without guile but the college age is the dangerous time when the young lady uses her head with a definite purpose in mind and the boy discovers the only girl. Together these periods include those years between the time when the stimulation of the gonads takes charge of the adolescent and keeps him in fetters and the time he lands at the threshold of the great adventure. This is not coextensive with adolescence, for many girls and some boys make alliances before they are mature, to their everlasting hurt, while others postpone the event indefinitely.

The period of adolescence, physically speaking, may arbitrarily be said to include the years between the budding of puberty and maturity. Puberty in the girl is that definite period when the endocrine glands take charge of her and develop her ability to reproduce. It is signalized by the appearance of menstruation. In achieving this development a number of years may be required in some; in others the transition seems to take place almost over night. Maturity is the state of the woman who is grown and physically mature; who is ready, without injury to herself, to take on in her turn the process of reproduction of the species, with the assurance of being able to present the best that is in her to her children. The law thinks this stage of development is achieved at sixteen years, but we doctors know it is not reached until the twentieth or even until the twenty-fourth year, depending on the individual. It is obvious that nature committed a terrible mistake when she made conception possible long before the time of physical maturity. To human intelligence was assigned the task of bridging that gap, a terribly misplaced confidence. Worst of all, the all too low legal age may be even further reduced by parental consent. Moronic parents are allowed to make their own interpretation of the law.

The age when the girl first menstruates varies. In our temperate climate from the eleventh to the fourteenth year is the usual age. A delay of several years is not abnormal, particularly if such delay is a family trait. However, beyond the later date a careful inquiry into the physical state should be made. If there is any evidence of abnormality the examination should be made earlier. In years gone by the usual cause of delay was tuberculosis of the lungs. Because of this association, the general impression was that the delay of menstruation was the cause of the tuberculosis. One rarely hears this theory now unless grandmother happens to accompany the young lady to the doctor.

To the great benefit of both patient and doctor most of these young girls either alone or with their mothers, discuss with the doctor any menstrual disturbance as frankly as they would a headache or indigestion. Our knowledge of endocrine disturbance has now reached such a point of development that their physical manifestations can be recognized as such and in many instances promptly remedied.

The two chief menstrual disturbances which bring the girl to the doctor's attention are painful menstruation and the prolongation of menstruation beyond the normal three or five days.

The location of menstrual pain is in the ovary. It is usually characterized by pain in the right groin—though it may be the left groin or both—often reflected to the lower back or down the outside or the inside of the thigh. The degree of pain may be only an inconvenience but it may incapacitate the patient for hours, even days. The fact that these pains occur more or less constantly, or at intervals, over considerable periods of time, distinguishes them from inflammations within the abdomen, notably appendicitis. There are no structural changes so that the term "ovarian headache" is apt; it emphasizes the fact that there is no more reason for removing the ovary or the appendix for these

pains than there is for removing the brain because of headache, a thing that is not done by even the most enthusiastic
operators.

Too frequent or delayed menstruation is usually found in
delicate girls of substandard constitution and may be remedied by tonics and proper diet. Another type is the young
woman of abnormal weight. This condition is due to endocrine deficiency and a remedy is uncertain. However, she
may console herself with the fact that her difficulty is due to
maladjustment in development, and that she is not really
sick. If the doctor wants to add a word of consolation he
points out that this over-plump constitution sometimes is
associated with unusually brilliant minds, and cites examples. The doctor withholds the fact, however, that this
plumpness is not a guarantee of a brilliant career.

Excessive menstrual flow is far less common than delayed
or painful menstruation but it also is a manifestation of
endocrine disturbance. In these cases the flow is often persistent, lasting weeks or even months, causing the patient
great annoyance and the mother distress. It often taxes the
resources of the doctor. Yet one can now say to the mother
that if she will keep the surgeon and the x-ray man away
the young patient will ultimately right herself. I have done
my share of useless operating in such cases and know whereof
I speak. These are problems for the doctor possessed of a
knowledge of the endocrine disturbances and their treatment, and require infinite patience on the part of the patient and her mother—and also of the doctor.

The physical changes at puberty are less obvious in the
boy than in the girl, consequently he receives little attention—less than he deserves. He subconsciously wants help,
and needs it, but unless it is tactfully given, more harm
than good is likely to result. At first glance it may seem
ridiculous to believe that a large young male comprised
chiefly of legs and lubricated hair should crave parental love,
but it is so. Things are happening to his body that he may
not understand. Ignorance of normal processes may disturb
his mental equilibrium.

Pimples on his face may but proclaim that he is a young male adolescent and to the doctor are unimportant, but to the boy they are a cause for distress. Pimples unimportant indeed! To him they are a large factor and make him feel uncertain of himself. He may be pondering the profound problem as to whether or not it will be necessary or correct, to kiss the young lady at the front door at parting. Pimply myself in my youth, I know now that the problem would have solved itself and that pimples are neither a bar nor a protection, if one chooses to view it that way in later life. Of course he does not yet know that the young ladies decide all those things. A conversation between a 'teen age boy and his uncle comes to mind. The young man told his advisor that he took a young lady to the movies the evening before, gave her an oyster stew afterwards, and then took her home. "Should I have kissed her at the door?" was the anxious question put to the uncle. The uncle, a practical old codger, made reply: "Well if you done all them things for her it seems to me that you done enough."

As I observe the high school kids pairing off in their little parties and promenades I have a feeling that the boy need not worry as to the proper procedure to be practiced at the front door. All he needs to do is take a deep breath and trust to the fates. He is about to be as near paradise as he will ever get. Puppy love indeed! It is the highest form of love between man and woman.

Each boy is a law unto himself and, believe it or not, the goings-on in his mind are more difficult to fathom than are those of the girls. The age of puberty varies as much in boys as in girls. One can say roughly that when they catch up with their legs puberty is past. This is likely to take place gradually about the age of sixteen, eighteen or twenty. At this period he is beset with many difficulties. Generally he is allowed to gain his information about himself the best way he can. Though usually ignored, the boy needs a father as much as the girl needs a mother, but he is much more difficult to approach. I always feel helpless when confronted by a boy I know needs information about himself. Why these things are so impossible to explain is hard to say, unless it is because one subconsciously remembers one's own timidity and early lack of a paternal advisor.

When one observes young people of the same age thrown together in high school activities, it is evident that girls usually mature earlier than boys. This is true of the mental as well as physical development. This in a way has unhappy repercussions. The girl at fourteen or sixteen is smarter than her male classmates and her obvious superiority at that age becomes a fixed idea so that she fails to realize that after a time the male catches up and becomes her equal. Sometimes a lifetime is not long enough to convince the lady of his mental maturity. The girls do the head work and the boys fall in line in a vague surprised sort of way. Blessed are those who never wake up.

It makes one's heart bleed to note how many children struggle with problems in distressed silence when frank inquiry addressed to an understanding person could dispel the perplexities in a moment. As an example I may present my own experience. For many years I kept silent about my desire to study medicine. I mentioned it to no one. When I did finally summon courage enough to tell my father, he said, with a kindly expression on his face: "All right, but there are so many doctors who do more harm than good that unless you can do better than the average you better stick to the farm. You really know how to plow corn." Yet these words were said in such a way that I knew he had full confidence that I would do better than the average. Thus a load was lifted from me, a load I had needlessly carried for many years because I had not realized I had one of the most understanding of fathers.

It is a tribute to the family doctor when the child will make a confidant of him although unwilling to go to a parent for consultation and advice. The child feels, and he is often right, that there would be no understanding, only criticism, if he consulted a parent. The parent often bases his judgment on his own experiences in a generation when everything that savored of sex was sinful. The doctor, on the other hand, has been obliged to keep up-to-date and can see the problem from the automobile angle rather than from the slow horse and buggy point of view. He knows, incidentally, that now the young people are less sex-minded than in the old days when all such thoughts were considered sinful.

One of the greatest mistakes that parents make, it seems to me, is in trying to make the child accept advice without acquainting him with the facts which underlie the adult point of view. This mistake is most often made by parents who still live in the far distant past. They were unloved by their parents and were pushed into a pen by themselves and allowed to find out what little they could. A child living in such an environment is either crushed and henceforth becomes a case in the doctor's record book—occupation: "at home"—or he escapes from parental influence entirely, and makes his own way, usually with credit.

Though the parent cannot direct the current which is sweeping his child to his destiny, a manifestation of constant interest in what the child is doing may make it possible to be of service in a crisis. This confidence must be built up through the years of infancy and childhood. The most prized compliment I have ever received came when one of my daughters, unduly driven on the athletic field, fainted because of a heart ailment. The athletic director had been duly informed about it, but had disregarded the information. Her sister remarked to the house mother: "Daddy will soon be here to see sister. He never sleeps." That meant that my daughters had full faith that their father was vigilant, ready to act at a moment's notice. They knew also, I may add to my own glory, that he never butted in on details.

If one could only live those years over again! While my girls were growing up I devoted one night each week exclusively to their wishes. Where they wanted to go, there also I went, even putting on a white tie and tails if necessary—greater love than that hath no father. Nothing but the direst surgical emergency was allowed to interfere with these dates. That idea was all right but it was just six days short. Had I my life to live over again I should be on guard like a fireman ready instantly to slide down a brass pole whenever my presence would be acceptable. True, the struggle to achieve professional distinction was the one god that led me, but once one sees the descending sun nothing counts but one's children. Inevitably, one comes to hate achievement gained at the expense of neglecting his children. That fickle goddess, ambition, leads us on and no matter how little or great the achievement we come sooner or later to realize that the lake of ambition has become a pool; in the end, we live only in the memory of the childhood of our children. It is inevitable—that as our children go forward in maturity, we go back to the early years.

We parents make our greatest mistake in trying to dictate in detail to our adolescents as to what they should do. We tell them that when they drive they must be careful at the corners, and go slow on icy pavements. But when they take the wheel all we can do is to put on good tires, see that the brakes and steering gear are in proper order, and then trust the fates. To cry out to them: "Look out for the curves and icy pavements" only aggravates them. The curves which interest them are not on the highway.

When our children are infants we can take them with us but in the adolescent years we must go with them or henceforth they, and we, travel alone. We would do a great deal of good if we went with them and learned to know what they think. I have often been amazed to discover that one of my young friends has been pondering a question sometimes for years without once mentioning it to me. I knew all the answers. But somehow I had failed to note the delicate feeling that was agitating him.

One of the wisest of my women friends teaches a Sunday-school class and she specializes in trying to find out what her young charges think about the things that are going on around them. For instance one young lass wanted to know if Moses was not the bastard son of the princess who rescued him. Where did she get the idea? That is the proper angle from which to view our young charges. What they think is of vastly more importance than what we think. If they refuse to believe things that never were true it is useless to try to convince them. Keep the kids talking and you are their friend.

Next to the influence of the home we must reckon the influence of the churches. It is pleasing to note that religion has expended much effort to keep up with the changing times. Unfortunately it must be admitted that greater concern is too often expended in keeping the doctrine on straight than in meeting the needs of the young people. It is what the children want and not our beliefs that should dictate the policy of the church. Good intentions may only chase them onto the street. Every parent should know that his first duty is to his children and not to the church.

I may make my point clear by citing two instances. One of the brightest of my boy friends, whom I had recently met at a father-son banquet, remarked to me what a fine thing such contacts were. He went on to say he enjoyed it thoroughly because not only was his father present but, because it was interesting to get to know the fathers of his friends. He continued: "I like Sunday-school and the activities in the basement, but listening to the stilted sermons upstairs," he paused and added, "it just can't be done." Whatever may have been preached to him was lost. Some one had lost his opportunity of meeting that boy's needs.

The boy above quoted, quickly added that he liked to hear the Reverend Mr. Doe preach, indicating the pastor of another church. I hastened to find out what those sermons were about that the boy liked to hear. They had to do with the problems of life as related to young folks, the value of industry, courage and honesty.

One Sunday morning one of my nurses came tripping down the hall, a magnificent symphony in blue, at least blue spots. "Going to church, Girlie?" I inquired. "No," she replied, "I am not going to church." Her tone of voice rather than her words convinced me that she was not going to church. I urged her to tell me why not. This is the reply

I got, in words with a ring of bitterness: "The last time I was in church the minister had the whale swallowing Jonah. I got to thinking that the available oxygen in the whale's stomach must be limited and the hydrochloric acid in the stomach within half an hour would have made Jonah as bare of skin as a peeled bologna. I just thought either the preacher is a fool or he thinks I am." That old tale was concocted before oxygen was discovered and before the physiology of digestion was thought of, and that girl simply would have nothing of it. Our children think, and we had better give heed to their thinking or we will lose them. What has Jonah got to offer a bright girl with her whole life before her?

I make it a point to listen in on radio sermons put on by the various members of a council of churches in a neighboring city. They contain nothing of interest to the young. The young will not listen to tales of things they believe never happened. Makes no difference if the old folks believe them or not. I was taught to believe prayers would be answered. Putting them to the test, I discovered that they were utterly impotent to help an exhausted boy to the end of the day. I have never recovered from that experience. It would have been better had I been taught that I was subject to the unchanging laws of muscle metabolism.

Young people are not interested in salvation nor in the problems of death. They are interested only in living. They subconsciously feel that they are the future parents of the next generation. We make a mistake when we condone sermons about things that never happened by pretending to listen to them. Or perhaps we do believe they did happen, once. But what difference does it make? Unless the young people voluntarily accept a like point of view we do them harm by making them listen as a matter of filial duty. As soon as they get from under the parental thumb they will cease to listen. Our young people are moulded by their environment and it is a question whether or not we are doing our best to make the influences salutary. It is their environment, but we made it for them. What we think as individuals has ceased to be a factor.

F

Not all children are so independent. Some retain full faith in the teaching of their fathers. One influence, most apt to occur at the 'teen age, is religious fervor. One would like to leave it unmentioned but a doctor cannot. Innocent children, told that they are by nature sinful and must repent to be saved, sometimes bring us our saddest problems. In my childhood, each child was given to understand that he must be able to point to a definite time when the transformation occurred. I never did; my father taught me that there never was any excuse for lying.

Perhaps the only sins these young folks can bring to mind are practices that are not nice but harmless; nevertheless these become fixed ideas. We find here an expression of the close relation of religion and sex which stands out in history. Everybody but the doctor can deny its most eloquent expression. In past years there were few great revivals which did not leave some child permanently unbalanced mentally, destined to spend the remaining years in an institution. These are now rare instances because the old time revivals are a thing of the past. Yet lighter forms of mental distress still come to haunt the doctor. The doctor may suspect that some such experience is the cause of a silent nervous disorder. Direct confirmation may be lacking. Yet in the very fervor of denial the doctor finds confirmation of his suspicions. Like a small boy emerging from a pantry with a jam-covered face bursting forth in denial before he is accused. Only a few years ago I was confronted by such a case; a girl headed for an asylum because of an unexplained melancholia. Had I not had personal, nonprofessional knowledge of an early religious experience it would have been inexplainable. The idea of original sin is an invention of the devil, and it is cruel to tell a child that he is lost unless he repents.

Equally tragic, perhaps even more tragic because they often are children of brilliant and independent minds, are those who, resisting the influence of their religious teaching, to the bewilderment of their parents strike out on paths of their own, too often to an unhappy end. These often present a subconscious sex background, so that the doctor has a premonition of what likely will some day become a surgical problem.

Let me repeat. If we could just suppress our own ideas and come to realize that religion, like methods of transportation, has changed with the passing years! Many ministers realize this fully. If we could just suppress our own prejudices or ideas, shave off our ecclesiastic whiskers so that the young people can see that we bear a kindly expression when we view their doings.

We are the product of the past, which is made up of our early teachings and our own experiences. Our boys and girls are the composite of the influences of today, like it or not.

In the girl in her 'teens we see first the conflict between the woman and the female. She has acquired a shape and, having viewed it, pronounces it good and proceeds to exhibit it where it will be likely to make the best impression. This is purely instinctive with her for likely she does not see beyond the next school party.

If my observations are correct, we are very apt to misjudge the doings of our young people. The young girl may be an artist in the exhibition of shape. The parents, having tasted life without exactly liking it, recoil at the exhibition, primarily because they had no shape to exhibit in their youth. The parents think only of sex consummated, because that is what they started with. The young lass likely has no such notion; she is still the artist attracting the world in the abstract. By undue anxiety the parent may direct the adolescent mind into channels it has not yet reached.

We wail: "Child, watch your step," yet neither our prayers nor our tears will guide her. All she has to guide her is what we implanted in her baby years. The value of our teaching is about to be put to the test. Did not we grown-ups do a lot of silly face licking before we thought of sex? If many an old horse could be resurrected and given the power of speech we might all be made to take a back seat. If we could make our children understand that at their age we had even less sense than they it would help to gain their confidence. As I view my grandchildren I am free to admit that they show much better judgment than their grandpa, chiefly because what they do is no longer forbidden, hence not sinful. We live in the past, and our bulging waist-lines and creaking joints force us to make a virtue of necessity.

Our children are a part of the world about them and we can serve them best by giving them a safe environment. Often when I am talking to a group of men, true representatives of their communities, about what they think of the environment they furnish for their young folks and their responsibility for it, I discover that they do not think. I have put this question to a goodly number, and they were astonished to learn that there was anything to think about. Environment must be adjusted to the needs of the children, or to what they think are their needs. The fundamental approach of young people toward their elders is: "Don't ask them, tell them." Even if they request our permission we must realize that after all, they do so only as a courtesy. They have already decided on what they are going to do.

It has been my great privilege to have had under my charge for màny years about a hundred pupil nurses. Most of these kids were just out of high school. They are in the full bloom of early womanhood. I have often said that I would be willing to take the judgment of that bunch of girls on any question of moral conduct. I would have more confidence in their judgment than in that of any hundred matrons. For instance, some years ago when girls first bobbed their hair my nurses wanted to join the parade. My superintendent promptly had a fit, declaring she would resign before she would have "boy-headed nurses." So I had a conference with the nurses and I agreed to follow their judgment. They went to their mothers with the statement that it was all right with me if they had their mothers' consent. I am afraid the superintendent's view-point was not mentioned. All but three got permission to bob, and bob they did. Nobody died in convulsions, not even the superintendent. The girls wanted to be like other girls. I did not like the closely cropped heads of that period any more than the superintendent but I had sense enough to know that when the cyclone of progress is headed our way we had better take to a cave in order to be among those present when the storm passes. Now the way the nurses fix their hair I regard as the most becoming within my recollection. The cute little curls make one want to touch them to see if they will unravel. They will.

If we do our best to mold our children's environment we should go to the trouble to keep track of their doings in order to see what influences are active. They have their concerts, their plays, their dances, and what not, to which we parents are invited or to which we may gain admittance. Do we go? Not many. When my young folks tell me that such and so is going to happen on a given night, it is to me not an invitation but a command. Sure grandpa is as proud of them as a peacock is of his tail and I believe it does us all good, even if our minds are filled with regrets at the memory that fifty years ago all the things the young folks now do were sinful in our parents' eyes and a transgression would lead to hell. But if we engage in these reveries, at least by our presence we show our approval, even though our creaky joints cry to high heaven for the comforts of the fireside.

Grown-ups are too ready to recoil in horror at something which they do not understand; but they are unwilling to do anything to anticipate it. The farmer, before he turns out a new bunch of calves, takes care that there are no harmful weeds which might poison them. Parents just tell their calves not to eat any harmful weeds, but don't trouble to furnish any botanical description of poisonous plants. We are of the preceding generation, or the one before that. If we show interest the young folks will teach their dads or even their granddads which are the harmful weeds.

People still act too much as individuals or as small groups. Although we are, in a measure, collectively responsible for the environment of our adolescents, we can achieve nothing unless we speak with a common voice. And we must realize that there are many factors that influence them.

The first, because the most obvious, is the matter of dress. Whether it is the result of education, or a subconscious expression of sex, is difficult to say. Very likely the motive varies. Certainly public opinion has much to do with the question of dress, or lack of it. We should realize that our child will be greatly influenced by what she wears. Clothes can help her to develop confidence, enable her to feel one of the group, or they can develop an inferiority complex in her because she appears different from her friends. I recall with blood in my eye that my sisters, skillful with the needle, were not allowed to dress attractively in their girl-hood because of the ecclesiastic edict that becoming clothes would attract the male, which was, of course, carnal. For reasons unknown to me, my parents submitted to this dictum to the permanent hurt of my sisters.

No matter how much we may try to concentrate on the doings of the young males, the girls constantly dominate the scenery. It is generally stated that the object in woman's dress is to attract the male. I believe this notion of the underlying object of dress, at least as it applies to young adolescent girls, is overstressed. They only want to join the parade, just as mama when she joins the parade on Easter morning, is concerned in knocking over Mrs. Smith with a new creation rather than with pleasing papa.

Girls are not so dumb. They know that they will attract the male, no matter how they dress. They have only themselves to please. If we look at the history of dress in the various periods this should be clear. Much has been made of the dresses "in the gay nineties." Look at them and weep. Those were my susceptible years. And believe it or not, we young yokels of that day thought the girls were beautiful. Bustles, hoops, long skirts, balloon sleeves, high choker collars, "rats" in the hair, and a lot of other things we never learned to identify. If the girls had deliberately decked themselves out with the design of frightening all the young males out of the neighborhood they could hardly have added a single touch. At any rate we young males hovered around the garden gate. Why our horses were not frightened is a

mystery to me. Perhaps they figured that it made no difference, since it was not they who had to marry the spectacles.

In the early period it seemed to be the general opinion
that the girl should be dressed modestly and comfortably.
Just what do those words mean? Today if girls act modest
their clothes are modest and if they look pretty they most
assuredly are comfortable. At least one would be led to believe this as one views the stream of young ladies headed
for high school. The boys are likely to be dressed for con-
venience and economy. It depends on what the other boys
wear. Nobody cares what they wear and neither do they,
just so they look like the other boys.

The various school activities furnish a fine chance to study
the effect of clothes. In the school band boy and girl are
equal because they dress alike. The mind is on the music,
or is it? At least viewing the magnificent young ladies it is
difficult for grandpa to keep his mind on the music, and
when the drum majorettes and cheer leaders prance out
leading the band no fool is so old but that he envies the
boys of today.

As we look at the clothes, first we see a close resemblance
to the prancing fillies in the ring at a horse show. The prancing at the horse show, at least, is not sex inspired, and I believe the same is true of the prancing band. To my eyes,
this is a pleasing scene because the minds of the girls and
boys are centered on the work at hand. But dominating all
is the sense of pride, the satisfaction of doing something or
being a part of the parade. Smart girls get the spirit before
the plaguing evidence of endocrine development absorbs
them. Young folks have more sense than their elders give
them credit for having. This can only mean that they have
more sense than their elders. Pants indeed! The young girls
look cute because they wear them without self-conscious-
ness. When pants are worn by grown-ups for exhibition
purposes, it is a different matter.

Perhaps we should take our young folks of 'teen age less
seriously and with less apprehension. They fall violently in
love. The worst case I ever saw was of a young boy who

walked in the middle of the street past his girl's home. I observed this for a period of several nights. One night I accosted him at 2 A.M. as I was returning from a professional call and asked him why he did not go home. He gave forth a wail, "Nobody knows how much I love that girl" or words to that effect. But he got over it and did not marry her. Good thing she had sense—he didn't seem to have any.

Such loves may be looked upon as acute psychoses. The prognosis is good. They recover in three or six months. The important thing is that they should be looked on as a mental aberration temporary in character. Their pains may be only remotely and subconsciously related to sex. Only general hygienic measures are required. Lost weight, though it may be considerable, is soon regained with the recovery from the spell. Of course the dangerous cliff of matrimony should not only be decorated with a "Danger" sign but also protected with a high fence. It is the parents' business to keep them under observation until they recover.

Beautiful as the association of the children in the 'teen age may be to the casual observer, and even to the parents, the doctor looks on many things he sees with apprehension. Boys and girls associate with each other and learn to see a difference. A certain girl may be outstanding for a certain boy for reasons he does not comprehend. The girl is likely to be even more strongly impressed by difference in boys. This is likely to result in a certain boy and girl withdrawing themselves from the common herd and devoting their entire available time to each other. These are classified by their fellow students as "steadies." That is, a boy and girl become so attached to each other that they have no association with other young people about them. I have no intention of telling the whole truth about such situations but so much of it should be said to make it clear that the endocrines in their development dominate the situation. What one sees here is the result of countless years of stimulation, stimulation, please note, in the name of God; and in our stupidity we call it love. The bud is crushed in the early hours of the morning just as the sun is rising.

But what shall we do about it? The children, knowing nothing about endocrinology, think it is love. They have no more sense than their parents. Mothers bring us these young people in the 'teen age and tell the doctor the patient is exhausted. The mothers say it is not so much the school work as the side activities that exhaust the patient. In the abstract they are quite right. I look at these mothers sometimes and wonder if they are thinking of the same thing that occupies my mind. Likely not. In some cases the young people are surreptitiously trying out Judge Lindsay's theory, with the inevitable result. Most cases happily do not go that far, but I have seen a lot that I wish I could wipe from my memory.

Even though things usually do not go so far, irreparable harm may be done. It is and remains but the manifestation of endocrine love. Even in its finest form the doctor sees enough to cause him apprehension. The stimulus of "necking" leaves the patient in a congestive state and the doctor knows that he will sooner or later have the patient to treat for painful menstruation or some other secondary disturbance. Fortunate is the girl who does not fall into the hands of an operator, allegedly a surgeon, who in his stupidity removes a "chronic appendix" or a "cystic ovary." If this happens she at once enters a lifetime of regret.

Nobody of course tells the doctor the truth but he can guess it, though what he can do about it remains unanswered. The only safe way, for the doctor, is to do nothing. When a girl child cannot bear to see its boy child friend associate with another child friend, there is the germlet of jealousy sprouting and it will endure. When a child is so far lost that he cannot take another to a social function for fear of exciting the wrath of his "steady" an irreparable injury has been done. The nervous manifestations of such situations are legion. Loss of weight, vomiting, headache, convulsions confront the doctor. Parents should realize that the child's weal or woe must be determined right there, and that the situation must be decided as intelligently as the problem of what to do if the child has an acute appendicitis. What one sees on the contrary is that the parents encourage the relationship, particularly the mother if she thinks the boy would make a good match for her daughter. Possibly so, but what are the children to do with the intervening ten or fifteen years? Besides it is not possible to tell just what kind of dog the pup will grow up to be.

When parents see their children caught up in this spell, what can be done about it? Perhaps if they see it coming and if they have sense enough to warn the children, they might do something about it, but usually it has got beyond the stage when warning will do any good before even the mother notices it. That forcible interdiction has its disasters, I have seen many times.

Unfortunately many parents encourage these early fascinations, to what extent I will not say. They must have their fling, the mothers tell the doctor. If the doctor has a knowledge of the childhood of the parents he knows just what they mean. But when disaster comes, they run to the doctor.

What can we doctors do about it? We can proceed on the basis that six months of separation will cure any case of endocrine love. Mother takes the daughter on a long journey. Europe is no longer available for such trips. This loss of terrain has not yet reached the eye of the alarmists but it is worthy of attention. Of course daughter must not know the basis of the plan or she will rebel. Happily this problem usually solves itself when one child goes to one school, the other to another. Some parents plan with this in mind and daughter is sent to a girls' school or a "finishing school."

I once talked to a mother about a sixteen-year-old daughter. The mother admitted that, although the daughter was afflicted with a most beautiful and most intense love, she knew she was too young. She said she prayed that the big love might cease; but if it did not she would know that it was God's will that it should continue and she must needs submit. I reminded the mother that we step on the gas and do ninety miles and pray that the tires will hold. I asked her if the fact that we were given brains enough to see about the tires before we start did not mean something to her.

Was it not sacrilege to fail to use what little brains we possess? She finished me off by asking what I would do if I were in her place. Discussing things in the abstract is a fairly safe diversion but when it comes to cases, it is a different matter.

We doctors sometimes get a backfire in our efforts to help our patients. An instance may be mentioned. One of these cases had to do with one of my medical students. In those days a high school education admitted one to the medical course. His sweetheart insisted on immediate marriage. Reasons obvious: she just could not live without him. They were married and he quit his studies and got a job. The boy, after the period of satiety, came to realize that he had been sidetracked from what he again came to believe was his lifework. Domestic disaster was the inevitable result. He came to blame his wife for diverting him, when in fact he was equally to blame for his boyhood weakness.

I have noted elsewhere the fine advantages children now have in the associated school activities, notably the study of music. As the child grows older, dancing quite naturally is added to music. Dancing presents a great variety of influences; in children it is always beautiful because it is only rhythm of action. In the adolescent period as much may be said of it, if confined to young people of a group and if properly supervised. At public dances, where young people meet as strangers, the idea of rhythm is likely to be lost and the dance in fact becomes just an endocrine orgy. The harm done depends on the individual.

It is interesting, from the doctor's point of view, to watch each couple and note how they react. It is possible to pick out those who will likely become a doctor's problem sooner or later. My father said to me fifty years ago, when the general opinion was that the devil played the fiddle at all dances, that dances may be good or bad depending on who was doing the dancing. I can add nothing to the viewpoint. Dances are good or bad depending entirely on why the participants dance.

Enough of this. To understand love we must study it in the beginning and the end of life, before the endocrines begin their rampage and after they have become atrophied. There are many factors that foster the intensity of child love. Things that stimulate a very natural function and may be influenced by the environment. The old saw that what is everybody's business is nobody's business is illustrated here. We approve of things by the simple act of neglecting them.

The indifference parents show to the environment of their children is the most serious indictment against our so-called civilization. In fact, we allow the environment to take care of itself. Sex lives on what it feeds on. It is susceptible to excitation by suggestive things. The baser elements of the human race seem to present the least resistance. This means that here lies the largest audience. Suggestiveness centers around the female form but even more about certain poses. The moral atmosphere which surrounds our young folks is measured by a commercial yardstick.

Who is responsible for the exhibition of nudity one sees on the screen and in the papers? Not our children. One finds behind it somewhere a commercial purpose. The female form appears in all sorts of advertisements when it is wholly extraneous to the thing advertised, such diverse things as an automobile or a hotel veranda. That universities should sell the advertising space on the back covers of their magazines to cigarette concerns whose ads picture all but nude females shows how high up the influence of the dollar extends in shaping the environment of our children. Perhaps cigarette smoking by girls is all right but certainly it should not be promoted by our university publications, nor should the impression be fostered that it is smart to smoke and go almost naked.

From beauties on the most prominent page of our university magazines we travel easily to the most deplorable exhibition of modern times, the so-called beauty contests. They are conceived by schemers for commercial purposes. They are degrading to the contestants and those who view them, except those for whom degradation is impossible.

Beauties are judged in these contests according to the rear or side view; the eyes—the windows of the intellect—do

not count. That the purely female element has a wide
appeal is manifested by the fact that the all but nude female
appears in so many pictures in our periodicals. I have twitted
some of my newspaper friends for publishing constantly and
persistently pages of beauty contests, bathing beauties, and
always legs and more legs. Since the press thinks it moulds
public opinion one might suppose that it is responsible for
nude shows. But that is wrong. No publishers go to work
with the idea of promoting a taste for the immodest and
vulgar. The fact is the press merely senses public desire and
caters to it, or at least it thinks it does. Evidently it is a
matter of individual opinion, for some newspapers are never
without such pictures, while others avoid them. My favorite
newspapers do avoid them and somehow they seem to pros-
per sufficiently to build galleries of real art.

Be this as it may, the step between the exhibitions, the
so-called beauty contests, and the illegal shows put on for the
Tired Business Man, is represented by a very small piece of
silk, or a fan. It is all very puzzling.

Nothing is immodest in art. Many uncivilized tribes are at
once nude and moral. However, even the small articles of
clothing they wear are designed to cover something. Our
beauty contestants, on the contrary, wear a little something
designed to meet police regulations, but it is so arranged
that it actually emphasizes what it is supposed to conceal.
That certainly is not art. There should be some difference
between art and nudity. Art is never vulgar. Even Eve, who
had no audience other than Adam, had a sense of modesty
(after she tasted of the apple of knowledge). It seems in the
end to be largely a matter of becoming accustomed to the
custom.

I would add here, in defense of my newspaper friends, that
it is a more a matter of position than nudity. It is left for
the magazines to exhibit suggestive poses. These are much
more morally devastating than simple nudity. Nudity may
be represented in many innocent ways, but the suggestive
poses can mean but one thing. If such poses do not violate
the laws of decency it is difficult to imagine how they can

be violated. To call such poses sexy would be to pay them an undeserved compliment. They depict lust, nothing else. The police chase solicitors from the streets, but these sheets are sent out to respectable districts and they may be on many readers' tables, brought in by themselves or their children. Without question, they are vulgar, and inimical to the morals of young people. Incidentally, the results give doctors headaches because we must treat the kind of people who read that sort of stuff. The road of lust leads to the doctor's door, and to the operating room. But who cares what the doctor thinks? His mission in life is to undo what fools do. My fingers ache from the incessant toil involved in digging out the natural result of these pictures. And what do I get for my labors? A woman condemned to a childless life, a life of silent regret. Complaining women, who have more different kinds of pains than you will find in all medical books, are a pain in the neck to the doctor. But the silent, uncomplaining woman who lives a life of disillusionment because as a girl she lacked the protecting care that a Christian community should have afforded her—that is what hurts the doctor. He hates the agencies which deliberately add to human suffering, by omission as much as by commission.

The effects of anatomical display on various audiences vary greatly. I had an experience a few years ago that illustrates this point. I was scheduled for a regular speech before a state medical meeting. I hadn't much of an audience so I abbreviated my talk in order to find out what the counter attraction was. I found it on the campus. It was archery practice hour. Grouped about on the grass were some twenty or thirty college girls. There were half a dozen archery targets. Some of the young ladies actually had bows and arrows, but all of them had shapes, shapes draped only with silk diapers and diminutive bibs. Yet there was my medical audience, made up of doctors of medicine of all ages from youth to incipient senility—just looking. Nor was it to be wondered at; even a doctor seldom sees so much female at one look as was exposed there. All these doctors had dissected the human body many times, all had examined various parts of it in the pursuit of their practice; but here the entire ensemble was exposed to view all at one time.

In contrast to this gawking audience of doctors were the boy students, who sauntered along the walks going to classes, without giving all that scenery even a fleeting glance. The girls, instead of attracting them, seemed to give them a pain. Perhaps one might use the old saw that familiarity breeds contempt. The girls were not smart enough to see that by overplaying the part, or over-exposing the parts, they were actually repelling the young males. Everyone is flattered if a little is left to his imagination. Many a doctor left that scene with the words: "Poor fools, even universities give them no protection."

Yet perhaps we judge them too harshly. Perhaps they were using the only means they had to secure themselves a meal ticket. A hen lays many eggs and for this reason is tolerated as a commercial asset. Peahens lay only two or three eggs a year and are allowed to live only because of their beautiful tails. That there is something to this law of compensation was evidenced by the fact that there were many young ladies about the buildings who were normally dressed, perhaps not possessed of shapes crying for exhibition; their attractiveness obviously was above the collarbone. They could learn enough so that they could earn a meal ticket.

I observed the power of public opinion in the matter of dress this summer. Teams of soft ball players made up of boys and girls were the subject, or object. At the first game all the boys were dressed in long pants as is usual in that game. Some of the girls also wore long pants but others rivalled the bathing beauties in garb. True, in repose their dress conformed to police regulations, but in the excitement of the game any observant officer might see the ordinance violated. In fact he could see everything. Remarkable was the confidence some of these girls placed in the integrity of a tiny string, more confidence, in fact, than most of us would have placed in a two-inch strap. The point is that after a few games all the girls were dressed as were the boys.

Somehow I was proud of the boys. By their example they caused the girls all to dress decently.

Yet this is no trifling matter. Public acclaim and approbation is a desirable thing in the eyes of most people, particularly the young, but to expose the human form for the delectation of the erotic population has a far reaching influence. When bathing beauties are selected in local contests it is bad enough, but when state representatives are selected in national contests it is certainly going too far. God forbid that the Queen of Kansas should ever be selected because of the shape of her legs, et cetera, particularly the et ceteras.

I want to emphasize particularly that it is the monthly magazines which are the chief offenders in the publication of pictures suggestive of immorality. I beg of the reader only to look over the periodicals exhibited on our newsstands. One wonders if there is really anything so rotten as to violate the law. The dividing line must be very narrow. Look at even some of the allegedly respectable magazines that defame youth by picturing come-on poses. Every time any one buys one of those damned rotten sheets he is kicking his own child in the face. The publishers publish such things because they believe it is what the public, including each of us, ordinarily wants.

The foregoing tirade has to do for the most part with girls of the 'teen age. But even mere children receive impressions which would shock us if we knew about them. In the day of the silent screen I used to collect a bunch of neighborhood children and take them to a movie. One evening the picture shown presented a young lady lying on a bed, very thinly clad, resting on one elbow. A male garbed in a bathrobe was walking across the room approaching the bed. I was nearly paralyzed when one of the little girls, certainly less than twelve, whispered: "Looky, she wants him to get in bed with her." Just then the scene changed. Even if children do not understand such scenes it will subconsciously dull the finer perceptions so that in later life they will regard such things with equanimity. Sure enough, we say they are love scenes; they are not love scenes, not even sex scenes—they depict nothing less than lust. Young people exposed to such scenes are much more likely to develop engine trouble on the way home than those not so exposed.

When young people are thrown together, one of them may have become accustomed to such scenes while the other may have been protected from them. These fundamental differences may not become immediately apparent. We, of an allegedly democratic society, prize highly the liberty of young people to select their life partners from a polyglot population. Yet after all it is an unfortunate situation; impossible combinations are made, largely due to the difference between moonlight and daylight. If a boy goes to buy a necktie, he consults his mother and his friends; but in the more serious problem he depends on his myopic vision to guide him, and by the light of the moon, at that.

We read of how "friendship ripened into love." Perhaps so, in a way. It would be better if we said, to friendship was added love and to love sex, for certainly before the marriage altar is reached, sex is added. Seldom does any one marry for love alone. Perhaps, indeed, we do not marry those we really have loved most deeply. In fact, love alone, unstimulated by sex, recoils from the final step. There is no definite line. Perhaps the first kiss defines the line between friendship and love or between love and sex. The kiss over the garden gate, between the screen and the front door, behind the steering wheel—there is bliss indeed. I wonder if there ever was an instance where the boy thought of it first.

I have previously referred to the menstrual difficulties which sometimes distress girls. Problems of quite a different character may distress the doctor. This comes about because so many of our most brilliant girls have delicate bodies. They strive to make high grades higher. Besides their school work they have their music. Because of their brilliance, they are drawn into all sorts of school activities. With the help of their doctor and his tonics, these girls struggle through to graduation, only to fall exhausted when it is over. Exhausted when their lives should be just beginning. The

G

damage is permanent. No achievement is worth a stunted growth. Of course the girl's achievements flatter her and particularly her parents, but the price is too great. They marry; and from then on they are a problem for some doctor. If he begins to operate the wreck is soon complete.

The other side of the case is represented by the girl who is not afflicted with outstanding brilliancy. She may have unusual talent, but she uses a part of it in the pursuit of things other than high grades. She seems not to have anything in mind beyond getting by. Don't be too sure she is not thinking. I still treasure a letter written from college by one of my daughters. She writes: "Well, Dad, my grades are nothing to delight papa but I like my victuals and I am having a good time," and, she might have added, preserving a fine physical reserve which is still paying dividends in a small group of children.

There are all kinds of girls and just as many ideas and outlooks on life. This brings to mind that one morning in the staff room one of my best friends remarked: "Well, my daughter is starting to college today. What she is going for I don't know; neither does she, but she is too young to marry and there is nothing else to do. It will fill in four years of her time." I hope the daughter did not know of the cynical outlook of her father, but it is difficult to fool children. Perhaps this was all true at the moment but the young lady received a degree of culture and some knowledge of the culinary arts. In addition she formed an alliance with a future young doctor that has endured. In so many cases children are smarter than their parents. But even so a child of college age, if properly reared, should have some idea of the possible benefit to be derived from a course of study in college. I hasten to add that I do not mean to cast aspersions on the young ladies who go to college with nothing but a domestic future in mind. In such cases even more heed should be given to those scholastic studies which will aid in preserving the catch, if any.

In this connection an amusing incident comes to my mind. A friend of mine who had taught Greek in a university for a number of years married a friend of mine. Once while making a visit to their home I was greeted half a block away by the lusty howls of an infant. As I hove into sight she remarked with asperity: "There isn't a single thing in Goodwin's Greek grammar that tells what to do for a yelling child." A trained nurse would have known what to do.

It has fallen to my lot to have educated a number of girls, in addition to my own. In my ignorance, I encouraged studies which would have a utilitarian end, since most of the girls wished to go to college in order to prepare for the teaching profession. But all have ended at the matrimonial altar, little prepared for the life before them by their school experience. I complained of this to a friend of mine after a young lady with an exceptional high school record failed utterly in college but came out attached to a young professional man. My friend replied that I had been a hundred per cent successful, that it was my own distorted view that was at the base of my lamentations. "What do you think a girl goes to college for?" he asked as a parting shot. But I still grumble at myself because I feel I paid too much for a raw graduate. That he was a young lawyer is purely incidental.

That my friend was at least partly right became evident soon after, when another young lady said quite frankly: "I'm going to do a little picking where and while the picking is good." Very well, such frankness clears the air, but here is the rub. When a girl goes out to find one where the picking is good she is on a sex quest, and the union is a sex union. True enough, in many cases love comes too if there is mutual respect, but it is taking a big risk. It is much safer to be guided by mutual respect first and let the other things come as a secondary consideration. Too often in such quests tragedy creeps in.

Years ago I observed the following case: A graduate of a training school for nurses, who had been raised in an excellent, intensely religious family who forbade the usual associations with young folks, became pregnant. She journeyed to a distant city, fell into the hands of a quack, and had an abortion performed, with the result that usually follows. She came back to my hospital afflicted with an uncontrollable streptococcic infection. She lingered for months, growing more emaciated day by day. Her eyes retracted into their sockets, and as they did so seemed to become more far-seeing. That infection causes little pain but speeds up the mental faculties and draws out time immeasurably. There was never a complaint, and I often wondered what was running through that brilliant mind. What is a fetus compared to the life of such a girl? I have always felt like a coward for denying her help when she came to me early when it would have been so simple. Yet a doctor cannot break the law of the land. But even now I sometimes feel it would have been more honorable to have rotted in jail than to have refused her help. If people who make the laws had to sit a few hours at such a bedside trying to figure out what those eyes were seeing— perhaps they would change those laws.

In late years new influences have entered. Indeed things have changed since the war now known as the World War I. In that war we saved democracy and of course ended all wars, but what else we have gained, or lost, is too deep for us old doctors to fathom. The utterly disgusting insane talk of "war babies," indulged in by parents, was made less serious because their children had more sense than their elders. In those insane years soldiers told me that mothers solicited war babies for their daughters. Sure, the thing to do now is to deny that such things ever happened. That should settle the question. Nevertheless we doctors could tell a lot, that is we could if we understood it all. I am not going to say that the hymen, the sign of virginity, disappeared from the nation with the war, but if some one does make that statement do not get too bold with him. He might add a lot more.

Lest I be misunderstood, I hasten to say that as I see them, girls now have more sense than at any other period of my experience. They know what they are about and keep their heads. Collectively speaking I believe our young women have more moral sense than their mothers. At least they escape many disasters which ignorance brought on their mothers.

Not all girls are able to acquire a college education or even to expose themselves to the possibility. The vast army of employed young women in cities are a separate problem. They are free from all home restraints, often the product of homes where the influence had been immoral or even vicious. The cramped quarters of a boarding house make it impossible for diversions to come to them, and being young, they seek entertainment where they can find it. To these, the basement of the church is a boon, but all too often they shy away from this because of what they have heard upstairs in years gone by of the universal presence of sin. The plain fact is they haven't sinned yet but the possibilities sound interesting. The church basement encourages the companionship of young people of both sexes, but from the lack of previous training they keep away. Sometimes the possibilities of finding attractive companions are limited. One young lady was heard to remark: "There ain't no man worth havin' in the church I go to. I've got to get me another church."

Numerous other societies are available to this class of young women. Their chief defect is that they lack the contact with members of the other sex that the coeducational schools and the churches afford. We provide places for the young folks to go, notably the Y.W.C.A. and like institutions, but no one goes to the trouble to lend their personal greeting. "Room and board" is not enough for young people.

To sum up, the crying need of the day is better parents, parents who appreciate that sex, a necessary thing is not the end of life and that it may terminate in lust unless it has a background of something nobler. Protect the children from those things that teach that the aim of life is lust. Changing the environment of our young people is the job for the community. It is every man's responsibility to give moral tone to his environment. All should be able to agree on the fundamental factors desirable. Little groups engaged in irrelevant matters will not accomplish it. Irrelevant matters are as the color of the spokes of a wheel. All of them lead to the hub. The most orthodox must admit that the matter of hell is a long way off but their moral conduct is an immediate need.

It is not enough that young people are supplied with the implements of entertainment. One should join them. Believe it or not, an old duffer like me is joyfully welcomed at all sorts of feeds, at the end of athletic seasons, appreciations for the band, endless things. Adult companionship, to be acceptable, must be free of any sense of chaperonage or policing but must have a full feeling of equality. People should remember that from such places of general gathering daughter or son may bring home a life partner. Thus, what seemed to have been a very impersonal problem may at any moment become a very personal one.

Even if young people escape immediate dire consequences, their experiences sometimes have repercussions that make real problems for the doctor. Looking back at her experiences from more mature years, the young woman wonders if it will ever be possible for her to marry a respectable man, and if so, must she tell him all of her past? Often she asks the doctor about it. If young people were frank with each other before the great event it would save the doctor a lot of trouble later. Therefore the doctor tells them that the future partner will receive the truth with greater equanimity before the marriage than afterwards. If it is learned from other sources, no matter how small the indiscretion may have been, trouble begins. Sex anticipated is much more tolerant than sex satisfied. Therefore all lies previously told or acts committed should be wiped off the slate before the clerk is paid his two dollars. The girl can tell her prospect anything on the calendar and the Lothario will still protest that he is unworthy of her. Even at that he may be telling the truth. As for telling the young lady the truth—never mind; she will already have drawn blueprints of the alterations she has in mind to make after the ceremony. Marrying some one in order to reform him has challenged many a disillusioned young lady worthy of a better fate. So in summary it may be said that it is all right to lie about the bait, but admit the misstatements before you take the hook out of the fish's mouth.

Fortunately for the comfort of the doctor, the young people of today know some of the pitfalls. They tell the repentant young man to show a clean bill of health from the doctor. Even then they may ask the old family doctor: "Just how reliable is the Wassermann test?" Some states now demand that a certificate be exhibited to the licensing clerk. This is a commendable step forward but there are too many loop holes; however, it is perhaps better than nothing. As for themselves, they tell the doctor the truth. Accustomed to seeing all there is to see from childhood on, the doctor is free to make whatever examination may seem to be required. Girls want to know if they have been unfortunate in this or that.

How wise young people can be is illustrated by the following incident: A lass of seventeen recently wanted to know the cause of an abdominal enlargement. She said she was not worried about pregnancy because she did not have any of the symptoms, which she recited with a detailed accuracy that would have done credit to a medical student. She concluded therefore that the tumor she had was an ovarian cyst, and she was exactly right. Such knowledge on the part of a mature woman the doctor has learned to take with a degree of equanimity, but in a tiny high school girl— Where did she get all that knowledge of the early symptoms of pregnancy? The wisdom of some of our young people jars even an old doctor.

How much should we teach the young folks and when? An amusing incident was recently related to me. The mother of a ten year old son told him that a neighbor had a baby inside her and some day she would give birth to it. "Oh yes," was his nonchalant reply: "just like all mammals." One of the most intelligent mothers I know, after being pestered by a pair of children aged eight and ten as to the wherefore and whence of puppies, secured a female dog and they found out all about the problem that perplexed them. This method seemed a bit bold at first but I believe the results have been salutary.

The adolescent male is not a great problem to the doctor. He is in periodic need of general repairs as a result of his activities, but save for automobile accidents his hurts are seldom serious. Given a decent environment he steers surprisingly free of the serious complications which cause the social reformers to pull out their hair in such large handfuls. Moral problems are more or less local affairs. If the boy thinks his father is the greatest man on earth in his adolescent years, given a decent environment he seldom needs a doctor.

One of the most serious problems confronting the boy in his early years is that of venereal disease. The best asset he can have is a good mother. It is his attitude toward her that will determine his attitude toward the girls with whom he associates. He will automatically discover the difference between women and females which, after all, is the greatest problem that confronts the male throughout his life. Fathers are too apt to feel that when they have sent their sons to the Y.M.C.A. to hear the secretary depict the horrors of venereal disease they have done their duty. Sometimes traveling secretaries are sent out with specimens showing the ravages of social diseases. But nobody ever was frightened into being good. They miss the point entirely. We doctors can cure venereal disease but the respect young men lose for all womankind by promiscuity is permanent.

Telling boys what not to do is not productive of any great good. Giving them something worth while to do is the best way to keep them in the straight and narrow path. Some years ago the boys in our town wanted to play baseball on Sunday. This had my hearty support but was viewed with grave apprehension by the churches. Several persons visited me to upbraid me for encouraging the boys to break the Sabbath. I replied that I had treated boys who had acquired a disease at all sorts of gatherings but nary a one that had contracted his trouble on a baseball diamond. I told them if they would go to the game and holler their fool heads off for the home team they would do more good than by worrying about the sanctity of the Sabbath. The boys got their baseball. The best boy in the world is a tired boy. It makes little difference how the fatigue is acquired, so long as it is by doing something attended by a real interest.

Too many boys, enamored of the scenery, contract marriage before they have taken a look at what the business of the world holds out for them. Too often a young man marries because he honestly believes that his sweetheart is a superior being, and if he allows the opportunity to slip past, he must needs marry an inferior person when the years of maturity come during which he would normally marry. Looking at it one way, he may be right. Nevertheless and notwithstanding, there is always alluring bait waiting for any fish to swallow.

Osler, who, like most of us, had seen the results of too early marriage, once advised a class of medical students to keep their affections on ice until they had established themselves in practice. No better advice was ever uttered, but too often the heat becomes so intense that, despite good intentions, the ice melts. No embryonic physician should marry before he sees his position in his profession secure. This means not until he has finished his internship and at least secured a decent residency. The same advice holds good, I dare say, for men in other professions. Yet in this, as in all else, many young men have defied the advice of their elders, married during the school course, and somehow limped through to a satisfactory end and lived happily ever after. Advice such as this has the advantage of never doing harm. Nobody pays any attention to it.

Most people can shut their eyes to facts; a doctor cannot. I once knew a community in which a girl, when approached for a date, inquired if the applicant was possessed of the usual means of contraception. In the name of God, can one think of anything more terrible! I have known mothers to regard such things with equanimity, dismissing the subject with the simple statement that young folks must have their' fling. I was once compelled to take cognizance of an instance in which the mother condoned a young daughter's wild life because it caused intense distress to the father. The mother was willing to see her daughter ruined just to spite the father. The officer of the law actually had to step in to control a situation the mother ignored.

The poorer sections of a city are supposed to provide the

greatest number of criminals, but statistics show quite as many are country boys who gravitated to the city. Broken homes provide more than their due proportion. By broken homes society means homes in which marriage is terminated by divorce. But homes that have never known a divorce may be as completely broken as those that have. A place to live in is not necessarily a home. Environment makes the home.

We doctors know that even our finest young people have a struggle with their celibate state. Excitation from their environment increases their suffering, and many a battle is lost because of the indecencies of surroundings from which they cannot escape. Nobody cares, nobody inquires into the misfortunes that beset some of them, the causes of secret marriages, elopements, and the endless variety of things that invite hazard. The doctor must inquire into the causes of things.

Many things go on about us which even the most obtuse and indifferent parents must realize are of vital concern to them. Normal young people suffer, but the burden placed on the pervert and the moron is even greater. Society offers the moron no protection from his folly. Nature's urge is intensified by lurid pictures. No matter how impossible the set-up, there is a license and a willing somebody to tie the holy bonds of matrimony. The utter folly of allowing some fool girl to marry a convict as he starts to prison is exceeded only by those who "save" the convict on the way to the lethal chamber, than which there is nothing more reprehensible. Only a society wholly dead to its responsibility would stand idly by and allow these poor deluded girls to start on a life of regrets. Of course, we console ourselves by the belief that none of these things can happen to our superior children.

Not only adolescents should be protected against an undesirable environment but also those who may be old in years while childish in intellect. Many people, whose positions give them some semblance of authority, say and write things that, wholly untrue and incalculably pernicious in their influence, only add fuel to the social conflagration. I have an aggravating example before me—a clipping from a publication. The source is not stated and the author is to me unknown. From the odor I dare say it is of a vintage of at least fifty years ago, perhaps two thousand.

I quote: "Says the sociologist: 'The idiot and imbecile are segregated. They cannot propagate. The weak minded are less fertile than normal people and have a shorter life span, and most of them fill their niche anyhow in the world's work. No danger at all from future defectives.'" That the weak minded are less fertile than the normal is of course a ridiculous statement, in fact, it can only be a willful distortion of the truth.

"Says the biologist: 'We know but little of human heredity; but we know that ninety-five per cent of the mental defectives come from normal parents and that sound children from mentally weak parents are common. We do know that crime and immorality are not inherited!'"

That too can be nothing less than a wilful misstatement. Mendel, a priest, established what is universally known as the Mendelian law and set forth clearly the facts of heredity.

"Says the theologian: 'Man as a person owns himself and has a right to all of himself and to the preservation and operation of all his functions. But as all men's bodies and souls belong to God, no one has a right to mutilate any part of himself or of any other man except when no other provision can be made for the good of the whole body.'" Let the pervert alone! If he murders a girl, save his soul and send him happily to his God. Sure, encourage him, protect him against society; he represents one more soul to be saved. The author of this screed certainly never had a daughter of his own.

Nothing reveals how deeply we are still submerged in the lust of a bygone age as the toleration we show sex fiends. "Castration removes neither desire nor power to act" we are told. That is not true. We condone the terrible acts of the sex fiend as long as he stops short of murder. Police have a list of sex fiends who are running loose because they have not yet committed murder. Doctors see these things in their incipiency. Most sex murderers have committed lesser crimes that should have put them out of reach of human beings for all time. It is a commentary on our intelligence and sense of justice that we let them run loose. We are told also that there is nothing we can do about it. Ask any ten-year-old farm boy whether there is or not. If the doctors were allowed to get to him, he would no longer be a problem for the police. But religion still teaches that he has the right to all his body, and by that very point of view condones the lesser crimes. What about the little girl who wants to keep her life? Has she no rights?

Every honorable citizen should ask the police for the list of the sex fiends who are known to them but who have not yet committed murder. The next one may know your child. He may take the precaution of marrying your daughter before committing rape. That holy right of every one to produce his kind, of which we hear, may suddenly become a very personal thing.

Take a look with me, see what I have seen, and it will be easy to understand why I am mad. A wretch murdered a little girl in lust, confessed his sins and gained eternal life, so he was told. "Jesus washed my sins away in his blood," intoned the criminal, only recently saved, as he walked after the man of God who led the way to the gallows. It was my job to listen to his heart and tell the sheriff when to cut the rope. Sixteen minutes—that is a long time to listen to ebbing heart beats. One can do a lot of thinking in that space of time. The picture of the little girl clutching her rag doll, described in the first chapter, came to my mind. Perhaps the summer complaint saved her from an attack from such a beast as this.

Birth, reproduction and death are biological processes, in man as well as in the lower animals, and are controlled by laws as immutable as the laws that govern the course of the planets. Those ignorant of these laws, even worse, those who pervert the truth for an ulterior purpose, should expend their energies in harmless ways, such as in praying for world peace or in figuring out how we can spend ourselves out of debt.

If I had my way I would begin with the child before it was six; I would show it the process of fertilization in flowers and incidentally explain the laws of heredity. I would anticipate its questions as to the physiological processes involved.

Most churches have been dehelled, so I would take the ministers into the basement, with the children to lead the parade. I would dip all ministers in the same vat so that they would all come out looking alike. In their talks, if any, I would admonish them to tell the children of life, the value of industry and kindness. Never mind about telling them of things that never happened or which don't matter if they did. I'd suppress the "inspired" persons whom no one would think of inviting out to supper to meet his wife and children, or even the dog.

I would clear the newsstands of obscene literature even if it required the destruction of some allegedly respectable magazines. I would keep from the fireside newspapers that help to commercialize the human form, in fact any printed matter that stimulates lust.

I would provide an environment with as much care as if each child in the community were my own. Every child running loose in the community is a potential life partner of a child of yours. Only God in his wisdom knows how true this is.

IV

Ticket to Paradise (History of Marriage)

A DOCTOR sometimes forms queer notions of the things which he sees going on about him, very unorthodox opinions. One of these things is the marriage ceremony. Some people are united by a very simple ceremony, some undergo a most elaborate affair. In either case, after it is all over everybody goes home. But the doctor, no matter what the nature of the ceremony, is likely to meet the couple again. After watching the parade for many years the doctor comes to the conclusion that the success of the marriage depends on the contracting parties, and not on who or what united them.

Whatever the conclusion he may have reached privately, he had better admit publicly that the bonds of matrimony are holy if he wants to avoid serious trouble. But the doctor who must be an honest historian will discover that the idea was strictly man-made. Nobody seems to remember that the ceremony is only what one thinks it is. If it is to be holy, a couple of people have a job which is going to require a lifetime of unselfish concerted effort to make it so.

The minister performs the ceremony; therefore it must be holy, and that is that. If one believes it holy, then very likely it is, at least for the time being. How it turns out is no affair of the minister. The ceremony has changed vastly in years past. It varies greatly among various peoples and seems in a measure to be dependent somewhat on climate. This in itself proves it to be a man-made institution or at least subject to great variations. There is no single source from which the procedure emanates.

Within my memory the procedure has changed. It used to take from two to three hours for my grandpa to perform a marriage ceremony for which he was paid nothing. I was recently told by one of the most brilliant representatives of grandpa's denomination that it takes him ten minutes. How

90

come this change? No answer. I was unable to find out the difference between his ceremony and my grandfather's. Either grandpa was wasting a lot of time or my modern friend is short-changing his customers.

When an officer of the civil law performs the ceremony he makes no pretenses except that he guarantees that his job is legal. He performs ten cents worth of service for which he gets two dollars. It seems to me that a phonograph could be rigged up so that a nickel in the slot would pronounce the words with as much feeling as Hizzoner the probate judge. A stamp could be fixed to mark the marriage license, say at a cost of a dime. Total cost, fifteen cents. That would be quite a saving for the young folks whose total assets are often characterized as a shoestring.

Under the present set-up the whole affair is beautiful, better admit that. The officiating person, considered in the abstract, gives no heed to what he is doing. There may be a display of fine linen and orange blossoms. I remember in my boyhood among certain peoples it took all day and many kegs of beer to do the job. It was considered to be particularly salutary if it was possible to get the bridegroom so drunk he did not know which was the bride. Funerals are becoming private affairs so perhaps in time weddings will be confined to the interested parties.

As one of the earliest recorded instances of marriage we may take a look at Boas. We read that Ruth's mother suggested that Ruth lie on Boas' loins at night. But Boas was sleepy and took no interest. When he awakened in the morning his first thought was of bacon and eggs. But he bought a farm on which Ruth was a chattel, a part of the farm. Evidently she looked better in the light of day after he had had his bacon and eggs, not in itself an unusual thing. At any rate their grandchild was David, and the descendant of David became the Light of the World. What was the ceremony? We are not told. She was his by right of purchase so likely he did not stand up three hours before one of my ancestral grandpas. It has always seemed to me that Shakespeare overlooked something when he did not take this incident as a basis for "All's Well that Ends Well."

Another instance intrigues us. There was Solomon who took unto himself seven hundred wives. Just what was the process by which he acquired them? Certainly not the three-hour ceremony of my grandpa. We may dispose of the problem by just assuming that he "Solomonized" them. Recalling these, and comparing them with the present ceremonies, one must conclude that it doesn't make much difference how you do it. Marriage is what one thinks it is and what one makes of it.

Suppose we doctors did our work as carelessly as the tiers of the marriage knot. Times a plenty a person comes to us desiring an operation which he thinks he needs. Do we do it? We do not. We take time to determine if there is need of the operation. Certainly we determine first of all if it will do more harm than good. Those who perform marriage ceremonies might study the methods of the medical practitioners. One of my most beloved teachers admonished over and over again: "Think what harm it may do before you pick up your knife."

In fact I believe the scheme as now followed by society is all wrong. We doctors should perform the marriage ceremony. We could give them something for their money. When a couple of candidates appeared before us we would get a complete history of the applicants to determine just what led up to the present complaint. Take an extreme case. The doctor could say to the child seeking the holy bonds: "Little girl, run home to your mama so she can wipe your nose." Or the other extreme: "Grandpa, go back to the home for the aged and tell the matron to put an ice cap on your head. You have a fever." That would be science. In medicine extreme cases are always easily solved.

Most cases naturally would require more intensive study. After we had studied the applicants we could form from past records some idea of what would likely follow after the operation. If the young man was enamoured only of the lady's shape we would try to get the angle from which the view was obtained. Thus we could forecast the probable course of the marriage. We would make three general classes: love, sex, lust. This would give them an idea of where they would end. The first we would label: "Chances excellent. With adequate aftercare life should be one sweet song." The second: "Well everybody is doing it. God help you." And the third: "Outlook absolutely bad and you will end just as you began." Out of nothing, nothing comes.

When a doctor dismisses patients on whom he has operated he gives them careful instructions as to the care they must exercise in order not to vitiate his efforts. "Don't over-eat, don't strain yourself; here is a diet list." His case book contains complete records of thousands of cases which enable him to know just how each case is likely to come out.

According to the church, marriage is the legal union of a man and woman for life, not capable of being terminated. Lawyers, I reckon, would add: "without the aid and advice of counsel." The right conferred by this article of union is the right to cohabit. If this is denied the husband can call for a new deal. That seems to be the only specific provision. Incompatibility is a general term and means just what one thinks it does. It comes distinctly as an afterthought, one may add, and is usually the result of ignoring the diet list.

Stripped of all trappings, marriage means that two persons are hereby united so that they may: a) cohabit; b) engage in certain occupations, voluntary or involuntary, namely the production of children and the raising of them, either with or without the aid of charitable institutions. Time was when a and b were classed together. But it is different now and rapidly becoming more so, like it or not. In the old days, there was no occasion for separating the two groups of activities. Everything was satisfactory to papa and he was boss. Even if the children were a byproduct they were desirable to him. The idea that the children were something to which one may, nay must, give heed was foreign to him. That is something new in the scheme of things.

In the usual ceremony the bride promises to love, honor and obey. Just what do these words mean, if anything? Do

H

they mean the vision of the garden gate, or does it mean submitting to the "right" the ceremony implies? It seems to me that they contain the same fallacy that the fundamentals of religion do. No one can love by an act of will. One can by an act of will say he does, but that is something different.

This mysterious word "love" has been much abused. In the dawn of my memory I see a very young man garbed in a long black coat who corners me and asks me if I love Jesus. I angrily yell "No" and run away. That attitude and that reply was supposed to be registered against me as evidence of my original sin. I have since learned what it means to develop an original idea and surely I desired no such credit for my childish act. Confronted by an unfamiliar situation, I was simply scared.

The promise to honor is in its meaning even more obscure than the promise to love. Nor can one will to honor. Honor is something that must come in response to an invitation tendered by a certain line of conduct. Its forerunner is respect. And it must, so far as I can see, come as a forerunner of love. It may be something one does as a matter of necessity, something like standing when the national anthem is played at a baseball game. One may or may not be thinking of something noble. At any rate one must believe the object of one's honor to be worthy of respect. Probably few husbands bat very high in the honor league.

The obligation to obey is just a hang-over from ancient times. Obviously as an act of compulsion or even as a voluntary act, it destroys love. Time was when the bride did obey her husband, but that was a long way back. If love existed, it did so under a serious handicap. As a matter of very obvious fact, if there is any considerable obeying done about well regulated households, the husband now does it, knowingly or unknowingly.

What is required of the groom? He promises to "protect" the bride. This looks fine in view of *a* above noted. It is ironical because what she may well need most is protection from her husband. It is the most meaningful word in the whole ceremony. As the bride leaves home the mother weeps

and implores the groom to be good to her daughter. Divested
of all camouflage this means, I am told, that he should not
knock her on the head and rape her.

The marriage ceremony is a funny institution. I have
endeavored to trace its history with indifferent success. I
could not even find out who said it was made in heaven. I
am told it was one Alfred Lord Tennyson. Maybe his middle
name gave him exaggerated ideas. I have never met Mrs.
Tennyson and possibly he was right. At any rate, it sounds
like a remark made by someone just before starting on the
journey to the altar.

You can't fool the old doctor. Don't get mad before the
whole problem is viewed deliberately and honestly. The
wedding ceremony may be beautiful but also it may be
sordid. Often I have been compelled to look on the marriage
contract as the acquisition of a concubine. If God joined
them, all right. But sometimes the devil moves in and takes
charge of the household, and it is the devil's doings that
come to the ears of the doctor.

It makes me mad when I hear of women's rights, of equality of the sexes and such rot. The right woman most needs
is the right to herself. The whole affair still reeks, if not of
the Old Testament, at least of the age of lust. It would help
a lot if we could study more closely the coincidental relationship of the two. If we were honest, we would clarify the
procedure by beginning at one end with affairs obviously
rotten, and at the other with the ceremony at its best, which
I would not deny is holy.

A state of equality is being reached by an ever increasing
number of women but it is coming about through something not necessarily a part of the marriage ceremony—
through the mutual feeling of two parents for a child.

I am neither a reformer nor a moralist. I see only as a
doctor who has been the buffer of the discord which appears
when a couple of strangers suddenly are thrown together. If
I were a dictator I would like the marriage contract to contain certain stipulations, the infraction of which would carry
certain penalties, for breach of contract, maybe the contempt

of court. Court contempt, so far as I can figure out, consists of lying to the court when the judge is in a bad humor.

Having considered what marriage implies we may as a matter of information trace its history. The lower creatures, like many people, produce offspring, and having produced them, cast them upon their environment. Most bugs lay eggs where they will hatch and call it a lifework. Many snakes do the same but also seek to protect their young.

Certain animal species have some sort of a family understanding. Most of the cloven-hoofed species have such a code. The males spruce up and act important around the herd so long as their company is agreeable. Afterwards they collect together into a sort of men's club and spend the remainder of the year wondering about the why-for of it.

One distinguished ornithologist has said that the only real lifetime marriage is found among birds. Most birds take their partners for life. Scientists of all kinds have sought to explain this. It seems to me to be simplicity itself. Mrs. Bird retains throughout life her youthful form and is always as neatly dressed as when Mr. Bird first met her. Mr. Bird, also being endowed with unchanging and unchangeable attire, is free from criticism as to the color of his necktie and the shape of his pants. Besides, Miss Bird knows, before she captures or is captured by Mr. Bird, just how many eggs she will be required to lay and when. She knows she will not be required to produce an indefinite number of eggs at unregulated seasons of the year, a proceeding which might rob her of her happiness and possibly her life. Also, all birds of a species are alike. No use nosing around: there are no beauty contests, no nothing, so Mr. Bird comes home to learn that the fates handed him their best. Why should birds not mate for life and in the doing, sing?

Many volumes have been written on the history of marriage but they contain little of a definite nature. Marriage by capture fills much of the early history, and falls into two categories. In the first, women are taken after the battle which killed off all their men folks. This is capture and no figure of speech. The other is capture after the modern method. The male thinks he does the capturing.

It is a fine myth, anticipating modern society, which says that the ardent swain cracked the desired young lady on the head with a baseball bat. Then as now, the lady in question merely radioed the already obvious fact that she was a candidate for capture. In cases when he did need to swipe the lady, it was because papa was holding her for a price beyond her fair worth or beyond the young man's means. In many of the primitive tribes, as with our Indians, the daughters were held for a regular price. We find here the beginnings of beauty contests. The bride brought papa a certain number of cocoanuts or ponies depending on her shape. Of course the element of supply and demand entered.

The males were fighting boys and when many got killed there was often an excess of girls, which beared the market. In some tribes this discrepancy was compensated for by one man acquiring many wives.

It is interesting to note that in some so-called savage tribes the maidens actually made inquiry: "What model car do you drive?" or words to that effect. That is to say, she desired to know his capacity to provide for her and her children. Sex was subservient to sense. Maybe our girls will some day catch up with these dusky maidens.

Usually the tribal requirements were that the candidate for matrimony give evidence of prowess either by slaying important game or a neighboring tribesman. This requirement had to be met, it is interesting to note, before the young man was eligible even in the abstract. He had to show that he could fight before the bride was handed him. They were amazingly frank in those tribes. Promises and large talk were not accepted. Only with pelt or scalp in hand did he carry weight with the tribal bigwigs. In some tribes if the young candidate brought in several tiger skins he was entitled to an equal number of wives. I have never been able to figure out whether that was in reward for past work or an implication of faith in his ability to protect himself in the future.

In some tribes of Luzon, the young men single out certain

maidens whom they wish to impress. They lay before the fathers of the maidens scalps they have collected from neighborhood tribes. This, apparently, is to prove that they are regular males, or possibly to warn the in-laws that interference with their future domestic arrangements might be fraught with disaster. After this they dance. These dances are held only when a certain tree is in bloom; possibly the forerunner of the mistletoe. But imagine the modern couple waiting for anything to bloom, or in many cases even for the sun to rise.

A primitive, personally organized white slave traffic was sometimes indulged in, in an attempt to corner the market. The lovelorn, usually accompanied by a number of associates, went forth to a neighboring tribe to swipe himself a wife. The best fighter among his friends was designated the best man, because he proved it. This practice was discouraged as much as possible by the visited tribe who despatched at once, without benefit of attorney for the defense and without benefit of clergy after conviction, anyone they captured. So it was literally hell if you got caught, and perhaps also if you did not.

In more modern times, when murder was committed in mass formation to the accompaniment of music and the prayers of the local clergy, the scarcity of males became alarming to eligible young ladies. The disproportion in some countries became extreme. For some strange reason the weak-kneed, saffron-hued males who did not go to war were not, as in the savage tribes, allowed to collect a number of wives.

This gave rise to competitive bidding with the dowry. For a long time it puzzled me how it was that young ladies who required backing of finance to make them attractive happened to have the coin. One day the explanation came to me. Men who are financially successful, or who are good fighters in a more direct way, are seldom noted for their beauty. One can note this in the average doctors' conventions. The only handsome men at the meetings are the presiding secretaries. One wonders how the rest ever acquired wives. Obviously enough, it was the anticipated earning power which the practice of medicine is supposed to hold. The point is the same in all cases: the prospect of unearned increment made up to some extent for the irregularities of shape and features, or perhaps better said, the absence of shape and the presence of features which never learned the importance of team work. But the delusion is only temporary and the deluded one wakes up some fine day with a pain in the neck. Possibly it is this pain that first gave rise to the saying that the spinal vertebrae were the seat of disease and osteopathy was born to correct it. I offer this as a possible explanation, there being no other.

Of course these circumlocutions and explanations are only to make it possible to avoid the truth. A glance at the history of the development of the marriage ceremony may here be a matter of interest.

Certain of the lowest races of Indians in Lower California have their rutting season as regularly as animals, notably the elk and antelope, unattended by ceremony. Certain Australian savages, in the middle of spring, have dances followed by religious ceremonies and then orgies of procreation, with marriage as a sort of accompanying ceremony, or afterthought. Some of the New Guinea savages, on the other hand, simply have orgies or annual feasts, followed by marriage and the exercise of sexual acts. These have no relation to any deity, being planned merely to stimulate the nervous system to a high pitch, and are accompanied by various violent dances.

Aside from these occasions it is said boys and girls play together in the spring evenings unmindful of sex. This annual recurrent love-making should give parents in these tribes a long surcease from anxiety. Sooner or later they will become civilized and read the papers and attend picture shows. Then love making will be perennial and there will be worry enough to go around, but they will have the satisfaction of knowing that they have become civilized.

Unhappily, as tribes advance in civilization these seasonal matings become diurnal periods of matchmaking. As a further evidence of civilization, unwilling maidens are killed if the capture technic is a little too rough. These rough boys are liquidated pronto. It must be remembered that they are only savages. To compensate, they have wife exchanges, right up to date, permitting everyone to guess again without going to the trouble of committing murder. Furthermore, no professional service is required. Papa just tells mama that he is tired of her shape. If one nowadays desires to express the same opinion in a more diplomatic refined way it is necessary to draw up papers beginning "Papa vs. mama." Being written in Latin this costs money.

In many tribal customs some sort of religious ceremony is involved. These we do not understand. Some religious denominations, including the one in which I was raised, make of the marriage ceremony and its indissolubility an essential factor in the achievement of salvation. That it does make for the integrity of marriage cannot be denied. This in part may be due to the fact that what cannot be cured must be endured as the old rheumatics say.

To an old doctor, it would seem that if the young people were allowed to work out their own marriage much grief might be spared. Say two young people find out that they respect each other, have the same tastes, the same abilities, and the same outlook on life. Suppose one day sex whispers to them and they go to their papas and mamas and tell them simply that they have concluded to be true to each other until death do them part. I am told the Quakers have some such simple sort of procedure. It looks to me as if that will be the salvation of a Christian civilization.

A couple so united would find the baby a part of themselves, a counterpart of the child in the manger, whether we regard Him as immaculately conceived, or as an allegorical figure. Happy marriages depend on what the couple bring to it and what they do with it. This means that the baby must be recognized as the light of the world. Any marriage that endures because of external pressure, whether it be fear of publicity, economic, or ecclesiastic, is not an ideal marriage.

V

Paradise Veiled (The Single Woman)

A DEEPLY rooted trait in humans is to do as they please, and having done so, to crown themselves for their noble deeds. Not only do they approve of their own doings, but they immediately assume that others should do as they have done if they wish to achieve a like noble plane. We see this best exemplified in the most elemental states. The easiest thing in the world people have to do is to produce children, but having done so, they seek to glorify themselves for responding to the elemental urge, even though the measure of achievement is just a matter of simple arithmetic. It is inevitable, therefore, that those whose only achievement is the production of children, being in the majority, have formed a doctrine that it is the duty of every woman to do as they have done.

We are at once confronted with the very obvious fact that many women do not reproduce their kind. We have not to do here with those who would but cannot. We are here concerned only with those who for some reason renounce, or are by circumstances shut off from, the exercise of the elemental urge. If we study this class we find that it is made up of various elements. We may note at once that their failure to reproduce may be due to choice, or to circumstances beyond their control. In so far as this is in a measure a problem of biology, it is right that biologists should examine the premises. But the biologist soon discovers that it extends far beyond his province because what he sees is not biology but the very negation of biologic laws. Therefore an attempt of an old doctor to view this problem is destined to be based on an assumption and is bound to end in confusion.

Single women fall naturally into several groups. The most outstanding is the group which enters into celibate life at an early age for religious reasons. Usually this occurs before the candidates learn the meaning of the biological urge. Whether or not there comes a time when they consciously or subconsciously regret their early action and wish they had followed the common herd is not disclosed to us. No doubt there is a great variation, depending on the biologic nature of the individual.

The next group enters celibate life without any definite avowal, many apparently as the result of circumstances over which they may or may not have control. Circumstances arise where duty calls, apparently temporarily but often for a lifetime. We see this most commonly in cases in which some member of the family requires care. The need may be either actual or imagined, a reflection of selfishness.

Next are the vast group of career women whose primary object in life does not fit in with a state of matrimony and the raising of a family. This group is by no means confined to celibate adults; in proper circumstances some marry and even raise children, but they are somewhat fastidious as to choice of a mate. This fastidiousness lessens as it becomes apparent that their lofty ideals find no counterpart in real life. One of these women told me quite frankly that she drifted along nursing a hope that was not realized until it finally was forced on her consciousness that the best of the species were appropriated by other damsels in their youth, and now, in midlife, she discovers that the leavings are becoming more and more impossible.

The final group is composed of those left single by circumstances, or personality or other factors beyond their control. Perhaps also widows should be classed in this group, women who return to the single state is due to the ravages of disease or accident, or whose husbands may have become entangled in the tall grass of domestic strife.

The first class comprises a most complex group which may collectively be called Sisters, who almost from infancy elect a lifetime of celibacy. They are found in a number of religious organizations. The early age at which consecration to celibacy is vowed in some recorded instances astonishes and puzzles me. For instance, one saint declared for a life of celibacy at the early age of seven years, as did St. Genevieve. St. Agnes was twelve. Such things defy the scientist, for certainly they did not adopt a *celibate* life as such at so early an age but entered a *religious* life of which celibacy was a part, and a part of which they were at that age wholly ignorant. Most young women, it may be noted, enter the sisterhood at an age when the full meaning of celibacy cannot possibly have been realized. Those who enter the sisterhood in the church in which I was reared enter at an age when the meaning of life should be clear to them. But it seems to spell the same thing in the end.

Generally speaking this great group, who renounce the world and devote themselves to a cause for the period of a lifetime, begin their service early in life and, having begun, continue. I dare say they are actuated by an envisioned love of the human race; they see the child in the manger instead of a child in their arms, emotionally stopping short this side of sex. That there is something as basic as the love of parents for their child is suggested by the fact that they accept Christ as spiritual bridegroom. These noble women are bound by eternal vows which bind their service to mankind from thence onward. How noble this service is every doctor, and only the doctor, knows. To the biologist they are of the greatest interest because they prove there is something in the human which can reach above sex and conquer it.

The next group comprises those who, whatever the cause, start out with a definite purpose and continue steadfast to the end, perhaps not without periods of regret. They are not bound to their place by any vows; they could at any time abandon their lot, but certainly they approach in their spiritual devotion those who are bound by vows. I will mention but one, Florence Nightingale. A girl born to high estate devoted her life to the sick and afflicted and set an example for the whole nursing profession for all time. What vision she may have had other than of caring for the afflicted soldiers, and what conscious purpose, whether religious or otherwise, we do not know. We do know that she continued to live in the hearts of future generations. It occurs at once to the biologist that possibly, in the persons of the sick soldiers, she vicariously took care of a child which she never knew.

Countless numbers of other women have lived, and lived equally noble lives, though their role has been cast in less dramatic situations. These women do not chart their course in adolescent years by any vows, but there is something equally profound since they remain permanently true to their celibate state. They represent a nobleness all their own. Whether they are single by choice or circumstance makes no difference; they are free at any period of their lives to change their course should they wish. Yet many are carried on by some unknown force as relentlessly as those who do take silent vows.

We should not fail to grasp the meaning of the lives of these two groups of women. They demonstrate that there is love without sex or that a sense of duty can control sex. They carry a beacon light that must lead the human race if a Christian civilization is ever to be anything more than a chorus of blatant Pharisees.

Every community has examples of this latter group. They give their lives to the service of some one else, an invalid relative often. All too often this service is claimed by a selfish mother who demands her daughter's life until she dies, leaving the daughter too old to establish a home of her own. I once had a friend who remained with her mother under these circumstances, and her sweetheart remained true to her until the mother died. Then they were married. Nothing more noble than such lives can be conceived, but they remain unnoticed and unsung.

In this group belong those who devote their lives to some permanently afflicted person. They literally give their life for the life of others, without complaint, putting aside their right to a life of their own.

Mother-son complexes sometimes work equal havoc with men. Such sons live their lives in devotion to their mothers just because mothers in their selfishness demand it. The son has his own life of business as an outlet and in this is less tragic than the daughter who has nothing to divert her mind. Such demands by a selfish parent should be ignored. The child has a moral right to establish a home as did the mother before him, and the selfishness of the one should not be allowed to kill the soul of the other.

Happily, parental domination has greatly lessened in recent years. In years gone by it was very common for mothers to consign their sons to the clergy in their infancy. Many met their mothers' desires but the study of biography tells us that many so destined fell by the wayside and took up other callings, most often literature or science, some even medicine, and occasionally banditry or piracy.

Less conspicuous because perhaps less common is the girl who rebels against the too strict religious teachings and the inevitable matrimony. Not only do some rebel against the teaching but against their teachers, notably their parents, leave home and, being rebellious, often meet with disaster. I have mentioned elsewhere that young persons impressed in their religious training by the idea of original sin may develop an ascetic slant, but more develop a sex complex, resulting in celibacy and painful sex neuroses, from which they never escape.

It is interesting to note that in years, not entirely past, when people tried to point to the day when they escaped from sin, in the majority of instances they fixed the date at puberty or adolescence. It is deplorable that our children should be taught that they were born in sin and must do something to escape it. Children are not born in sin and are only unfortunate in that they are the progeny of fool parents, who have made them a private hell from which there is no escape. Since original sin is brought to the attention of the child at about the age of puberty he is apt to connect his sense of guilt with some event of this epoch. Many children indulge in practices at this period which are not nice but entirely harmless. Fools who think they are reformers, noting that sometimes idiots engage in these practices, ascribe the idiotic state to the practice. The idiots were born idiots, just a little too dumb to join the rank of the reformers.

These patients are frequent visitors to the clinic. Some of them frankly declare their trouble is due to sinful practices. These are headed for the asylum. By far the greater number have stomach trouble, fatigability, or sleeplessness, not physical signs of disease, and the doctor is left to guess.

The group of career women strike us with less awe though they are none the less noble. They mingle with us common mortals, and devote their lives to the unending pursuit of some object, but retain a mental reserve which will allow them to change their course if at any time they wish to do so. One finds many of these women in the professions, including medicine, I am pleased to say. All occupations claim them. In many offices executive heads of responsible businesses have their "confidential secretaries." Usually a glance at the office set-up tells which one of those present occupies the responsible position. The boss leans heavily on her because her ability and faithfulness know no deviation, no letting down. Her interest in the work sometimes exceeds that of the boss himself. He forgets something, she reminds him of it. He loses something, she knows what he did with it. The devotion of such women passes understanding. One hesitates to use such a vulgar term as love to designate their devotion because they never show a tingle of the female, are never conscious of their own charm, never seek an end except the faithful performance of their work. Their undeviating faithfulness is equal to a daughter's.

Perhaps the largest number of this group of women are found in the teaching profession. Many of course teach as an interval occupation, one might say, although they are none the less noble for that. Others continue their course throughout life. They devote their lives unselfishly to the attempt to civilize the young brats we produce, finding in this perhaps a vicarious outlet for the instinct of motherhood. Who does not cherish in his heart an enduring affection for some teacher who touched him in some inexplicable way in his childhood? These women commonly represent the most intelligent, and one might add, the most attractive of their sex. Many of these women come to the doctor chiefly because

of sleeplessness. When he seeks to find the cause of a nervous
disorder some will frankly state that they suffer from lone-
liness, from the want of some man they could honor and
respect; but that when they think of all that marriage implies
they recoil from it. There is something infinitely fine there.
Just what it is they yearn for, what it is they fear, defies understanding. Obviously their attitude at least implies a lack
of faith in the male of the species. These women represent
some of our finest. Somehow they seem different from the
business group that we meet daily and have learned in a
measure to obey.

More tragic is the great group who remain single throughout life without any definite object in view. The crosses in
Flanders field are emblematic of just that number of spiritual
widows in the home land, women designated as "old maids."
Some remain single because of an unending grief for a particular man who did not return; others, in an abstract sense
perhaps, remain single because not enough soldiers returned
after democracy had been duly saved. There is the real tragedy
which has been largely overlooked; not the dead but the
living suffer.

Many of these women accept their fate silently, occupying
their lives in an endless number of ways. What heartaches
they may conceal no one knows. But some of them become a
problem for the doctor because they find their conflicts with
biologic forces annoying, even difficult or wholly confusing.
They mistake their complaints for something the doctor can
remedy. Fundamentally they are just different.

One finds such women particularly in families whose members marry early and specialize in a numerous progeny. It is
interesting to note the difference in the reproductive urge
in members of different families. Indeed, how women react
to the single state is in large measure hereditary. If a woman
has a number of maiden sisters or aunts, and many bachelor
brothers or cousins, sex is not likely to trouble her over
much. So the doctor writes this fact into his case-book. On
the other hand, if the patient has a prolific ancestry, particularly if the relatives are prone to marry young, the doctor is

likely to have a permanent patient if, for whatever cause, she does not marry. Many of them battle bravely. Sometimes it seems an unconscious struggle, but more often they are aware of it and proclaim it. Then, almost in midlife, the endocrines suddenly become angry because of years of neglect, and the unfortunate victims marry any one who comes along, too often some one wholly beneath them. It has always seemed to me that this is the meanest trick fate plays on humans. To defy sex throughout half a lifetime, only to be kicked into an ill-advised union by the final act of the endocrine glands!

That is the saddest part of the story. Before the endocrine system becomes stable the victim must have borne a child. The fates are not mathematicians and seem unable to count above one. One sees this law operative in the case of women who have had their ovaries removed before they had borne children. They become at once nervous wrecks and remain so from then on.

It is tragic to note that most women who marry at or near midlife forsake a brilliant career and are content to bask at ease in the sunlight of domesticity. Why they suddenly renounced their obligations to their lifework is as puzzling as it is distressing. Yet few remain true to their profession once they marry.

The disaster some of the single women meet is illustrated in the following case. As I was seated in my office one morning, my attention was attracted by a grunt which might vaguely be interpreted as "Good morning." I looked up and beheld a middle aged squattish male dressed in old clothes obviously intended for a tall man. A glance was enough to reveal that he was a recent graduate from a moron academy; perhaps he flunked his final. Behind him was a woman of like age, equally poorly dressed. She startled me by addressing me in a melodious voice in charming English. She related that she had a black spot on her foot which had been gradually increasing in size for a year. Her physician did not know its meaning so he had advised her to see me. After she had removed her shoe, the cheapest kind of footwear, I saw a delicately molded foot which certainly had not spent its adolescent years in such shoes as she was then wearing. She said she wanted to know the facts, whatever they might be. A doctor must know when a patient means it when she asks for the truth. The pleading look in this patient's eyes told me plainly that she hoped for the worst. The truth was that the course of the disease would be short. In a year she was dead. I got in touch with her physician, who told me that she had been the head of the English Department in the local college for twenty years. Suddenly, to the consternation of her friends, she had married a share-cropping farmer of low mentality. I have learned that a woman who meets the verdict of a fatal disease with a joyous look, has been putting up a noble fight from which she is glad to be released.

Why do not women, when they find themselves caught in a terrifying, unnavigable stream of sex, consult their doctors? This woman's doctor would have known the answer and to some extent could have controlled the rampant endocrine glands until the passing years brought relief.

Many women do consult their doctors, but they complain only of fatigue and sleeplessness. They look at the endless years before them and their faces declare their distress. A wise doctor understands, asks no questions, prescribes the proper sedative and thereby makes a friend.

Many try to find a vicarious outlet in church work or some other altruistic occupation. One of these who had labored for years startled me one day by crying: "One dose of your medicine did more good than all the prayers I ever uttered." Of course if I suggested that in some cases religious work only aggravates this state I would be berated. Fortunately when a doctor confronts a patient he may think silently. No doctor would ask a question in such an instance, or make a comment. Thirty or sixty grains of sodium bromide after supper in such cases is more efficient than prayer. There is no doubt of it.

Some women remain single for reasons which puzzle the neighbors—attractive women who reject all suitors. Sometimes in such cases there is a complex; something they heard their elders, or their sisters say in early life has influenced

I

them. In dealing with these patients the doctor is likely to receive some surprises. Most commonly there has been a disappointment: she was left at the gate by the only one; or there was some girlhood slip which damned her, in her own mind, for life. Most tragic of all is she whose Lothario is wholly imaginary. Those left at the gate at least may live in hope that the faithless suitor will some day return. It is tragic to be consulted as to whether or not the patient is physically fit for marriage when there is not the remotest chance that her condition will ever be put to a test.

Sometimes these patients label themselves for the old doctor when without sufficient cause, they vow eternal celibacy. One knows then which little devil is disturbing their tranquillity and that they are putting up a false front. This condition is found most commonly as the menopause is approached. They become nervous and have hot flashes. As before noted, the fates are cruel to these women either because the period of transition is usually more stormy and extends over a greater number of years than in women who have borne children. Nature is angry with them because they have resisted the urge to reproduce. Some badly informed doctors advise such patients to take a year or two off from their work. This is unfortunate advice. He should advise them to continue on their jobs with increasing industry. The best antidote against the sex urge in any form or at any age is work and yet more work, and that applies particularly to women at this stage. Any wise doctor can alleviate the suffering of these patients until the endocrines have done their worst and have retired into atrophy. Many new endocrine extracts are being discovered which in some cases work wonders, and there are always the never failing bromides when all else fails. The real tragedy comes when some doctor who owns a knife finds a tumor, in itself innocent, and proceeds to remove the uterus. Then the wreck is complete. I have seen literally carloads of these unfortunates made worse by ill-advised operations. For those who suffered such needless operations there is no help. One cannot put back what has been removed.

Some of these women who have the mother instinct yet

shy away from actual motherhood because of some complex which they will never overcome, find a relative's child who needs their care, and they give it without measure. Others attach themselves to institutions devoted to the care of children, while still others simplify matters by acquiring cats or dogs. Fortunate are those women who have no career marked out for themselves if they can achieve vicarious motherhood. Many an adult praises the virtues of an aunt who became his mother in time of need.

Perhaps we should include the women who achieve a single state through some accident to their marriage. They form a heterogeneous group. Sexual desire can be stimulated, and the greater the stimulation and the more sudden the interruption, the greater the suffering is likely to be. If such women have a number of children, their chance of acquiring a new mate is remote unless they find a widower to whom more or fewer progeny makes little difference. The grass widow, ending her married state in a hyperexcited sex condition due to the nature of the conflict, is, because of her previous experience, mostly likely to salve her wounded heart by a successful conquest. For more the bereavement is genuine, particularly for those whose husband's death has been preceded by a long illness; they find themselves prepared for a period of single blessedness. Many of these are cautious about acquiring new alliances because candidates do not measure up spiritually or financially to the husband whom they have lost.

We need not long consider those who are widowed because they misplaced their hubby in the grass. They will rectify this oversight before they become a problem to the doctor. The acceptance of the single state by widows who have children is comprehensible. They have paid their debt to the fates and can devote their years contentedly to the care of their children. Ultimately they will live again in their children's children.

Many who have not borne children likewise continue their reclaimed celibate state. Why these widows do not remarry is difficult to understand. Sometimes, I am sure, it is a devotion to the memory of a real love. I sometimes wish these women would complain so that I might find out what is going on in their minds. I once asked one of my old patients what was the secret of her tranquil widowhood. She replied promptly and simply: "Work and yet more work." If these patients have spells of insomnia the doctor asks no questions. He gives them sedatives.

Sometimes, no doubt, women choose a continued widowhood because their experience of sex life was such that they are unwilling to risk a repetition. Sometimes they definitely have flown from an experience which they did not anticipate. These latter usually are easily detected by the observing doctor. Their faces bear permanently the expression of having undergone a great disaster. This is in contrast to those who are widowed by the death of a truly loved one; they bear a serene, resigned expression that beggars description. One such was my patient more than thirty years. Her noble bearing always impressed me.

Generally speaking, widowed women who have become accustomed to a regular sex life suffer more than those who are strangers to such experiences. Some of these during their wedded life made wide acquaintances which in their widowhood stand them in good stead.

And the single woman, single not from choice but from necessity, what of her? Many of these women have no outlet for their sex urge or their grief as they are not career women. The life of a domestic is their portion from now on. They complain to the doctor of nervousness and that just about ends the list of complaints. They have no memory, no solace, no visioned hope of a different state.

During the years I worked in a foreign clinic it was not a rare thing to find women, seeing themselves approach middle life without prospect of marriage, deliberately bear a bastard child, and having borne it, seem supremely happy in their anomalous state. It was pitiable in the last degree to hear these women relate at which battle the child's father died. They did not say that at such a battle her sweetheart died. To them the child was not a bastard, and spiritually, I believe they were right.

Some single women seek to circumvent their state by

clandestine means. The fuss and uncertainty attending this
produces nervous states, and sometimes unwanted diseases
are acquired. Endless grief is in the offing. Clandestine indulgence certainly is not the answer because unless the endocrines
are appeased by the bearing of a child, sex will not be satisfied. One reads much of homosexual practices and other
things that are not nice, but if they are common here I have
missed my diagnoses for I have seen but few. Even if it be so,
one cannot say that women are injured by it, except possibly
if they close the door to any attraction to a male suitor, who
is rather a remote hope in any event. The great difficulty in
these attempts to circumvent the demands of nature is that
at best the sex urge is satisfied only momentarily. The
endocrines continue their incessant demands.

No one can write on the subject of this chapter without
the feeling that he has bungled the job. Nevertheless, these
single women offer a most interesting study, one which shows
that there is a noble side of life that is above sex or can rise
above it or nobly struggle to rise above it. These women
give us cause to hope that lust, which dominated the life of
our ancestors, and is still with us, may some day be overcome. When this happens, and when the significance of the
child in the manger is realized, we may achieve a Christian
civilization. A futile twenty centuries spent in this attempt
should not discourage us. We have traveled at least part way
with the new woman.

When I contemplate the great group of women who have
in common the celibate state I am reminded of what Professor
Royce once wrote: "Life is true and deep only in so far as it
is tragic." If the kind fates would grant me the power to
make one discovery I would elect to produce something
which would neutralize the endocrine substance which brings
needless suffering to the nobles of our race.

We doctors do not know much. When cells fight bacteria
or unduly multiply, or tissues degenerate, we can find our
way about within limitations. But there is a point beyond
which all is confusion, and that is why we do not know why
women do what they do—and neither do they.

Having written the foregoing it would seem that anyone

should be able to figure out his own status in this troubled world. But many do not understand that their whole lives must harmonize with the state in which they find themselves. No one can be a physical celibate and a mental profligate. A mental profligate may be defined as one who exposes herself to certain types of literature, certain types of stage presentations, certain types of periodicals, and of all things, certain types of so-called music. This list, it is true, seems to include about all that goes on about us.

I have hinted that there are certain drugs that alleviate this state but few apply to the doctor, even to a woman doctor. When they do go to a doctor it is for headache, sleeplessness, backache or several of innumerable other complaints and the doctor must guess the rest. In my earlier years of practice I sometimes gently suggested to such patients that their symptoms were never found in ladies pushing perambulators. That well intentioned observation was a mistake, because to make a diagnosis when there is no available remedy only increases the difficulty. The sensible doctor prescribes sedatives and says nothing. Mild sedatives are taken by some of these women for years and even decades.

The best remedy is work and yet more work to a definite purpose. Yet even so most will fall sooner or later. I cannot help but regard as tragic a woman who, having devoted many years to useful life, casts aside the use of her talents to become a beater of biscuits and a puddler of gravy. Yet they are content. These things being so, it would seem wiser if young women could realize in early life just what the future will bring. They should start with the firm determination to order their entire lives to a visioned end, or accept life as the fates decree and save physical and mental distress in resisting the inevitable.

Obviously our alleged civilization has constantly emphasized the biologic. A spiritual view of life now glows only in the early morning. We males have been good scientists, explorers, and masters of commerce but we have made a mess of the general fellowship of man and of Christian civilization.

VI

Dream of Paradise (The Honeymoon and After)

LOVE which leads to the altar is a complicated phenomenon. At best it is made up in part of that spiritual something which began as a gentle whisper back in the early days of a girl and boy's first contact and has its germ in the infinitely fine something that cries out in childhood. It carries with it mutual honor and respect. This implies that the parties bring to the contract a degree of civilization beyond that of the great common herd. It is a delicate thing sensitive to slight influence. Therefore it must be carefully guarded. A single slip may silence it forever.

Yet so-called love, as we see it at the altar, may range all the way from the delicate state above noted to a sensuous vulgarity reaching a depth below that of any other animal. If one calmly studies the things which are done at weddings in their historical settings, we soon discover that the whole procedure is a very human phenomenon. If we study mating —it is not worthy of being called marriage—in the uncivilized tribes, we discover that the process differs but little from the practice of the lower animals and is simply on a higher moral plane. It is sex that calls and that only, sex frank and unadorned. If we will observe the phenomena going on about us we must realize that it is motivated in the same way as are the physiological processes of the lower tribes. Love, then, as we are to view it at the altar, is a mysterious combination of an indefinable spiritual quality and sex. Therein lies the problem, for the proportion of the ingredients is infinitely variable. Spiritual love may be present, but if so it finds itself in very strange surroundings. Yet sometimes when a man starts to find a mate, he may have underneath the surface the same attitude as a person setting out with a rifle to bag game. Even so, people drawn by a sex urge sometimes have a more noble side which, when sex is satisfied, comes to the fore. Then mutual respect may permit love to bloom again.

The uncivilized peoples have a much better chance to escape misery than we have, though from the nature of things they are excluded from the finer companionship of civilized people. They are subject to the same experiences, they are actuated by the same motive, sex. It is desirable to note that without any pretense or subtlety they are destined for the same end as their civilized cousins: namely, to produce children like themselves. And many of the lower tribes love their children. But in this lies the difference: they have no hope of the future; they will leave the world just as they found it. Contrast this with civilized peoples who have a vision of the future, a dream of a better life than their ancestors knew. This we call the advancement of civilization, or at least the yearning for it.

In comparison with the savages, we allegedly civilized peoples have a far reaching job before us in this melting pot of ours. The savage pair have the common background of countless generations. Their wives cook their yams just as their mothers did. Change from mother to wife means simply a change in scenery. No other adjustments are necessary.

We civilized Americans are made up of a polyglot population, except in sections restricted by religious influences, and wholly different types are thrown together. Man and wife may have wholly different backgrounds, wholly different natures, wholly different notions as to what the purpose of life may be. It is well to keep in mind that these are fundamental social, not moral, questions. We are constantly uniting in wedlock Chinese and Eskimos. Yet we expect them, through some mysterious ritual, to work a change whereby they will agree on whether their garments shall be made of fur or cloth, and whether the food shall be blubber or rice. Expecting love to bridge such differences is apt to invite disaster.

Many statistics have been compiled by sociologists to determine what brought the young people together, that is to say, why A married B. Such inquiries are about as productive of results as is inquiry into why one gets up after sitting briefly on a tack. Looking backward, half the women when filling out a card which they are not required to sign, admit that they married for security. In other words, what they visioned was a permanent meal ticket. Some also seek prestige, station, or what not. By a simple ceremony they expect to be lifted to an estate better than they had previously known. They are wholly unmindful that many personal qualities will be required before they can really share the new estate. One might as well call an Eskimo out of the igloo, put on him a Chinaman's shirt and say to him: "Now you are a Chinaman." Certainly the picture would be no more ludicrous, or tragic, than that of women marrying for a meal ticket or position some man as unlike them as it is possible to be. Some women say they married because they desired children, the acquisition of a husband being incidental. Of course they are not quite so frank about it but it is true just the same. Generally speaking, children just happened to arrive as an after event, but since they devote themselves to their offspring one need not trouble about the primary motive. Many who say they married for love, on cold analysis are shown to have been wrong. They married for sex pure and simple. When I was a child I had to repeat after a preacher whom I detested for good reason: "I believe in the Father, the Son and the Holy Ghost." I have never found out what is meant by the holy ghost. I dare not be so frank about this love business, so any doubts I may entertain I had best keep to myself.

A fine young nurse once told me with the greatest frankness that she was going to find herself a husband while the picking was good. She and the gentleman with his bow and arrow strode forth in the wilderness in quest of game. She soon found one she considered a buck with a great spread of horns, as hunters say. Unfortunately what she bagged was not a deer, as she had expected, but a caribou; an excellent specimen it was, but it was not just what she wanted. Many like-minded women are less frank. Some say on their card that they married for love, just that. And then they spend the rest of their lives wondering what it was they married for.

The young girl who goes to college to find a mate, or the girls who journey to other climes and other scenes, declare the same thing. It is interesting to note how smart some of these young women are. They discover that long residence in a particular neighborhood has made them a part of the scenery, and that the eligible young men have "developed an amazing sales resistance to their charms" as one clever girl expressed it. So she moves to a different neighborhood, where she is something new and interesting to the young eligibles of the community, who have of course become accustomed to their local scenery but have developed no resistance against the newcomer. Books have been written on the technic of this communal interchange.

If they succeed by this manoeuvre in securing a mate, as most of them do, it is sex that unites them, not love. The little cherub that goes forth armed with bow and arrow is a most efficient person but he does not represent love. If he represented love he would at least put on a diaper. At best, therefore, what he brings together is just a couple of shapes; thereafter his concern ceases. He makes no promises for the future. If the young couple find or develop mutual respect, out of which love may grow purely as a byproduct, he has had nothing to do with it; his sale is based on a down payment and so much per day from now on. No one has a right to expect more than he bargains for, because of course he seldom gets it. Don't blame cupid.

These young people are exactly right. The fates tell the girl, "You get yourself a baby and straighten out your endocrine system or I will see to it that you spend a lifetime of regret. By doing as I say you may escape it." The young man has been told by his elders, "It is hell if you do and hell if you don't." With these glowing prospects, the fates have reduced the resistance of the pair to a very low point.

When one considers the complicated process that leads to the altar, one wonders why it succeeds as often as it does. Somewhere in that picture of love, respect and sex, each newly wed pair find their place. The reason they married then comes to the fore; they may have misunderstood their motive before. When the marrying parson says "for better or worse," he says a-plenty. I have been unable to find out where those words came from. It is poor coaching. Suppose a third base coach should yell out to a ball player approaching the plate: "Johnnie, you are swinging for better or worse, you have one chance in three or four to make a hit." Instead the coach yells: "Johnnie, bust one, you can do it." There are times when a constructive lie is good technic. I believe the ultimate history of most contracting parties to a marriage shows that the words should have been "for better and worse." Marriage is a constantly changing panorama, sometimes better, sometimes worse, depending on the variations of conditions. It is a mistake to allow young people to believe the great adventure is perpetual bliss or total failure. It is rarely all the first and seldom needs to be all of the latter.

The really important point is that a young couple should take a complete inventory of themselves and each other. They should realize that adjustments are constantly necessary. It has often been said that the first five years of wedded life are the hardest. There is much to this, because small differences may smolder for years. Mutual respect, unfailing regard for the rights of the partner, are the basis on which a satisfactory life can be builded. If each regards the final result as a personal responsibility, much more will be accomplished than will follow the use of high sounding phrases alone.

If one makes an honest study of marriage as a ceremony or a rite, it does not seem that the form matters a great deal. The marriage ceremony is in its significance as impossible of realization as a religious vow. Of course the marriage ceremony has changed. The word "obey" has been replaced by "cherish," which is even worse. The old boys used to compel their brides to obey, and there was no if about it, but the same technic never caused them to cherish. One can obey against one's will but to cherish, the impulse must come from within. Nowadays some brides request that the word "obey" be left out. That seems funny to me, because that kind of bride has never obeyed any one and never will. I have come to hate the word. Generally speaking it implies certain rights which the groom has over the bride, but it may include anything. Many years ago a delicate young woman married. The first night at home her husband ordered her to go out and milk five cows. She had never milked one cow, but he told her it was time she learned, that she had promised to obey and she had to do it. I learned these facts when the father brought her to me because she had a nervous breakdown. Marriage was sacred to those people. Who remembers when they first tried to milk a cow? Suppose you were not raised for such work but a recently acquired husband insisted that you do it. Only hate could be the result. "A nervous breakdown" in such cases can mean only that hate has destroyed the nervous equilibrium.

The instance above related shocks our finer sensibilities, but things we are more accustomed to may cause as deep a hurt as the things that are less familiar. Anything that one of the partners does which offends the sensibilities of the other spells disaster. Brides more often offend in our higher society than grooms. The sweet young things try to remodel their catch along lines which they are convinced are right and proper. Go milk the cows. Don't smoke in the house. Don't bring your roughneck old friends into my house. All the same language. That is the first step. As a result, a wholly selfish person makes the home a mockery. When the mess is complete the doctor comes in. He points out that if the husband had demanded his rights to his share of the home in the beginning the whole aspect might have been different.

Experiences such as this caused me once to make the mistake of writing that marriage is not in itself holy; it has to be made so by the parties concerned. I have been severely criticized for this assertion and consequently have no intention of repeating the indiscretion. I now humbly admit that marriage is holy, but as a doctor I must add the mental reservation that sometimes it simply does not stay that way. Some one has facetiously said that marriage is a ceremony in which two persons are made one, but which one it will turn out to be only the passing years can decide.

It would broaden our point of view if we analyzed the marriage ceremony and went back into history to determine just how the thing started, best man, shoes, rice, flowing robes and flowers. These are only symbols to us now, of course. It would help us perhaps if we realized that all the fool things that are done at weddings today, to which we add a few of our own, have been done down through all time.

Divested of flowers and fine linen, the marriage ceremony itself is not lovely to look at. What it means is that two people now have the right to cohabit. They have now the right, not only the right but the duty, to produce children who are, in the light of crude laws, to be considered legitimate. What can be made of marriage beyond this depends on the individuals. The ceremony as such is not concerned with eventualities.

That the premarital scene admits of any exercise of intelligence on the part of the contracting parties is generally recognized as a pleasant myth. Fortunately, unions that started with sex may result in love. The young lady may find, after the period of deflation, that the mate in the package she drew has turned out to be a considerate gentleman, and as such he excites her respect. If the package contains only sex, then henceforth that remains the single bond.

The backstage whisper: "What did she ever see in him," catty though it is, may be the only intelligent observation. It makes my heart bleed to think of what I have seen: mere children mumbled over a bit and then pushed out on their own, lacking even the most elemental knowledge. If ever any one needed a guiding hand it is these poor young folks, and they have no one to go to for advice, except the family doctor. What do people think goes on in a doctor's mind when he sees such things and pictures the probable outcome? Do they think he just runs around in circles in smug complacency like the fools about him? Sometimes I feel real proud of myself when I recall that I have never committed murder.

Of course in the higher circles the postnuptial period has

a pretty name. That period of deflation is euphoniously called the "honeymoon." To any one with half an eye it is a travesty. It is sex saying in effect: "Come on, the preacher says it will be all right."

Even if the attendants at the wedding refrain from the utterly silly procedure of throwing old shoes and rice, the journey is in itself a warning for those having the finer sentiments that they had better stay home. "Maybe we'll be back," should be the parting adieu to love as they start on their journey. How much safer it would be to go at once to the place where they hope to build a future home, there to await the awakening of sanity. The vast sea of mental aberration in which the recently married couple find themselves is purely a sex phenomenon, even if there is love in the background.

When I see a young couple starting out on their honeymoon, endowed with no more sense than their elders, I feel like crying out to them to watch their step, that the honeymoon is as senseless as the fine raiment and orange blossoms. They must look out what they do. Satiety is a dangerous thing at any stage of the matrimonial journey, and particularly perilous in the beginning because it may cause one to fall over the cliff into the valley of disgust from which there is no rescue. Satiety loosens the temper and shows the unvarnished elements in their ugliness. A honeymoon offers the poorest possible chance for adjustment. Labor at the regular job would be better, with extra pay for overtime.

Shakespeare cautioned the new couple as follows: "These violent delights have violent ends and in their triumphs die, like fire and powder, which, as they kiss, consume. The sweetest honey is loathesome in his own deliciousness . . . therefore love moderately."

I would suggest to every groom that before he says an unkind word to his bride, he stop to consider what the boss would say if he used the same words to his wife. Let him confine his vocabulary, in his conversation with his bride, to words which he used before he smelled the orange blossoms.

The early home is to the newlyweds what an empty beehive

is to a newly housed swarm of bees. The hive is a vast empty space in which, by assiduous cooperative labor, it will be possible to store a lot of honey on which to feed when the winter comes. If a boarding house, or papa's and mama's home, is to be the abode of the newlyweds they are sunk before they start. It means, without frills, that they could not wait until they were ready to build a home. Uncomplicated love is never in a hurry. It can wait indefinitely.

I pause here for station identification. I am not concerned with cases which are alleged to be the result of love at first sight and which compel the couple to call some one out of bed to marry them at three A.M. An ungodly hour, I would say, to perform the holy rites, and also a hard way to earn a few dollars. Tomcat stuff. A few weeks in jail on a diet of bromides would convince the agitated couple that what they regard as love at first sight will really turn out to be hate at hind sight. It's a matter of the point of view. Such people should not be considered in a serious study of the marriage relation.

The foregoing may seem to be entirely foreign to the affairs of the doctor, but it is not. When we hear of a wedding it is already time for us to begin to speculate on whether the consequences will become our problem. Remember that it is the doctor's chief job in life to prevent suffering, though we occasionally do save a life. The organic diseases which may develop in married people do not concern us here. They can be diagnosed by the ordinary scientific methods. The situation with which we are now concerned demands the exercise of understanding, the recognition of conditions before they are described in words. The adequate medical care, of which we now hear so much, does not include diagnosis of these problems. The relation of the doctor to these young wanderers is not taught in books.

Only we doctors ever know how far reaching are the conditions attending a false start in marriage. We know that the young people must first learn to adjust themselves to each other as animals. The most sordid pictures I have seen are centered about a wrong start. The lower animals have their sex life charted for them. Even the savages have their definite periods of sex activity. But we civilized folks, by centuries of cultivation of the sordid things in life, have developed a sex urge that is ever present and always ready to answer a signal. Just why the Fates made things so complicated for the human is beyond comprehension. Why did they not give us brains before they gave us sex urge? I sometimes wonder what is the significance of the fact that the concubines came before Christ. The two things do not fit together. The indulgence of many allegedly human males would wreck most of the lower animals who have never had concubines to exercise and increase their capacity.

If I could have one wish, I would ask that all I have seen of those early days of wedded life be blotted from my memory. The young people do things so badly. In the hour of need they have no guiding star. After the rice and old shoes have been cleaned away, and father has paid the bills incurred by mama's wedding show, there is still a long road ahead. Not long ago, when a young couple were starting on their honeymoon, I reminded them that the first fifty years would be the hardest. In due time, I got the cheery assurance that they had survived the first month. I hope they told the truth.

We have societies devoted to the early recognition of cancer. In comparison with the cankers the honeymoon may produce, cancer is a merciful disease. Cancer kills after a year or two; but the sores which develop from lust, destroy all but life itself. One can paint a picture of this ulcer just as a doctor can write a book illustrating the various early forms of cancer. Our talk about the prevention of cancer is empty. We cannot prevent cancer because we do not know the cause. What we mean by prevention is the recognition of simple lesions in their early stages. Simple lesions may lead to an incurable lesion if unrecognized and neglected, and proper treatment delayed.

In the same way, many disorders of a sexual origin can be prevented. I have seen a number of people who were willing to listen to the advice of the doctor and who have profited by a simple word of caution such as is possible within the limits of the law. Even a mathematician must have at least one basic fact to work with, but many young couples have nothing, nothing but a blind urge which may lead to endless suffering.

The most vicious idea ever promulgated is that sex satisfied represents the pinnacle of love. This shows how inadequate is our vocabulary. Of course, nature had to see to it that the race was replenished. Were it not so, people who knew love would be content to bask in it forever. Therefore both love and intelligence must be temporarily blended with sex.

I wonder to what point those who say that sex satisfied is the highest state of love would be willing to see their dictum carried out. Apparently to excess, or even to a point which would be rape if the act were committed out of wedlock. Perhaps they would even include physical injury and finally sex murder. Evidently, to say that the sex act is the pinnacle of love leads to dangerous lanes. The fact is, as any one should know, love is one thing, sex another.

To approach such a situation as a medical problem involves the necessity of compiling facts, putting them together, and then seeing how they add up. On the whole, this has been largely futile, but general groups of facts can be recognized.

Nobody but a nasty old doctor would think of such things. More accurately, however, he simply remembers them. In the old days, when a young bride left her newly acquired husband at daybreak and went home to mother, everybody understood, and many laughed. The doctor remembers instances where the young bride said to her mother: "I did not know one had to do that and I'm not going to do it." There follow admonitions and explanations from the fond mother that everybody does it. This may induce the bride to return to her husband or the groom may save the situation by going west to get himself a job on a cattle ranch. One historic character went to the Southwest and made the great state of Texas a fact.

Of course such extreme ignorance on the part of brides is

K

now rare although not unheard of. However, the young ladies had to go out on the highways and byways to gain their information. Their mothers did not teach them the facts of life. Even today, for one who does go home to her mother there are a thousand who wish that they had done so when they discovered that their Lothario was very much a sensuous being. I have heard "If I had only known" so often that I am sick of it. When I see a patient come into the office with that look, I feel like shouting: "For God's sake, don't say it. I understand." If they would yell their plight at the top of their voices, swear like a mule driver, as I feel like doing, it would not be so bad, and it would do them a lot of good. Say what one will, profanity has opened portals which prayers failed to budge. In my last conscious moment I am sure I shall hear two sentences: "Oh, God, put life back into my child," and "If I had only known."

Concrete cases sometimes are useful in clarifying a point. I remember with agony of spirit one scene in which I, as a young doctor, played a part. A prospective bride collapsed just before the happy event. I was called to administer a restorative and stimulant so she would be able to stand up through the ordeal. I did. I was not jailed, as I should have been, as an accessory before the act. That girl was crying for a protector and I turned only an unheeding professional ear. If she had been a heifer and I a farmer, I would have raised my hand and said: "Don't put her in, boys, she is not ready yet."

It is pleasant for us doctors to note that, in general, brides now have more sense than their mothers. Before marriage they may consult the doctor to find out about certain things, whether they are physically fit for marriage for instance, indicating of course that they understand what is ahead. If one knows there are no ghosts there just aren't any. That they seek information is evidence that they have superior intelligence. Unfortunately those who really need advice do not seek it. There are still mothers who evade and even snub children when they inevitably express curiosity about sex matters.

Even intelligent young women, who are fully informed as to what marriage implies, perhaps assured by their doctors that everything is all right, hesitate to undress before a strange man. Sure enough, I know how little the lover days provide scenery which will help them identify the stranger without pants as the same man who was the lover at the garden gate. Many a home has been lost in these early days because some erotic old fools have told the bride that sex is the consummation of love.

Even if the bride has a general notion of what marriage implies and thinks she is prepared to meet it, her sensibilities may be shocked when details fail to check with things as her inexperienced mind had pictured them. There is an endless variation, and most of them do not register until marriage places them in their true setting.

I have put off as long as possible the mention of the more terrible scenes which may have ensued during the first night. An instance: A cultivated, delicate young girl married something which she mistook for a man. I saw her two days later in the most terrible state of hysterical delirium I have ever witnessed. The anguished cries ring in my ears yet. I literally heard them when I came within a block of the house. In the delirium I learned that she had been raped seven times on her wedding night! Raped—that is the word—in the holy bonds of matrimony. Except that he had taken the precaution of undergoing a ceremony before committing the act, the groom could have been hanged for his brutality, as he should have been. Of course that girl was marked for life, and I presume a doctor somewhere is trying to find out to this day why she is nervous, because one may be sure she never would tell anyone, even a doctor, of the experience. The memory of that scene, even to this day, makes my trigger finger tingle.

Everything had started out so beautifully and had lasted from high noon until night. Her father pronounced the rites himself and everything was up-to-date. Nothing was omitted, except the things that were essential. It was all very puzzling to the family. "Oh, he was such a nice, virtuous boy"—except that he was beset with the accumulated rage of a long and ardent courtship.

If I should say that it is just such nice boys, likely to infest parsonages, who are most apt to make up for lost time, I would be hanged, quartered, and burned at the stake. Before judging anyone who makes such a statement, one should read history. One can get an idea by studying the camp meetings of my boyhood. My father once hied himself to one of these with the declaration that he would be gone ten days. He returned in a day. We boys knew he was not open to an interview. About that time a minister invited him to take part in a revival. "No, don't like revivals; too emotional." That was quite a speech for dad to make. That word "emotional" was quite a poser to us boys; we did not know what the word meant, so we proceeded to do a little scouting on our own account and thereby got a general idea of what Dad had meant. I regret to be compelled to say that the public would be better able to understand this paragraph if they would study the history of religions. Don't blame me: I have just been around watching people perform in this old world for about seventy years.

Of course the extreme cases above related are unusual, but less aggravated instances, not requiring the immediate care of a doctor, are not unknown today though apparently they are less common than formerly. Only we doctors learn about the disturbances of the early days, often not until years after when we search for unexplained causes for nervousness. It is the finest tribute women pay us doctors that they will tell us things they would not tell any one else in the world.

Is such treatment cause for divorce? Not at all, it is entirely legal. I do not know of a single case in which rape on the honeymoon was given as a cause for divorce. The judge does not hear of it, though it may be the underlying cause for the cure which he is about to perform under a wholly different diagnosis, which nowadays is generally "incompatibility."

I will illustrate such cases by describing one which properly begins in this chapter, although the end of the story belongs to a later one. When I was a young doctor, a little lady came

to me because she could not sleep. She told me that after the
first night she had hated her husband; that ever since his
touch had been as welcome as a snake's. In this case there
was no intermediary stage of disgust. She told me that when
she married she supposed that a woman had the same privi-
leges as a cow; that a woman had to submit only when she
wanted a baby. She told me of the horrors of her life. She
remained my patient thirty-three years—until the story was
finally all told. When she was sleepless, I gave her a sedative;
when she was weak, I gave her a tonic. The cause of her
troubles were never mentioned after the first visit. Her husband was a good provider and was one of our respected and
prosperous citizens, but he knew his rights. One day he
came to me with a very small tumor on his leg. It didn't
amount to much he said, he'd had it for years but lately it
oozed so that it became attached to his clothing. I removed
it but gave no prognosis because I was not asked for one.
Remembering his wife, I had a peculiar feeling as I calculated
that in a year and a half he would be dead. My calculations
were correct. A few hours after his demise the frail little
woman tiptoed into my office. I didn't notice her until she
laid her hand gently on my shoulder, and fairly hissed her
hate: "Now at last the old devil is dead." To the community,
this was a happy Christian family; they raised a number of
very creditable children. Only she and I knew how terribly
cruel life had been to her. Hell from the wedding night
until her husband died, forty years later. Two things might
have averted this disaster: early understanding on her part
of what the minister was saying, and consideration and an
understanding of the rights of others on the part of the
husband.

Many instances are not so aggravated as these, but for
related causes come to the attention of the doctor. The most
usual cause, pain caused by the act itself or some other incident, produces a more or less permanent frigidity. Here is an
example: A woman told me that her husband was an ideal
lover, had done everything one could expect from a future
husband. During their courtship, to be in his arms was bliss

indeed. Her thoughts did not reach beyond this; she was too happy. Had he just held her in his arms the first few nights, until she could have had time to realize exactly what marriage meant, which she knew theoretically of course, all might have been well. The result was a frigidity that she was never able to overcome. Was there no remedy? None. Too late. She believed in the sanctity of the marriage ceremony, so she endured the hell which she had entered so blithely carrying a spray of orange blossoms. Funny combination here: she loathed her husband sexually but loved him as a man—and he was blissfully ignorant of why his wife was nervous.

Perhaps the doctor does not know what he is talking about, but the first night may be extended to several, also to several decades. Listen to the case-book; here's another which begins in this chapter and ends thirty-six years later. A high type of business man consulted me about a lesion his home doctors could not diagnose. I told him that an operation was necessary, one that would render him permanently impotent. He looked at me with a mixture of incredulity and horror. "Unthinkable!" he exploded. "Do you know," he went on, "that I haven't missed a night since the wedding night in thirty-six years?" I told him my obligations were fulfilled when I told him the truth about his ailment. He replied that he would rather be dead, that he would go home and shoot himself. In exasperation I exploded: "Wonder you hadn't thought of that long ago." Imagine my feelings when a few days later the newspapers carried the notice that he had blown off the top of his head with the saddle gun of his cowboy days.

I sent for the local newspaper carrying his obituary notice, which was written by his local minister. It stated that in a fit of insanity the Brother had taken his own life. It extolled his virtues as a citizen and as a deacon of the church. He left a bereaved (probably a misprint, should have been relieved) widow but no children, three brothers and three sisters, besides a considerable property. I have thought about that instance many times. I really had not taken his threat seriously. Those who threaten to take their lives rarely do so. Temporary insanity the paper said. It was the noblest impulse he ever had, though he had been unconscious of that interpretation. Yet it is a sad picture. No children. Perhaps if thirty-odd years previously he had had a little daughter to crawl upon his lap, love for the child might have modified his lust. Life might then have assumed an entirely different form, for he was fundamentally a high type of man. Disappointments sometimes take funny forms.

Sometimes such excesses result in a loathing that leads to the judge. It is interesting to note that most women in this class are highly sensitive, which is the real trouble; but in addition they are high minded, which means they are ready to live a life of hell before they will tell a judge. Indeed, there is often nothing to tell, because the husband may walk the straight and narrow road according to the moral standards of the community, be a model husband in the daytime, and provide well for his family, meeting all the requirements of modern society. He may have everything, in fact, but an understanding of his obligations to his partner.

Some of these maladjusted women enter the marriage state with their fingers crossed. They conclude beforehand that if they are not satisfied with the result they will cancel the deal. This idea is particularly attractive if such a step carries with it a permanent meal ticket. Women of that type pronounce the word "alimony" with the same enthusiasm that a colored urchin says "watermelon."

I repeat that all brides should be warned that although aversions may develop during the first night, they are usually psychic and are capable of correction. In fact they usually correct themselves in time. There is naturally a reluctance to mention the difficulty, even to the doctor. Mothers of such unfortunate women seldom have the confidence of their daughters, because they failed to give them advice beforehand. Even the doctor is handicapped because the complaint reaches him in a much disguised form. It is easiest for a woman to go to the old family doctor who has perhaps known her from childhood. It is no task for a clinic or a specialist.

Such topics are avoided because they are not nice. All the lady need say is, "Doc, I'm nervous and can't sleep." He need ask no questions. If she goes to the clinic where she can have "adequate medical care," and the Wassermann and other tests all prove negative, she is branded a malingerer. She would rather go to the judge, who in his kind understanding makes the word "incompatible" cover whatever is needed to meet the law.

Sometimes these early nuptial difficulties have an anatomic basis. An unusually rigid hymen or an adherent clitoris is assumed because there are a few such cases on record, and attempts are made to relieve the condition by operative means. I have encountered many cases in which this was done not by spinal manipulation but with metal instruments, almost always by irregulars ignorant of fundamentals. If nothing in particular is removed, as seems usually to be the case, no harm is done, but if too much is removed the mischief is complete and permanent. It is like hitting a fiddle with a hammer because it is out of tune.

One thing should be particularly emphasized: If there is pain, the young bride should see her doctor, and take her husband along. Most likely the trouble is caused by a spasm due to fright, and a statement of the fact from the doctor, reinforced perhaps by a little sedative, will relieve it. Occasionally there is an anatomic basis. If the couple even suspect this, they should consult the doctor at once. If there is an anatomic difficulty it should be remedied by operation. Go together to the doctor, I say to the young people. The foxy old doctor will take one look at the husband and see a lot. There is no need to worry; he is not going to ask any questions. He will estimate the husband's athletic achievements and drop a suggestion which may do a vast deal of good. Many husbands act as they do act because they misread the instructions on the card which they received at the start. Perhaps owing to previous experiences it has not occurred to him that there is a difference between a woman and a female. Many young husbands have been grateful to me for this simple suggestion. Let me repeat: If there is any difficulty, see your doctor, and go together. The failure to do so may cause a fissure to appear which will only widen in the ensuing years.

Difficulties arise in the beginning which many young couples iron out for themselves, if love survives the ceremony. The most common is frigidity on the part of the bride, even though she is intelligent and has an abstract notion of the events to be anticipated. Perfect frankness and the ability to discuss more intimate matters as freely as headaches and stomach trouble is the first essential. Even here, the doctor, knowing the difficulty, may have suggestions to make. A few concrete examples may clear up the point.

Farmer boys know that before turning a cow into a lot, certain preliminary physiologic processes are necessary. He forgets this by sundown. Often I have heard brides say in agony of spirit: "If he would only hold me a while as he used to do." She knows what she needs, but is too embarrassed to tell her husband. Satiety removes this obvious need from the mind of the husband, but with the wife it is different.

An instance comes to mind, the recollection of which amuses me still. A young husband came to me complaining that his bride was frigid. I knew the upbringing of the young lady and also his. I suggested that he take a bath before going to bed and put on a night shirt. He flared up in anger: "You think I am a hog." I replied that I knew he was not a hog because hogs are really clean animals and sit down in the mud only when they want to cool off. All his life he had been going to bed in his sweaty shirt, smelling to high heaven, which naturally was repulsive to a girl of a different breeding. I record with a bit of glee that my advice was followed and it worked; also he learned to like the daily ablutions.

But the doctor's troubles are not yet over. To start with, the idea seems to be that the sex act now is theirs to "enjoy" (God save the word), and the more of it the better. I have been asked countless times how often indulgence was permissible. A fine steak is good for the stomach, why not a whole beef? That seems to be the idea, particularly since the butcher man has sent no bill, yet. How often can it be done?

This is a constant question. Never yet have I been asked how little is advisable or what the real purpose of it all may be.

Unfortunately one starts with two unequal people, two utterly unknown equations, variables as the mathematicians say—and we doctors are supposed to be able to solve the problem without a single known factor. Perhaps one is experienced, the other not. So far as I have been able to see, herein lies the chief evil of the so-called double standard for men and women. Too often the experienced stranger sets the pace, or tries to. A person who has never seen a golf club is handicapped if she enters a game with a professional.

As with alcohol and opium, toleration is increased by constant use. But as with the excessive use of these drugs, there will surely come a day of reckoning. Then they want to cry on the doctor's shoulder. All this because the idea persists that the sex act is the height of love. It might help a little if people could get the very obvious fact into their fool heads that the sex act has nothing to do with love.

I sometimes think it might also help if the bride could know whether she is to meet a novice like herself or an experienced campaigner. But as long as everything is considered so beautiful any practical point of view is unthinkable. I have already mentioned the disaster likely to result if the novice is an emotionally highly strung person. He is a greater menace than an experienced campaigner. Golf players have a way of classifying each other in order to level off unequal matches.

After difficulties have arisen, the doctor may be asked just how much the husband has a right to expect. I am not going to display any mathematical calculations. When I think of what I have listened to in days gone by, my pen goes dry. To begin with, Martin Luther wrote a "poem" in which he expressed the opinion that twice a week was a moderate indulgence. That may be a conservative figure for a gentleman of leisure but for any one engaged in the serious problems of life it would be a sad waste of energy, to say the least. The limit of sordidness has been illustrated by a case in a previous paragraph. Here we have to do, it is assumed, with honest people seeking the way to light. The doings of sex athletes do not interest us here. It all depends on what a man's purpose in life may be. If sex is his god, no rules can be laid down. He who drives himself at high speed for a great purpose is likely to be a failure as a sex partner.

Here it need only be remarked that the essential factor is a common agreement. The distressing thing is that the husband often thinks things have all been ironed out because the wife does not complain. But the wife may tell a different tale, although she doesn't really need to, for an experienced doctor knows the physical signs of satiety.

Of course the husband sometimes receives the surprise. He may have regarded himself as quite a fellow, only to discover that he is a piker. Many years ago I was consulted by the husband of a thrice daily female. I can see his hollow eyes as he blurted forth: "Say, Doc, by gawd." I advised him to get all his money together and buy one one-way ticket and travel as far as it would take him. I explained that what he needed was a change of climate, direction immaterial. As I have remarked before, this is a funny world.

When the day of satiety appears the wife can pretend but the husband cannot, and he hies himself to the doctor for a tonic. The honeymoon may be abbreviated because of an urgent desire to see the home doctor. Just where the boundary lies between normal and abnormal indulgence, it is impossible to say. Sometimes I think the person who divided the day into twenty-four hour intervals must have been a lady Solomon.

That adjustments must be made, owing to differences in sex capacity, has been generally recognized and various suggestions have been offered. Judge Lindsey, when he proposed companionate marriages, attempted a solution by way of trial marriages. If the differences were insurmountable after a year the trial marriage was to terminate spontaneously. Such an arrangement is defeated before it starts, because it ignores the finer sentiments and concentrates on the sex act as the sole test of connubial bliss. It is, in fact, nothing more noble than a sex marathon. Such ladies should not be called trial wives but concubines. To the medical man it is an impossible proposition, because it presumes there will be no pregnancies during this period. Few loves, even if decent to start with, would survive the use of the necessary contraceptive measures, particularly when the gate is open for escape. This in itself brings a definite hazard. The Judge certainly has not found the answer. The sad part of it is that the learned judge seemed to think that happiness was only a matter of sex. Or did he think that love, if it ever existed, might survive the ordeal? Not a chance.

It might help in reaching an adjustment if at the outset it were understood that the woman and man are anatomically different. The glands in the woman are mucous glands and, like a cow's udder, are ready constantly to secrete. Her test of endurance is the nervous system. The man on the contrary is constructed like a snake, or say a skunk; once the "poison" gland is emptied he is harmless for a period until he has accumulated more. One may observe the bull. Once through, he wants to eat grass. The most attractive bovine bathing beauty interests him not in the least, for the time being. In fact the sight of the beauty gives him a pain in the neck.

The woman should remember this; if she sleeps late and her husband is peevish because the biscuits are just a bit doughy on the inside, it is only a temporary state due to their anatomic differences. Many early fights begin at the breakfast table because neither understands. Don't blame the biscuits.

There is a fundamental factor here that is unpleasant to think about, doubly difficult to write about, but of all factors in the process of sex adjustment, by all odds the most important. An exhausted animal is grouchy, no matter what the cause of fatigue may be. Four times a night, a recent honeymooner told me, and pleadingly added that he just could not keep up the pace.

Nature fixed it for the lower animals so that no exercise of intelligence is necessary. But humans are supposed to have some sense—rankest flattery. Humans must understand that

the act should, nay must, end in mutual satisfaction. The
sex act reaches its height in a contraction of various muscles.
This is called the orgasm. The majority of inexperienced
young husbands believe that a single orgasm means satisfaction for the wife. This may be true, but women differ
greatly. A number may be required before she feels relaxed.
The husband must determine how many she needs and
withhold his until she has achieved her required number.
That is what is meant by sex adjustment. The sad fact is that
such adjustment requires more intelligence and knowledge
of physiology than the vast majority of young people possess. Yet the failure to achieve an adjustment is going to
breed much unhappiness, and is the most common fork in
the road that may lead to the divorce court. Of course they
do not know where the difficulty lies.

No one need take my word for the importance of mutual
satisfaction. Harken to the voice of an expert:

"O maidens of Jerusalem, I charge you, by the roe-deer
  And the hinds, never rouse lovers, never stir them,
  'Til they are satisfied." Songs of Solomon, 2:7.

Imagine a big mature party with whiskers singing about
that! Yet in the writing of that song lies his reputation for
being the wisest man who ever lived.

As far as frequency of indulgence is concerned, generally
speaking the wife should be allowed to wind the clock,
albeit one must admit some women have abnormally strong
fingers. The doctor is seldom consulted about this, and if
he should be he cannot give a more definite answer than
the statement I have just made. But excess, it must be
warned, expressed in a feeling of exhaustion, is disastrous
and tends to destroy the import of the whole thing. Many
women complain that they still like to be held and loved,
but, though married, want to go no further. To the cow,
certain preliminary endocrine stimulation is necessary; the
bull can interrupt the business of eating grass without notice. The great difficulty is that complete confidence does

not always exist and possibly people never heard of the song above quoted.

That feature of our national life, the double bed, tends to lead to excesses. Half awake in the morning, the couple are in no state of mind to exercise any sense of proportion. Morning indulgences usually mean excess. It is like eating a piece of pumpkin pie after a turkey dinner. It is not the fault of the pie, but the sequence, which causes the indigestion. The first thought on awakening in the morning should be of bacon and eggs, and there should be a rivalry to see who gets to the kitchen first.

It has always been my belief that ideally, the partners should have separate rooms or at least separate beds. It seems I do not know much. An enterprising furniture manufacturer recently sent a questionnaire to five hundred wives inquiring if they preferred double or single beds. Three-fourths declared in favor of the double beds. The reporter of these facts facetiously remarked that he reckoned women preferred the double beds because it was harder to keep up a quarrel in separate beds. Be that as it may, I am confident many rows start because of the double beds. The fundamental fact behind the preference for double beds is that many women want only to be held. One of the noblest of my friends told me that he and his wife always had had separate rooms, and that he never once in thirty years entered her room without first knocking and receiving a welcoming word. She was equally considerate. They are sweethearts still. Maintaining that high personal regard which marked the days of courtship is the key to marital happiness.

But judging from the results of the questionnaire above mentioned, the ladies have a different idea. Certainly they should have the right to indicate when they want simply to be held and loved, and when they want to go further. But holding just as a manual exercise becomes uninteresting to the husband and leads to excesses because he does not understand.

With excess comes the feeling of exhaustion. If there is a tendency for either party to be grouchy at breakfast it is time for a little exercise in mathematical calculation. The doctor is likely to be appealed to for a tonic, but if he is dumb enough to comply with the request he only adds to the vicious circle. That a courageous inquiry into facts may solve misunderstandings, smooth out irregularities, I have abundantly proved in practice. In some instances the husband is amazed when told that he has been unreasonable; it excites in him a willingness to meet the wishes of this less amorous partner. More often, however, he just stands on his rights.

There are two classes of patients I refuse to consider: One, the drunk with a headache; the other, the man who complains that he can't keep up the pace. What I say to him may sound like a prayer that got mixed up in an electric fan. But it is not swearing; it is merely making a comprehensive diagnosis.

If we could get that word "obey" out of all marriage contracts and insert instead the provision that the bride shall always be the master of her own person, the changed point of view would I am sure work much good, but to achieve that the whole scheme of things must be altered. Sometimes I feel it might help if fine linen were changed to sackcloth and ashes, and an honest functionary performed the rites. But it would never do; the bride looks too beautiful.

With the adjustment period comes another problem. It is vulgar for a young couple to produce a baby in regulation time; and it might even be premature, as many first babies are—much to the delight of the neighboring dowagers who scent a delicious scandal. How to have babies presents difficulties; how not to have them brings even greater problems. Societies exist for the promulgation of such knowledge and many couples know much more about it than the doctor. All the doctor knows is that all methods have their hazards, both because of their inefficiency and their effect on the psychology of those practicing them. The early months in which prevention of conception is practiced are more hazardous than the later years because complete adjustment has not yet been reached.

Sometimes an old acquaintance greets the family physician with: "Say, Doc, I am to be married next week. My salary is only fifteen dollars a week; I need some information, etc." Here unhappily the doctor is silent, not through fear however, at least not through moral fear. The law decrees that the doctor must not know anything. Don't blame him; the laws are what the people make them. This reminds me that Will Rogers once said that some legislators vote dry as long as they can stagger to the polls. The people likewise vote laws that, individually, they may some time ask the doctor to violate. They believe he should violate a law that the general public has made, aided and abetted by a lobby anchored somewhere two thousand years back.

The bare outline presented in this chapter is sufficient to show how complicated is the life that confronts a young couple as they go forth to make a home. It seems plain that their chief trouble lies in the fact that love and sex are confused. Mutual respect is indispensable, and to this must be added love. Sex, a necessary end, is not a part of love, and excessive indulgence does more than anything else to drive love away. But the advent of a child may excite a love when only sex existed before.

VII

The Struggle for Paradise (The Happy American Home)

IT IS pleasant for the doctor, in his professional capacity, to mingle with families in which the parents are in entire accord, devoted to each other and to the children. The doctor's role then is to combat the things fate brings along in the way of sickness to a parent or to the children. One does sometimes see such a utopian state, but far more often the parents, being human, experience little frictions. Things happen to them despite their best efforts, but being honorable, they meet them with frankness and honesty, and thus achieve a state of domestic bliss approaching the ideal.

In the preceding chapter the struggle for animal adjustment was considered. It meant a constant consideration of the rights of each. It meant the conquering, in a measure at least, of the poorly veiled implication behind the marriage ceremony that sex is the primary end of life. The newly-wed couple, by their own efforts, may measure up to the fine linen and the orange blossoms if they discount the "rights" of the contract. Even so, the solution of the adjustment problem in most cases is not complete, or refuses to stay solved, because one or the other alters his point of view. Biological differences continue to appear in many cases, usually as the result of changing conditions in after years. Life is constantly in need of readjustment, and in many phases of it the doctor may be of service.

Even if the problem of sex during the honeymoon is satisfactorily solved the real struggle is only beginning. The couple may still be far apart, still harassed by the fundamental sex urge. Some rugged people will eat a beefsteak every day; others by over-use of a protein diet lose a taste for it, and become vegetarians. There is always a need of guidance in the selection of the moral or spiritual diet. We doc-

L

tors cannot hold up our hands and say everything is very nice. We know that the results are going to depend largely on the capacity of the couple to manage their own affairs despite what aid the doctor can give. Much more often than formerly, these people will ask him to prescribe a compromise diet.

People come to doctors with complaints none the less real because they have but little pathological basis. The distinction between mind and body is chiefly physiologic. The problem is usually presented in a veiled form and the doctor must read the real cause out of his past experience. One will say: "Doc, I can't digest my food, I must have an ulcer. I just can't eat meat." The difficulty is the wrong partner complains. If the big meat eater complained we might prescribe something that would lessen his appetite for meat. We would say: "You have an ulcer and I must put you on a restricted diet." The old spinach gag has gone out but one could put him on alfalfa, which is said to contain large amounts of some vitamin or other. It might even do to put him on some medicine which would lessen his appetite for anything much.

It would be pleasant for us doctors if we could assume that once a pair has found an equitable adjustment that the union is launched on still waters and the sailing from then on will be a pleasant dream. We get the diet fixed—and behold something else comes up. Doctors must anticipate these problems, often little things in themselves which become large only by neglect.

Let us assume there has been a measure of human understanding after the honeymoon. For the first time in history young people discuss the question of parenthood. Nearly all agree that they will want children. When do we begin and how many will we want? In other words, for the first time, parenthood is looked upon as a responsibility to be solved by them rather than by rules laid down by some one in the distant past.

Nevertheless, the question of children is one of the most usual causes of domestic unhappiness. The doctor meets the madonnas in their early pregnancy, sometimes long before they themselves have waked up to the fact that life is real and the pale blue moon has set and their future is in their own hands. The lady comes to the doctor and says that our diet worked very well for a time but now everything is worse than ever. In fact, just this morning she vomited her breakfast. A tactful, sympathetic understanding does much to quiet this surprised and startled patient. The doctor says, "Well, well, something must have come up, besides your breakfast. You haven't got to eating too much steak, have you?" Being assured that such is not the case, he proceeds to investigate and discovers what he knew all the time. Many a doctor has made a friendship which has lasted until his dying day by showing a sympathetic understanding and avoiding a blunt diagnosis. He tells the lady he finds her afflicted with a slight touch of pregnancy, only slight. She may be mad at the doctor for his diagnosis, but he skillfully leads her around to the cause of such things. If she is merely surprised, that is no concern of the doctor; if really angry, she will direct her remarks in a direction which will not hurt the doctor. But if she is frightened, the doctor can reassure her by calling attention to the fact that many women have recovered from a like condition. Of course the doctor may reflect that she has overlooked the fact that this is what she asked for, but he does not mention it. The beautiful blue moon did not tell her all the possibilities. If, however, as so often happens, she secures an abortion, procurable in most states only from quacks, an infection results. If death follows, it isn't so bad; there is always peace in the grave. But the more common infection produces permanent invalidism. Then it becomes a major tragedy, starting from just a little rebellion against nature. Such misfortunes usually do not produce a rift between the couple. They bear it as a common grievance, but the most pleasant anticipations in life are out for good.

Sometimes the doctor is met by the frank statement that of course they want children some time but can't afford them now, because there are so many counter attractions that appeal to them for the moment. I tell these people: "All right, bring the baby to me—I'll raise it until you can afford to keep it." I am still waiting for my first one.

Women sometimes play mean tricks on young doctors. In years gone by before women got wise, they could be roughly divided into two classes: those who had too many children to suit them, and those who wanted them but could not have them. A married patient, childless for years, desired to know why she was denied a family. I examined her carefully and I was sure I demonstrated an infantile uterus. So I told her emphatically that, owing to a lack of development of her genital organs, she would never be able to bear a child. Within a year she had a baby and then four more followed at two year intervals. Not satisfied with showing me up thus she ended by producing twins. Worst of all, in an attempt to be facetious I had suggested that she buy a pup. For years she taunted me by inquiring if I had any young dogs for sale. That cured me. Never since have I told a woman in like circumstances what she cannot do and what she should do.

To couples whose wish is not anticipated by nature, comes a day when a baby is desired. Whether the wife's sterility is due to causes unknown or to some misfortune above noted, they appeal to the doctor. If the sterility is due to unknown causes, it is the medical man's job to find out what the difficulty may be. We know many ways to demonstrate the cause, but if found, it is seldom remediable.

When denied a child of their own, many couples seek to fill the void by adopting a child. This involves many hazards the discussion of which I would gladly avoid. However, there recently appeared in a book a discussion of this subject which is so misleading that I believe a doctor's point of view is due these people. This writer painted the prospect in such glowing terms that one equally devoid of information might be misled. According to this author, all the couple needs to do when they desire a child is to go to a second-hand shop and select a baby they like, and presto all the requirements of parenthood are met. This cheerful point of view disregards wholly the changes in the endocrine system produced by pregnancy. It also ignores the laws of heredity, and certainly it is counter to the experience of the medical man.

Of course, those concerned with finding homes for children have Wassermanns done to assure the prospective parents that the child they are about to adopt is free from syphilis. This is likely to be eighty per cent right. The possibility of other hereditary diseases, including tuberculosis, that are prone to come on later in life, are even more difficult to exclude. Their number is great. Aside from the physical defects, there are other considerations. The baby may be the product of an unfortunate girl, say seventeen years old. The adopted infant may possibly be unfortunate at the same age, much to the distress of the foster parents. Many other defects likewise are more or less hereditary.

I will say as kindly as possible that I cannot conceive of anyone so obtuse to facts that he could visit an institution of neglected children without going away with a stronger hope that the problem will be met at its source. The way to lessen the number of unfortunate children is to lessen the number of unfortunate parents.

This recalls an observation I had a chance to make years ago. A friend was very positive that environment was everything, heredity nothing. To prove his point he secured an Indian infant and brought it up in the strict tenets of his religion. All went very well until the boy was sixteen years old, when one day, without warning, he stole all the money he could find, took a gun and a horse and headed for the Indian Territory. Total failure; exit one fine theory.

Being a doctor, if I were to adopt a child I would insist on knowing his antecedents. How did it happen that the child was placed for adoption? If this information were not available, I would play safe and buy a dog. Some children's homes refuse to give out any information except that the child is healthy—which of course nobody knows. It only means that for the moment there is no demonstrable disease.

Sometimes the genesis of the child is well known. It happened that some relatives of mine adopted children. In one case the parents had died of typhoid. In the other, measles caused the death of the parents. These children grew up true to type and developed into respectable citizens, filling roles in the less pretentious walks of life, but the proffered higher education was beyond them.

Occasionally one is confronted by a problem such as this: The woman says of course she wants children, but she feels it would be nobler if, instead of adding to the race, she would adopt some children, and make them a Christian home. It sounds noble, but often spells disaster.

Certainly the parents of the child should not be told who the foster parents are or there is very apt to be trouble: a demand for the return of the child, blackmail, and many other things. It is aggravating to see a parent who has ignored her child for years, when she sees the product of the foster parents, forthwith demand him back.

The question of whether or not the child should be told he was adopted often comes up. Certainly the child should not be told a lie. Sooner or later someone will let out the information. For instance, a couple moved into our neighborhood bringing an adopted child. Aunt Mary from Ohio visited her sister, Mrs. Doe. As soon as she got her hat off she asked her sister if she knew Mrs. Roe's daughter was an adopted child. Exit all the household of the Does, who went forth with "Hear ye, hear ye, Mrs. Roe's daughter is adopted. 'Taint theirn at all." The little girl runs home, asks is it true that mother is not her real mother. Mrs. Roe makes reply, "The Does had to take the children that were given them. Papa and I went to where there were a lot of babies and we picked you out from the whole bunch." Goes Miss Roe forth and declares she was a picked child: "The rest of you kids, your parents just had to take what was given them." That is an entente cordiale which will do credit to an umbrella statesman and a paperhanger. That reply was a masterpiece. Not all foster mothers have the tact of this one, but many do solve the problem in their own way. The fact to be remembered is that in few cases is it possible to keep the child permanently ignorant of the true status of the child-parent relationship.

To most couples, however, there comes the day when their own baby arrives. The thrill felt with the first kiss over the garden gate or behind the steering-wheel, comes again, comes to stay in the person of the baby. The baby— that's the important thing now. The voice of the baby, indistinct at first, gains volume as time progresses. Eventually it smiles. Henceforth the preservation of that smile is the all important thing for the happiness of that particular family, and for the good of civilization.

With the arrival of the baby comes a new crisis. This, it hardly need be mentioned, does not occur when a baby is secured at the second-hand store. Only when a woman produces her own baby is there a readjustment of her endocrines; and she comes out a different person than she was when she conceived.

It is generally assumed that it is the baby, as a separate individual, that influences the sex life of the parents. This is true, but it is quite apart from the changes in the mother herself. After the baby is born, if sex is the bond that brought the parents together, sex life is resumed, at worst within a few days, within ten days often, and within three weeks as a rule. Such things are unbelievable but they are true. There is no other beast that sinks so low. I have listened to such tales with murder in my heart.

But there is a finer side. The presence of a baby may change the entire sex life of the father as well as of the mother. His entire instinct may be to assume the spirit of a father and to forget sex. The whole family relationship may change from the instant the child is born. Is there a male parent so obtuse that he has not felt something changed in his soul when he first held his baby daughter? The marriage "rights" are out for good. The mother, through the mediation of her child, becomes the captain of her fate, also of his. Even many considerate husbands do not realize that so long as a mother is nursing her baby her sex instinct is satisfied, and they need to be told. The most hopeful sign I have seen that perhaps some time a Christian civilization will ensue is that the father will, when the good of the mother demands it, restrain himself for months, even years. These fine things never get into the books, and even the neighbors miss them.

Though I shall consider this subject later, there cannot be too much repetition of the facts relative to the influence of a child on its parents. The child has been holding up its arms for two thousand years, without takers. Nothing curbs lust so effectively as love for a child, and secondarily for its mother. Many a time have I studied a young father's face with interest when I explained: "Mother is feeding two people now, and the less additional strain placed on her the better." There are a lot of noble men in the world who, though ignorant, will understand when the doctor tells them the truth and will receive the obvious facts gladly.

An interesting observation well known to all doctors may be made here. When I was young in the profession, I encountered women nursing their babies after two or more years. This was not discussed in the books, and I had to be told by the mothers themselves that they did this because as long as they nursed the baby they would not become pregnant. This was the first evidence I met indicating that women had a desire to limit the output. This attempt of the mother to slow up production apparently went on without the attention of the husband. It was years later that he joined his wife in the effort to limit production. Somehow the idea gained ground that the relation of wife and husband had something to it besides procreation.

With the advent of the baby we're not yet through with the adjustments which the pair must undergo. A fine relationship between husband and wife brings its complications, and eternal vigilance is needed to preserve it. Perhaps following that baby, will come another, and even yet another. "Hold on here," cries the husband. "Where is this thing leading to? Let's see, it cost Pa a hundred dollars a month to send me through college. Three times a hundred is three hundred a month; how is one going to meet that expense on a hundred and forty a month? Say, Doc!" Here father raises his voice in approval of the purpose of the wife when she sought to limit output by prolonging the lactation period. Limitation of population has taken on an economic aspect.

"Doc," a young father told me, "I would not take a million dollars for this baby but I would not give fifty cents for another. Three is all we can afford." All the doctor can say is: "Sorry, but there are the civil and ecclesiastic laws that restrain us. You will have to muddle along the best you can until the laws of mankind are changed." Muddle they do, and new disaster impends in the muddling. One young man, when I told him the profession was silenced, asked me why the teachings of Christ do not say how many children one should have. "Son," I replied, "you must remember that religion, a purely man-made conglomeration of opinions and beliefs, runs this world. In that wild scramble the teachings of Christ have been submerged."

What will the answer be? Nobody knows. So long as the making of the laws is the exclusive privilege of those who know nothing of the struggles of the people and who, having no responsibilities, insist on pious declarations, we cannot hope for any fundamental change. Certainly not so long as those who control us persist in singing the songs of Solomon.

We must here digress and point out that there are other things that appear to influence the relations of the man and his wife during their early period of married life. As a doctor, I feel there are a number of things young people should know more about, side-lights on sex, which, misunderstood or unrecognized, may mar the happiness of the pair. Final understanding can come only when both are perfectly frank with each other and are willing to meet the problems as they are. The law says ignorance excuses no man. Never was this more true than here.

The first has to do with normal menstruation. There are often minor disturbances which make the wife nervous, petulant, and unapproachable. Many wives have a slight fever at this time, lasting a day or two. Yet she feels a strong need for sympathy, wants to be held, even though to the confused husband it may seem that what she wants more than anything else is to be left alone. If attention is denied her through ignorance, she may conceive the notion that the husband no longer loves her, and a gap in their affections may appear.

Menstrual disorders attended by pain or excessive hemorrhage furnish the doctor with some of his most perplexing problems. Treatment is urgently indicated, not only because of the physical suffering, but more because the husband does not understand why the wife should be abed hours or days each month. The husband feels like a spare tire, and a deflated one at that. Left to his own devices he may wander down to the corner drug store to see what the boys are doing. But the suffering woman craves sympathy and should have it. Woe betide the husband who overlooks his obligation. The doctor must think back to such instances if he is to understand obscure nervous disorders. Few women will volunteer this information, even if she is cognizant of it, and the doctor must search for the elemental facts. A woman will best serve herself if she will frankly tell the doctor the truth of the case.

Happy is the couple who have such full confidence in each other that the wife feels free to tell her husband that she feels nervous and wants only to be held. Of all created things, woman is the least capable of growing up. She clings to the things of the old courtship days.

With the menopause, nervous disorders increase. The endocrine glands, with almost inhuman perverseness, seem to realize that they are at last to lose their grasp on their victim and they proceed to raise as much hob as possible. The woman feels nervous, feels consumed by heat, skin vessels dilate and a flushing of the skin may be noted. These are the "hot flashes" of common parlance. She may be in a mood for combat; sex desire may be lessened or increased or unchanged. The disturbance may last for years or may pass in a short time, and some women are fortunate enough to escape all the unpleasant manifestations. Sometimes the degree and duration of the flow is increased. Such disturbances require medical investigation because they may hide a lurking cancer, but here great caution is needed on the part of the medical man. Far too often a cancer diagnosis is missed, but it is equally necessary to warn that still more often a cancer is diagnosed when none exists, and a needless operation is the result. I once heard a distinguished surgeon say that when in doubt, operate. That clears the surgeon of responsibility, for a normal organ removed does not haunt the surgeon, though it may the patient. Any surgeon who knows his business can tell the patient yes or no without equivocation. There is one thing that every woman should know: once menstruation has ceased and a bloody discharge appears, say after a year or more of cessation, careful investigation is imperative.

The emotional disturbances at the time of the menopause are likely to be more significant than the physical. The woman is apt to be cranky, critical, suspicious. Mental aberration may reach such a degree that the patient may need to be confined to an institution for a time. They usually recover eventually, though there are distressing symptoms. Many divorces in middle life are purely the result of misunderstood reactions of the physiological regression of the endocrine system. If ever a wife, and equally a husband, need a protecting arm it is here. In case of doubt, better stop in to see old doc, and tell him the truth, before going to the judge. Rash acts at that time may result in long regrets once the endocrine involution is complete and sanity returns.

It is pleasing to note that the nervous disorders resulting from the menstrual period and menopause are much more widely understood than formerly. The woman has knowledge which raises her above the prudery of the past; to her facts are facts which she and her husband discuss together, and together they go to see the doctor. There are many things he can do to lessen the suffering of both. The hot flashes or nervousness can be controlled with drugs until nature completes the normal process of involution.

Nature has a hateful way of punishing those who ignore her laws. Women who have borne no children or those who have borne only one, perhaps long ago, suffer more from the disturbances of the menopause than those who have borne a large number right up to the final bell.

Having disposed of the less desirable aspects of acquiring children, we may return to the young couple as one finds them today. The old order has changed. I have in mind now only the finest of our young couples, who are anxious to do the right thing by themselves and their children, and to produce no more than they can properly care for. According to our present set-up regulated by those who rule without responsibility, the right to limit the size of one's family is not recognized. The less intelligence the parents have, the more apt are they to listen to the dictum of "the more the better." Just in what way the world will be better off by an additional half dozen morons staggers the understanding.

Many now believe that we will be better off if we regard bringing a child into the world as a privilege, a responsibility, and not a duty; if we realize that producing a baby is from the beginning to the end a selfish thing, justifiable only if we exert ourselves to the utmost to meet our obligations. Who has not looked at his baby trying to devour its big toe and wondered whether it would be possible to make that baby's life more of joy than pain? Maybe that is a Christ idea, too. At any rate when religion condemns those who try to figure out how best to meet the responsibility of children, there is in the offing an ever increasing conflict. Suppose the subject of debate, instead of being the number of children produced, were "Religion versus the Christ idea in our relation to our children." That would be something new and would require a lot of readjustment. Like it or not, that is the subject of debate right today.

I sometimes find myself speculating about this problem of how many children should be born. I had one brother. Suppose I was entitled to two more, which the times would have warranted. Suppose sometime I should meet these two non-existent brothers on some Elysian shore, and they should quiz me on the desirability of getting themselves born. Suppose I call them Jacob and Henry after my uncles. Uncle

Jake died in early middle-life of tuberculosis, leaving a squalid underfed family. Helpless for years, he had to see his brood starving around him. Clearly it would have been better if he had never lived. He produced only suffering. Uncle Henry never married; raised a good Mennonite boy, he nevertheless disregarded his religious teachings and volunteered for the army and was placed in the 43rd Illinois Regiment. We still have his last letter written on the eve of the battle of Shiloh. It is the most heart-rending document I have ever read. It is written in German and I have had to make my own rather free translation. It starts by detailing the trip on the boat, during which wet and cold caused great suffering. Camped at Pittsburg Landing, the poor boys were sober, whatever may be said for their commanders. "Grant and Sherman are sure Johnson, camped at Corinth, will not seek battle," he writes. But this soldier, in agony of spirit, was sure battle was imminent as he bewailed the total lack of entrenchments. In despair he writes: "Both armies pray to the same God, so it looks to me as if we soldiers will have to fight it out in order that God might be spared the responsibility of taking sides." These words represent my translation. Then in a final paragraph he assures his brother—my father: "I place full faith in the goodness of God to protect me." He was killed at the first charge under conditions which need not be mentioned. It does seem to the eyes of mortal man that he was forgotten by God. In those four days he suffered more anguish of spirit than he could possibly have been compensated for by the accumulated joy of a lifetime, had he lived. It would have been far better if he had not been born. And that is true of countless thousands who are being born even today to serve as cannon fodder to appease the hate of those who rule. So I would advise my imaginary brothers, Jacob and Henry, to keep on being unborn. It is the only sure way of escaping the fate that might be awaiting them should they be thrust into this world.

Yet, I am not so sure when I look about me and see but few children starved or whipped, none beaten, nor spanked save only hard enough to cause a pleasant memory in later life. I see happy children going to school, their faces bright, unclouded by the pain that marked them in a bygone age, and in spirit I join the happy throng. I am assistant cheer leader for our high school—assistant, not honorary—and I yell and wave my arms when instructed to do so, and feel for the first time the thrill of childhood, a thrill I missed in my own adolescence. And then I take great joy in my wonderful pupil nurses, a hundred strong, who give me the affection of granddaughters. I would be a cynic indeed not to want to live life over again so that I might see these girls seek families of their own, as many of them will, fortified by the knowledge their training has gained them. Whoopee, they are my girls and will always remain so.

Hell gone, in spirit and in truth, a new womanhood arises, giving the lie to the old inspired figures of the past with their lust and murders. Happy small families are in prospect, busy teaching their parents the new birth which means that instead of wailing to the unhearing Fates to bring about the brotherhood of man, they can now achieve it by eliminating strife and hate from the fireside.

I believe *wanted* children are more numerous now than at any other time in history. Everyone loves children, but to want them—is it not selfish? The responsibility of parenthood cries out for help in vain in our pagan civilization. Nevertheless certain facts may be put down. Would it not be a great boon to the happiness of the home if it were assumed that the doctor has some sense, and should it not be permissible for him to offer advice when the desired family has arrived? Does not the fact that they are concerned with the welfare of the child mean that they have an intelligence exceeding that of those who made the rules in a bygone age, when infectious disease and limitless reproduction ran a merry race?

Those without responsibility may complacently say what the Eternal wishes. They certainly have their nerve to assume that they alone are attuned to the wishes of the Eternal. Who shall judge how many children the mother must bear? Hardly one who, because of his sex, is in no danger of ever bearing any. Responsibility, personally met, sometimes places an altogether different aspect on the face of things.

In times past the Fates took care of the excess population through infectious diseases and war. Just as a concrete example: Four miles from where I sit is a little long-neglected cemetery where lie five children dead of diphtheria, members of one family. Three of these were girls with no chance to be wiped out by war. Only one child was left, a magnificent girl. Would the other three have been equal to the one remaining, had they lived? Those who died did so because God willed it. I heard the minister say so, but that was more than forty years ago. Would any minister dare to say the same thing now? Religion also advances.

How select the number? The average family desires two or three. Of course we are met with the objection that if people could decide, many would have none. Well, what of it? Have we not seen enough of people who had unwanted children? A woman who does not want a baby should not have one. She is not going to give it a mother's love, and it would be better off if it were never born. Suppose I should write down an account of the doings of women who had children they didn't want. It would shock any one to know that such heartless creatures ever lived. It seems to me that the rearing of children is a privilege and not a duty.

No one can deny that the noblest couples, as I have mentioned before, are those who think of the welfare of the children they now have. We hear the complaint that it is the most desirable families who produce the fewest children and the lower classes who produce the big broods. It seems strange that no one has been able to see the answer. It is not the lack of intelligence. It is lack of courage to admit that a belief fostered sometime in the past is wrong.

Perhaps we doctors are somewhat at fault because we have not made clear to the public some things that are obvious to us. When the doctors think of sterilization they think only of the limitation of the size of the family. The layman

I dare say, often thinks that it means the loss of his potency. He thinks his own particular cat is to be silenced. Indeed not. Let him howl, let his joy be unconfined! The only difference is there will be no kittens to neglect.

Get this straight. There is no use in getting mad at doctors and calling in the law. We have not brought about the present tendency to limit families. The problem has been thrust upon us. We see family ties being gradually weakened and know that if disharmony does not cease the judge will be consulted. Many a family started out with high purpose, only to be wrecked by a little difference in mathematics, or diet. A woman comes to the consulting room with two children, seven and five. That is enough for the doctor. He knows that two are all she wants because she tells him so, and no gentleman would doubt the veracity of a lady. All we doctors can do is study what is going on about us, simply and honestly, pretend the difficulty does not exist, but be ever ready to limit the suffering as much as we can with our tonics and nerve sedatives.

Like it or not, families are being limited, but limited at too great a cost and in the wrong places. The limitations are taking place in the families of higher economic status and intellect.

It is among the lower economic classes that the old tomcat hollers most loudly and uninterruptedly. While visionaries desire to bring the "more abundant life" to the "underprivileged," morons must after all be dependent on the earning power of the prudent who are now engaged in figuring offspring in terms of maintenance cost. This idea of free food and free raiment will bring complications, just as it did in old Rome. Old Rome, it may be remembered, shed so many tears for the underprivileged voters that they ultimately became restless in seeking the more abundant life and upset the apple cart. Civilization went into eclipse for more than a thousand years. When that happens here, will the ecclesiastics declare that the tomcats stand higher in the sight of God than the woman who thinks of how many children she can care for?

Doctors have won the debate so far as the control of infectious disease is concerned, but in the debate as to who shall say how many babies Mary and John shall have we are not yet victors. However that the problem does exist is being recognized. This is made evident by the fact that an eminent divine has discussed it in a recent magazine. We are now told that it will be all right to limit the size of the family. The advice is simple: "Just don't do it." That is perplexing advice, although to one not tempted by the scenery about him at the break of dawn it may seem logical and adequate. But despite the admonition, the night cometh. It appears that although the problem is recognized, there is a lack of moral courage to face it. Any one who knows human nature knows that the advice above given will fall on unhearing ears. Perhaps some noble characters will heed it. But on the whole, it has little chance when it conflicts with a law permitting the unlimited coinage of morons. Admonitions, no matter how vociferously uttered, do not interest the author of the wail on the alley fence. It requires something more tangible to bring silence.

This reminds me of an incident I once witnessed. Johnnie Evers, the greatest second baseman of the Cubs, became peeved at the decision of an umpire. There was a stone mason making some belated repairs off first base where I was perched. Johnnie approached the workmen with the query: "Do you understand baseball?" The somewhat startled mechanic stopped his labors and gravely shook his head: "No, I no understan' him." "Fine," yells Johnnie, "come out here and umpire this game."

But in contrast with the advice of the eminent divine is a recent magazine article by some unregenerated person, explaining how birth control centers are operated in one state. They offer information to the lower classes, where it is most needed, and where interestingly enough, it is eagerly accepted. Here is evidence that somebody has recognized a desperate condition and is willing to do something about it.

I have before me a newspaper which gives an account of a meeting in which the problem of birth control was

M

boldly discussed, by women of course. The lady president explained that, by a very simple surgical operation, the expensive and unsatisfactory methods followed by most people might be dispensed with. No medical journal would publish anything so bold. This reminds me that once a convention of women advocated and won a radical change in the city administration. An old friend of mine commented: "Them wimmin."

When "them wimmin" get mad, cases such as the following will become ancient history. But that it is not yet ancient history is evidenced by a mortality slip before me: woman, aged twenty-eight; died in her ninth delivery. Also: child, married at thirteen; died at twenty-four in ninth pregnancy. That is civilized life up to date. In the old days, as I jogged along making my annual pilgrimage to such families, I used to speculate on the outcome. Because of the exhausted state of the muscle of the uterus, postpartum hemorrhage was dreaded. In such cases, after the baby was born, see-wish and a spurt of blood inundated the bed and the floor ten times faster than it takes to pen this line. Perhaps owing to lack of resistance, the patient frequently succumbed to respiratory or other infection, and usually in a week or two was dead. Sometimes, of course, she lingered for months, or even a survival as a permanent invalid. That these things can happen right today is neither God's fault nor the doctor's. It lies with those who insist that the old things be allowed to go on even today. Needless tragedy.

For instance, today a young matron told me that she and her husband have two children, are on relief, and that they live in the dust bowl and cannot afford to have any more. Measures to prevent conception, method not stated, have led to frigidity, and she feels that she is beginning to hate her husband. What shall she do? I said: "Lady, unfortunately the only legal thing for you to do in this state is to pray." I felt like a skunk. She looked at me with hate in her eyes. She thought I was making fun of her. I was not. I was filled with anger at the limitations placed on me. I could have referred her to the lady president of the newspaper article above referred to, but that would have been illegal. Only "them wimmin" have the courage of their convictions.

Here I can view the contest complacently. Is God backing the law as we have it or is he backing "them wimmin"? I am glad I am not in on the contest.

But never fear, the great American home, the workshop of civilization, is operating. Somehow the parents keep the smile of the child, the gage of a happy home, from disappearing. Let us not fight the writing on the wall. The children are educating their parents with a speed and thoroughness heretofore never dreamed of. If we would inquire silently or vocally what our children think of us instead of constantly telling them, it might be productive of results. They are not impressed by the teachings of the past. Sometime there is going to be a collective voice, and some folks are going to have to readjust their notions as to who is running the world. The women are running the world, all right. All that is needed is that they all get mad at the same time. Then the only "belief" that will avail is the conviction that the safest place is in some cavern. We doctors know that it is the kids who are backing "them wimmin," kids whispering from the manger.

Suppose I get real bold and ask what would happen if doctors were allowed to sterilize people after they have the desired number of children. What effect would it have on the home life of the couple if they were permanently relieved of fear, relieved of the necessity of doing what they do? There is evidence aplenty. Tumors of the uterus which cause bleeding are common, and a portion of the offending organ must be removed to save the patient from death from hemorrhage. The removal of the diseased portion leaves the patient spiritually and sexually unchanged, but does make pregnancy definitely impossible. The fear is permanently lifted. These people bloom out with a happy smile, ever grateful to the doctor for doing only what he was obliged to do. Even without the operation they would, from the nature of the tumor, have been permanently sterile, but there would still have been in their minds the theoretical possibility of pregnancy and the fear would have continued. I have seen hundreds of such women and they naturally make an impression on the doctor's mind.

One of the simplest and perhaps the most common cause of domestic tragedy is economic in character. That these conditions may lead ultimately to a broken home is made the matter of discussion in a later chapter. It may seem that such things do not concern the doctor in his professional capacity, but take a look at this. A young woman in near collapse enters the clinic. Obviously there are no physical causes. What is behind it? The husband is an engineer. The company for which he has worked was in a somewhat hazardous business, big income one year, low the next. Last year was an exceptionally good year, this year exceptionally bad. This year's income not being sufficient to pay the income tax of last year, the company folded up. This meant no job for the husband. He desires his wife to go home to her mother until he can find a job. Go home to a mother's love, a mother's sympathy—and domestic disaster. I have never felt more sorry for two young people in my life. Standing bravely together appealing to the doctor. I do not know even now why they came to me, unless it was a vague general idea that when you suffer, you go to the doctor.

Financial worries cause disturbances in health, make everybody sleepless and irritable, and the happy home suffers. I mention this here because many a happy home has been wrecked on the installment plan, by the installment plan. Next to the fear of pregnancy as a cause of human suffering comes digestive disturbances due to business worry. The outlet of the stomach contracts; plyorospasm, the doctor says. If it is unrelieved, an ulcer may form; from ulcer, perforation ensues. I am sometimes reminded of that fine poem "The Night Before Waterloo" which might be paraphrased thusly: "Calm slumber enveloped the household. Then came a cry. 'Hush! Hark! What was that sound, was it a cry of pain?' 'No 'twas but the wind. Let slumber be resumed.' But the cry grows louder. There is a scurry of flying feet as the nurses prepare the operating room for action." Then comes the sleepy voice of the resident surgeon: " 'Chief, sorry but that ulcer has ruptured.' The clock says two A.M." That would be a poor time to tell the doctor that the financial doings of the community are no concern of the medical profession.

There is yet another frequent cause of discord, and it has to do with the environment. It is both amazing, and distressing to the doctor to see so many fine homes broken up by outside influences for which the young couple are not to blame. For instance, long ago I was sitting in my office when in came a husky corn-fed dame, carrying a baby about nine months old. Behind her was a young woman obviously under great mental distress. Husband died, was the thought that flashed through my mind. At the time I did not realize how nearly I was right. The mother, in a firm voice, told me her daughter was nervous and didn't sleep. I saw at once that here was a real problem. Paying no attention to the talk of the old lady, I proceeded to have a high time with the baby, keeping my eye on its mother. At first a bit apprehensive—that was in the days when I wore whiskers—he soon relaxed and showed me two teeth above, four below. With a yell of delight he grabbed my spectacles. A wan smile came over the mother's face. While apparently chiefly occupied with the baby, I got the history from its mother: She and her husband had moved to Idaho after their marriage, bought a little ranch and were happy and prosperous. Baby came, and she brought him home to show mother. The old lady scowled as I got this history bit by bit, at such intervals as his young lordship saw fit to loosen his hold on my whiskers.

"Now mother insists that the baby and I shall not go back to Idaho," the young mother told me. Friend husband must come back and work mother's farm. It was perfectly clear to me that the husband was a fugitive from that mother-in-law.

That is as far as the history got. Without further questioning I said to the mother:

"Take that baby back to your husband where the eternal stars are calling you." Turning to the mother I said:

"You blankety-blank old fool; you are perfectly willing to sacrifice your daughter's life for your own selfish ends. If a real mother's love should ever penetrate your heart, if you have any, you will die of mortification. From now on, if there be a God in Israel, you are the one who will have the sleepless nights." She seemed to shrink to half her size while a new glow came to the daughter's face.

Gentle reader, do not get the idea that a doctor ever uses profane language before a lady, but the exactions of a correct diagnosis are such that sometimes one is obliged to use unconventional phrases. That's science. After nearly forty years I received recently from a lady a remembrance with a little note which I cannot quote. It was written for "her doctor" and made no mention of the fact that she was once my patient. Yes verily, the doctor has his reward even for swearing at a lady. Funny world!

It is seldom that I now see a complete picture as in the case above related. Perhaps it is because I haven't the time, nor the whiskers, but it is maddening to see how many mothers are willing to wreck a home to satisfy their own selfishness. In many cases the family is broken up before there are any children, but the presence of a child naturally makes the incentive for the grandmother to break it up much greater, because she wants to keep the baby. To my mind human cussedness can go no deeper. How these cases escape the Federal kidnapping laws puzzles me.

It is distressing to see the large number of fine women who have made themselves happy homes, but who come to the doctor exhausted, nervous wrecks, saying that they just can't take care of his folks any longer. Of course if they are her folks, the distress is much less. In that case, it is the husband who develops indigestion. Well, what do they expect the doctor to do about it? Poison the folks? Not a bad idea, but it is against the law. I tell such couples frankly that some other arrangement must be made for the visitors or they will break up the home. If I have the chance I tell the offending person directly. Since I am still in active practice, it would be inadvisable for me to tell my methods. I may say, however, that if I should write daughter-in-law a letter setting forth the situation as it is, and some nosey old mother-in-law should get hold of it and absorb the contents, it would be no fault of mine.

When there is economic need for such sacrifice there may be some excuse for the old folks to live with the children, but many old folks, particularly widows, prefer to live in a home where there is some one to boss. In former years, grandmother was a most important accessory because she was always available to care for the numerous children. She was a part of the family in spirit and in truth. But when she seeks to supersede the daughter in the household it is a different matter. The remedy for such situations was dispensed some years ago by a young woman who told her mother: "You chased father away from home. You are not going to chase my husband away. You are welcome in my home as long as you remember it is my home."

Many of the most aggravating cases have nothing to do with permanent residency. The occasional visit of the inlaws may start the fire-works. It is then not so much a matter of exhaustion as of temper. Mama pities her daughter because she has such a hard time, but reminds her that she warned her before she married. Daughter has been happy all these years because she thought her mother opposed the match just because she set the bid, unmindful of the fact that women change their minds. Taken by surprise, she bawls and sleeps on the spare bed. There is dynamite there. The doctor must recognize these cases, and when he does meet with such situations he is a coward if he does not institute vigorous measures. I give the wife sedatives a-plenty and tell the husband just what is wrong and that if he wants to preserve his home it is up to him to act. Then I recite for him some choice language appropriate for such occasions. Such language takes practice, and I find most men who thought they had a happy home are apt to find themselves without words. That "eternal vigilance is the price of liberty" applies to homes as well as nations.

Persons of advanced age make demands on their children which are essentially selfish. Having cared for their parents in their old age, they naturally feel that they will in turn be cared for by their children. These are difficult cases to manage for all concerned. The aged parents fail to see that the times have changed and the presence of an aged person, no matter how tactful he may be, causes disturbance in the home.

For example, one of my fine old friends lost his wife late in life. He wanted to spend the rest of his days with his daughter. The daughter was a faithful child and had a nice home. But she had several budding daughters and the home was then the proving ground for their future life, and she knew the addition of her father would threaten the congenial home machinery. Her proposal was that he go to an old folks home, one of the best of its kind. I had been his physician for forty years, and I was called by him ostensibly because he could not sleep, but really to intercede with the daughter. Here the problem was easy for an old doctor. I was too smart to use the argument that the daughter's first obligation was now to her children. I explained that he needed a tonic, snowed him under with sedatives, and he went serenely to the home for the aged.

It is pleasant to look back and realize that happy families are increasing. The new woman has brought vast changes. Where she came from is a puzzle, but she is here. The most important factor, I believe, is the early association of boys and girls in school, in the basements of churches, and particularly at little home parties. The children first learn mutual respect and on this follows love. When sex enters it may pester but it cannot destroy respect.

It is inspiring to see the fine struggle people are making to maintain a home and to educate the children, and, despite the spirit of the times, to secure a competence for old age. The way some of our citizens battle the vicissitudes of our own celebrated dust bowl staggers understanding and excites profoundest admiration. Hope, persevering hope that this year there will be a crop, or if not this year, then the next. That is the spirit that turns out some great citizens and will save the nation, if it can be saved, from those who would destroy it and deprive the people of the very thing for which they have made a relentless battle against fate.

The great American home is often to be found among people who, in official circles, would be regarded with pity. It is pictured as offering adequate housing including a bath tub in which to keep the vegetables, and everything in proportion. Those not adequately housed from the point of view of those who have never toiled, bring crocodile tears about election time. Any sort of housing may seem adequate if one is not accustomed to anything better. He who has never kicked snow out of his pants in the morning before he puts them on can never know how delightful these garments can be after everything becomes warm. The dietary efforts of the inspired dieticians are misdirected. After children have been pestered for a decade to eat spinach, it is discovered that the mess has no real dietary value. Somehow, people from simple homes, where children ate what appeared on the table, are in large measure doing the work of the nation today.

The satisfaction of knowing that one has earned what he received does more than anything to build self-reliance. The old pioneers knew what famine and privation meant, but they fought their own battles without thought of leaning on the more prosperous. Here is a good example: Several years ago one of my old patients came into my office and announced that he was opposed to all the lettered organizations designed to care for certain classes of people. He proudly held out one hand and smacked it with the other, and said most emphatically, "No dollar has ever touched that palm that old Mark has not earned." And then with a derisive chuckle he added: "Sure, the Government should help the poor farmer, the good ones don't need it." That was the spirit of the pioneer.

The struggle of many people to keep from the degrading

influence of charity is the finest thing I know of. Wife and husband bending every effort to get by through their own efforts. Often do I hear that when the wife learns that she needs an operation, she hesitates. I can guess the rest. They have struggled for years to keep off relief but the cost of an operation would be the last straw. Could any doctor ask for greater compensation than to render such patients his services free of charge? Such parents as these avert the disaster now threatening a cockeyed politically-ridden nation.

Formerly every family was a unit in itself. It had its own religion and its own way of making the sauerkraut and seasoning the sausage. Time was when I could find my way around the neighborhood by just sampling these things. Sauerkraut now comes in cans and sausages are made in Kansas City. By sampling these commodities today, all the expert could say is that he is somewhere in America.

While family isolation formerly was the rule, now cooperation and standardization have taken charge. Many changes have come about to aid the influence of the home. The basements of the modern churches alone interest the young folks. Kids no longer are born sinful, requiring saving before they raise whiskers, and they remain sin-free unless they are spoiled by their parents. If we could but realize that their needs are our needs, their wishes would excite our profound consideration, always. Our environment fairly buzzes with the brotherhood and sisterhood of kids. In time they will be grown up, and then there will be a dawn of a new day. They are now putting a new meaning into the overworked term "the great American home" and they are preparing to make such institutions in spirit and in truth. If the fool population could only get it through its head that a happy home is possible only when and where there are happy children.

If I am ahead of my time, it is so because the young folks have taught me. Young folks of all sizes and shapes have accorded me their confidences and companionship. Meeting in their first childhood and perhaps in my second, we have complete accord. The most pronounced change I find is that they are not worried about hell, not even about dying. They have their hopes, their futures. Why should they not be happy and why should one not rejoice that sin and hell have gone out of a child's life forever?

The parent-teachers associations are evidence of the awakened new order. Parents want to know what the teacher is trying to do for their children. They indicate by their interest that they recognize that the great need of the time is for better parents. Too often, however, they are as ready to criticize as to help. Even so, the teacher may exert an influence on the parents and thus lessen the chance that their fine work may be undone at home. Parents who know their children's teachers are at least less likely to criticize. It is constant criticism which destroys the influence of the home.

To revert to the problems of the married couple, I might point out that the complications of their life can be realized only if we understand that the fates do not care whether or not they become or remain happy. The race must be perpetuated; it is a necessary end, though the happiness of the pair thereby be imperiled. That does not seem right. Just when people are most in the need of guidance they are left to the teaching of a fool ancestry.

There is yet another factor. Before approaching the marriage altar, the young man should realize that he is accepting a dual role, his life work and his family. Unless he is willing to accept this, he had better stick to his single state—wedded to his life work. The problem of serving two masters has been set forth as a difficult undertaking under other circumstances.

I have never known a man who achieved anything worth while who did not place his life work above any woman, certainly above any female. That does not sound well, but it is true. It all depends on what one's purpose in life may be. This, and the price, is well expressed by George Arnold:

"Ah, many a one has started forth with hope and purpose
        high,
   Has fought throughout a weary life, and passed all pleasure
        by;

Has burst all flowery chains by which men aye have been
　　enthralled;
Has been stone-deaf to voices sweet, that softly, sadly called;
Has scorned the flashing goblet with the bubbles on its brim;
Has turned his back on jewelled hands that madly beckoned
　　him;
Has in a word condemned himself to follow out his plan
By stern and lonely labor—and has died a conquered man!"

In the end, the scientific man finds only disappointment.
Achievement means nothing; it is the things just beyond his
reach that beckon him on to an unhappy old age. In other
words, nature asks every man to take his turn at reproducing
his species. Only with wife and children can he face a happy
old age. The same thing applies to the career-minded
woman, and even to a greater degree. It does not seem right
that it should be so—noble effort throughout life, disappointment in the end. Yet our commencement orators encourage
this delusion.

"Better or worse" indeed; the end, with a child to smooth
the pillow, proclaims the experiment to have been for the
better, although the intervening time may have leaned very
much to the worse side. One hasn't much choice in this
world.

Considered as a purely biological problem, a happy home
is quite within reach. Certain problems must be viewed as
matters of fact and freed from tradition. This requires a
degree of intelligence, high character and unremitting attention to detail. That is the price.

I can close this chapter no better than to quote from a
letter I received in response to one of my speeches. It reveals
at once a lofty mind and a home which may sometime become
universal:

"I suppose you would call me a modern woman; I am just
one of many like me. A college degree, a few years of teaching, a husband, a family. Now I do spend the greater part of
my time at home; I am still in love with my husband, after
ten years of marriage, and I enjoy our two sons, aged nine

and six. But that leaves me still a margin of time and interest for outside activities. We can thank you men for your labor-saving inventions for that. And I do thank you because I believe that women are better wives and mothers for maintaining outside interests. The modern home can be kept clean and in order in at least one-third the time formerly given just to keeping house, and that with the help of one or more dependent women who used to clutter up most homelife.

"Modern cooking is a help, and the services performed outside the home cut a little more off the time required for the job of homemaking, and who gains the most: the woman with the extra time for civic and personal activities outside the home, the husband whose wife can meet him halfway in his mental outlook, the children whose well-informed mother can often anticipate the problems of the growing child?

"You ask how did the modern woman cut loose from the church? You mean why isn't she still the slave of all the religious taboos of the past, don't you? You men permitted her to get an education, or, as the feminists would put it, the women got too much for you and demanded education. Well, education, however got, does dispel superstitious fears. I grew up through a troubled childhood of religious preachment of "hellfire and damnation," as my father used to call it. Then I got the philosophical slant, and, after all, isn't philosophy just religion grown up? My boys are going to Sunday school, but I don't think they take the Old Testament tales much more seriously than they do Santa Claus. With a little careful guidance they won't. They need the church, if only for its social background, all the way through adolescence. Most of them do, and our children are no better than the average. But by the time you've reached adulthood, if you haven't a working philosophy that's personal to yourself, well, you belong with the herd, don't you?"

"Them wimmin."

VIII

Tragedies in Paradise

IN PRECEDING chapters I have tried to picture a couple of young people starting after the marriage ceremony, trying to adjust themselves to each other, as animals and spiritual beings, in an honest endeavor to find the place in which love and the inevitable sex urge may allow them to live in harmony. In the next chapter I have presented pictures showing the difficulties, incident to parenthood, which may arise in families, and the long hard struggle of parents to subordinate themselves to their children and to each other. There are many things which keep the domestic team more or less in combat, but which for some reason or other stop short of a legal break, even though the recurrent strife may last throughout a lifetime.

We have in this chapter to consider incidents that may border on the tragic but which are met with more or less fortitude. These usually are not matters for which the couple is responsible, being due in large measure to unfavorable and uncontrollable incidents. They are often beyond their own sphere of control, and may be but temporary in action or may continue without end. The disturbances in many of these cases may be due to the dereliction of society. If the public had any sense of moral responsibility for the common good, these conditions could largely be wiped out in a generation. Society is so completely bound by tradition, to use a polite term, that it refuses to see what any honest person cannot possibly overlook. Besides, the public assumes no responsibility. It passes by on the other side. If it had to see what we doctors are obliged to experience, the whole picture, I am sure, would be changed.

Many events in the lives even of couples that start with good prospects of achieving happiness, seem to fit nowhere in the picture, but do upset the regular course of things. It is important to recognize that these events may be but temporary ripples, disturbing only for a time the normal course of life. If their transient nature is realized, life will become smooth again. If not, they may assume an undue importance, and ruin what might otherwise have been a happy life.

Often desire lags behind ability. In the dawn of our present era, the doctor was frequently confronted by a dame who, with great show of reasoning, declared it just could not be that she was going to have a baby. However, most of these women, if not reconciled to their lot before, capitulated with the first squawk of the new arrival. Many interesting sequelae were encountered, mostly comical, some tragic.

One of my patients' chief grievance was that it was undignified for a mother to have a child after she had daughters old enough to entertain company. The argument was well taken. No doubt it was disconcerting to a timid young swain to have his train of thought interrupted by the squawk of a new baby elsewhere in the house.

Some of these patients made themselves a sore trial to the doctor by their persistent howling against fate, some of them even going so far as to express the wish that the child might be born dead. The maddest woman I ever met in such a situation, despite her wishes, went through a perfectly normal pregnancy. She was an intelligent woman and had only two children, but she stormed and ranted. On my first visit after delivery I took along a full sized ball bat. Her eyes turned big as she saw the strange implement I was carrying. I did not wait for a question, but said that I had brought something along so that she could knock the new arrival in the head, since she did not want it. Now, I told her, she could dispose of the brat without injury to herself and without making me a murderer.

The child grew into a beautiful girl, and the cloud that had hung over the household for nine months floated away. The girl died in her 'teens, after a short illness. As the bereaved mother's eyes met mine after life was extinct, they had an expression I have never seen before nor since, and hope never to see again. That was a real tragedy that never lifted, never modified. I was then profoundly sorry for the low comedy I had once played.

Only in rare instances do women refuse to be reconciled to the newcomer, once it has arrived. But the exceptions do occur. The most aggravated and aggravating case I have encountered had to do with a woman who had vowed never to bear a child. After the child was born she continued to heap vituperations on the unwelcome guest and swore never to lay hands on it. The father and the nurse gave the child every care except a mother's. The father suddenly died, and the widow in her stunned state resolved to claim the child. She believed the disaster was the visitation of fate, and it seemed to me that if the Fates do pay attention to such details, here certainly was an ideal case. She became silent, completely silent. When a rip-snorting, voluble woman suddenly becomes silent, it is a manifestation of the depth of her grief. Nothing else will shut her up.

A woman, seriously sick, required an operation necessitating the removal of a very small fetus. The patient's brother was a priest and so positively refused to sanction the operation. The doctor, a friend of mine and one of the greatest surgeons of my time, said to the priest: "The responsibility for your sister's life is your own but do not compel me to see a woman die whom I am able to save." That was too close to home—a sister. The patient was removed to a private home and was operated on by my friend and promptly recovered. Standing firm for an abstract principle and assuming responsibility for a sister's death are different things. I only ask what difference it would make if all patients were our sisters, and who established that abstract principle.

To the doctor all patients are alike. A patient who dies is to us a failure. That is a fact that is incontrovertible. Yet sometimes we must stand by and see a patient die because of a religious prohibition against an operation which may save him. When we doctors consider who first made those prohibitions, we are confused. It doesn't seem right.

But such cases are now rare. Any one desiring detailed information may obtain same by calling over any alley fence.

In this week's Journal a supreme judge rendered the decision that no doctor was permitted by law to give any information, even if the life of the patient depended on it. This opinion was rendered in a Republican state. This will give any informed person one chance in two of picking the state.

Most of the instances that come across the domestic horizon are more obscure in etiology than the cases above related, and in consequence are more puzzling to the doctor. This chapter must therefore be made up of odds and ends of events which deal with a number of things which may appear singly or collectively in the later chapters. Some, indeed, have no relation to domestic discord, but present so much of human interest, visible only to the doctor, that it seems they should be presented. They show in many instances the nobility humans are capable of achieving, and do achieve despite their environment. By viewing these events as entities, we can more easily comprehend them than when we consider them as a part of the whole. We can view bricks the better by examining them singly as bricks than after they have been made into a wall. This applies particularly to the inside bricks not easily seen yet just as important, since they make up the greater part of the supporting wall. We know they are there whether we see them or not.

In other words, we have here to do with the struggle of serious people to ascend in the scale of civilization. They struggle unseen and unsung, achieving no other reward than the consciousness of having done their best. Many never become a problem for the doctor, but he may meet them at any time even literally unto the third and fourth generation. Viewing some of these people, I have become convinced they show far more evidence of divine inspiration than did the prophets of long ago, whose teachings they vainly try to follow.

In the main, this chapter has to do with people in general, but more particularly with a couple of people trying to raise their family amidst conditions which they do not understand or which, if understood, can be altered little or not at all. Decent people doing their best in the world, living frugally

N

and honestly are so uninteresting, it seems. They use their brains, great or small, to achieve their own ends simply and earnestly. To an old doctor it seems as though the Fates are set against these simple folks. George Sand said: "By the sweat of thy brow, thou shalt make a wretched living, and at the end there is death to await thee."

We make large talk about the greatness of our nation. What made it so has been individual effort of people with the courage to work out their own salvation. Now designated as the underprivileged, they spend no time in pitying themselves, accepting with a grim determination what others would regard as intolerable situations. It is the "underprivileged" people who have made our nation great. I have known many of the old pioneers who endured hardship beyond words to express, and asked no quarter. Looking back many years, I think of a young expectant father trying to feed cornstalks into a stove fast enough to maintain warmth in a miserable room while the doctor is busy delivering the wife of a child. That couple was certainly underprivileged, and so was the doctor.

Yet I have never heard a complaint uttered by people in such surroundings. They had to be told they were underprivileged. They had their reward. Such homes were not dominated by the alleged wisdom of an ignorant sensuous period.

It is said that newspapers publish what people want to read. If so, what they want must be regarded as a measure of our civilization. Then what is news—the things which interest the average reading citizen? I look in vain in the papers for accounts of the noble struggles of small people as we doctors see them; because they are never news their efforts go unrecorded. Noble effort, the finer things of life, devoid of lust or blood, it seems are never news. I can point to numerous instances when the noblest traits of human character have been unfolded, quite unobserved by the neighbors. Yet if played up, they would make most interesting life stories. Achievement is measured by the capacity of the individual to do something worthwhile. In this list should be recorded, on the first line, the conquering of poverty or a heroic adaptation to it. From these miserable homes have come men and women who have emblazoned their names in the records of their time. Opulence, not poverty, puts the strain on the best there is in people.

It is a trite saying that "the wind is tempered to the shorn lamb." This simile is not correct. What is meant is a lamb which never had any hair. The term "shorn lamb" should be reserved for those who have just paid their taxes. The funny thing about the whole business is that poverty and want are not so bad until someone tells the victim how much he suffers.

But such struggles never make news. A simple line in the local paper is their portion. It seems to me a great service could be rendered society if our newspapers would hold up achievement of honest people to the public gaze rather than devote their space to the doings of criminals. I sometimes think that if the papers printed the noble things in life, people might come to like them, and business would be just as good as it is now.

If a woman gives birth to more than two babies, that is news; if a woman has four or five that is a wow, a matter of international importance, though if a dog has the same number that is not news. If a woman during her lifetime has a dozen or twenty children, that is news. A picture of the children lined up in a stepladder array is a work of art, even though they obviously may be a lot of undernourished morons. The father and mother form the central feature of the picture, though their faces indicate a moronic heredity.

If a man marries a woman, that is not news. If he marries several, he makes the front page, even though he is in jail, looking out. If he marries a child, that is news. If that child gives birth to a child, that is front page stuff, also a work of art. These works of art usually lack the chief item of interest, the moral derelict who performed the marriage ceremony. His nefarious work goes unheeded and unhindered by law, civil or religious.

Things are much more impressive when witnessed at two

in the morning than when read about in the evening paper. Sit with a young doctor beside a girl less than fifteen years old. Through the long weary night, this child labored to produce her child. No one was present except her husband and the doctor. To heighten the nervousness of the young doctor, a terrible storm was raging, and a few blocks away his father lay dying. He was torn between professional and filial duty. Professional duty won. The father died at almost the same moment the baby was born; he died alone. It has often been noted how close tragedy and comedy follow upon each other. As the baby was being born, the husband flopped on the floor in a dead faint. The new mother, seeing this, screamed and tried to get out of the bed with her baby half born. A large basin of bichloride solution was on a chair beside the bed. This the doctor doused over the half-born's papa, who at once recovered and started to scramble out of the room on all fours. As he went through the door the doctor threw at him a blade of the obstetric forceps, now no longer needed, and scored a perfect hit. It was such a ridiculous sight that, despite the double emotional strain the doctor was under, he burst out in boisterous laughter. The final tragedy, which brings this scene into this chapter, lies in the fact that the family discovered the father was insane, which the doctor had known for some years before the couple were married. Child wife, worse than a widow, because her imbecile husband still lived. He had his rights. The town slept, except of course for the doctor.

Another instance comes to mind. My patient was fourteen years old. A labor lasting thirty-six hours completely ruined my disposition. As the baby was born, the mother of the patient gleefully shouted: "Me a grandmother at twenty-eight. Did you ever know of one younger?" I knew the proper language, young as I was, and what is more I used it. The husband, it must be said to complete the picture, was an unemployed gentleman of sixteen. He took one look at the baby and disappeared, and was seen no more. Two widows and one orphaned child, all destitute. The young husband, we may assume, was a modest young man properly reared, who did not realize just what was happening until he saw the baby. That was enough. He has not been heard from since, and that was forty years ago.

These are examples of what I mean by domestic tragedies happening to persons who are not morally guilty, but are only following the well trodden path made by law and custom. Yet these things will not happen if or when the public is awakened to their common responsibility. It would be a good thing if the public would understand that child marriages are hereditary and represent but the first step toward the sex murders against which I have exercised the limit of my invectives in another chapter. That parents of low mentality should be allowed to say whether or not a minimum legal age for marriage should be set aside outrages our sense of justice, is an affront to our intelligence, and places a heavy handicap on our faith in the final justice of all things.

What has this to do with the subject at issue? Simply this: The publication of these things is not a matter of indifference. Human conduct is imitative. The blunt fact is by that allowing stupid parents to set aside an already inadequate law we form a bridge for the potential sex criminal. A mother once replied, when I asked her why she was so persistent in securing a marriage license: "Will is a good boy. I am afraid if he don't get married, he will do something awful." How serious a problem this is is manifested by the fact that when a sex crime is committed, the police round up all sex perverts for questioning, knowing that any of them are capable of having committed the crime in question. This means that society allows potential murderers to go about the streets until they murder someone else's daughter. Then it becomes a tragedy in someone's domestic paradise. The idea seems to be to marry these perverts off so young that they will not be liable to criminal law. I am concerned here only with those innocent parents who suffer because the law offers their own children no protection. Don't blame the law enforcement officers. Had they the right to do what they feel like doing, they would line up this whole breed against the wall at sunrise. Here before me is a newspaper which records that after a sex crime recently committed, the police rounded up nineteen persons capable of such an act. Rounded them up today. Why not yesterday? And, I may add, nothing was really done with the lot of them.

I am just now observing such a drama. A person with prominent family connections assaulted a young girl. He is being defended by one of our ablest and most honorable members of the bar. If he is cleared of the offense now at issue, there is the possibility that, should he again engage in a like act and the victim should scream, he might choke her to death in order to quiet her. That is the usual sequence. That will be too bad. Another unsolved crime goes on the police records. Because of the prominent family connections and the able criminal lawyers, the police are helpless. It seems to a doctor that the defense counsel sometimes shoulders a tremendous moral responsibility for he does, in fact, makes himself responsible for the future conduct of his "patient."

We cannot deny that our civilization protects the potential criminal until he commits a crime, outside of wedlock of course. That such persons, by reproducing their kind, are a detriment to the social welfare, I believe all criminologists are agreed, and no one else with the brains of a squirrel doubts it. Has society done anything to prevent these persons from producing their kind? Not long ago a state institution sought to sterilize, not castrate, some of these people. What happened? A flock of cornfed dowagers let out a cry to high heaven demanding that the officials stay their hand. Hopeless morons though they be—meaning the inmates, not the rampant dowagers—these girls have their rights, we are told. If an inmate be turned loose and marry your son then the picture belongs in this chapter. I have seen this very thing happen more than once.

Perhaps we doctors have been derelict. I believe a part of the difficulty lies in the fact that the public does not know what we have in mind when we rave against such things. To sterilize, it is only necessary to clip a tube no larger than a knitting needle. The patients are still free to exercise all their lustful functions unhindered. They have no desire to produce children, and I do not believe their defenders desire that they should do so. Nevertheless, religion teaches that the individual has that inherent right, no matter how it affects society in general. Even though mere sterilization does not prevent marriage, but means only that the moron or pervert will produce no more of his kind.

On the other hand, by castration doctors mean the removal of the sex glands and thereby all desire, at least in nearly all cases. But there is much misunderstanding. If one really wanted to lessen human suffering, he would be doing these patients a service by castration. It would relieve them of an eternal urge that nearly, sometimes actually, drives some of them insane. I know of no more miserable person than the man with some moral sense, who finds himself driven by an unending sex urge which he fears he will not be able to control. I have as a patient a nationally known man of high type who belongs in this category. The only advice I am able to offer is: "Work until you drop and then start in again as soon as you awaken."

We doctors could prevent a lot of suffering in this world if we were not restrained by the pagan philosophy which still retains the old primitive conceptions of personal rights. Go read history. We doctors are still struggling with influences that antedate history. I have already related an instance of a man who committed rape in wedlock. That case brought tragedy to the respectable parents and wrecked the life of the fine daughter. Nor have I by any means exhausted my fund of experience in relating one case. Who gains by such liberties? Someone once suggested that the common good is paramount to the good of the individual. That seems to be partly recognized, that is until "personal liberties" become involved.

I venture to relate a very common experience doctors have. It is easier to get mad if one has been put to physical discomfort because of what is obviously a public dereliction. Many years ago a male citizen was confined to an insane asylum, curiously enough because people thought he was crazy. During the summer months each year he had a period of slight mental improvement, and in consequence he was allowed to spend a month or two at home. After his vacation he was returned to the asylum. Each year I was obliged to journey no inconsiderable distance to deliver the wife of a child sired by this insane person. Why was I not photographed at my task in that hovel, bringing forth a new candidate for the asylum? Sure, I was a hero, but I did my stunt in the small hours of the night, muddy roads and all that. I am sure it would make a very interesting picture, me standing beside mama resuscitating a baby, successfully, which I hoped to God would die. To make the picture complete, of course, one should have a picture of the asylum with an arrow pointing to a window, marked "Papa's room." I may say in passing that, in my opinion, the papers miss a good chance by not having an old doctor on their editorial staffs. Too many of the really dramatic things are overlooked. Of course I realize would-be heroes should pull their stunts at convenient times and places. All I was out was my time and axle grease, but it made me mad. Any doctor could in ten minutes, by a slight operation, have saved me all this trouble, and it would have made not the slightest difference to Papa. The morons so produced were companions of normal children during the school age. If one of them should marry into your family, your domestic harmony would most certainly be jarred and make a nice illustrative case for this chapter. Of course we complacently hope these morons will not marry into our people's family.

One of the daughters of this moronic father did marry the son of a friend of mine. She unfortunately was, and is, not quite insane enough to warrant commitment to an asylum. Two tragedies again, my friend and his son. The moron mother was not disturbed by her brood of children, and the father contributed the only thing to society he could. A picture of this family should be printed alongside the one showing the father framed in the asylum window. If we are going to have the news, let us have the whole picture.

I do not understand the public. Why are allegedly Christian people so interested in the sordid things of life? Things

noble and beautiful are not news. Or if they are, it is only
when there is also a sordid connotation. If a woman gets into
a jam she is always "attractive." Don't homely women ever
shoot their husbands? To whom do they appear attractive?
Strange thing, the mean women I see in the clinic are old
hags, repellent in the extreme, obviously paying the penalty
for their misdeeds. Attractive? Happily, the "attractive"
female criminals, if they get sick, at least spare the country
doctors.

But our children read about the attractive molls who accompany major criminals. It is natural for young people to
be attracted by things that bring them into the public eye.
Suppose we were collectively to tell the newspaper man that
we do not believe it is good for our children to have crime
depicted as attractive. The children are not told that each
crime is a tragedy. Let us see the tragedy traced and in all
its ramifications.

Why God keeps his noblest children hidden from the
public eye and interest has long caused me wonderment.
Why would it not be a fine thing if the papers published a
picture of a shriveled little woman, who subjected herself
to untold toil in order that her children might be educated?
It is just possible that such a picture might bring to other
children's minds the fact that their own mother is making an
equally great struggle. Countless children loaf through college while parents toil to keep them there in the vain hope
that they are doing them a good service. Tragedies a-plenty
loaf through college.

I have seen many pertinent examples. Of course there is
the difficulty that real grief, unlike joy, cannot be seen; it
can only be felt by personal contact. The infinite silence of
real grief has been the hardest thing I have had to bear in
dealing with my patients. Just recently a man who brought
his wife for consultation came into my office and asked what
education was good for. "Ma and I worked hard to put our
boy through college. He is through now, has no job and he
is too proud to work with me." I asked the father the nature
of the studies the boy had pursued. He did not know—

something like sociology and business. That told it all. He did not know why the boy was in school any more than the boy did. He did not know that the boy's mother, who was then the problem of the clinic, was simply suffering from a broken heart under the guise of a nervous breakdown. After all their effort to educate the boy, he returned rebellious toward his parents. They had spent all their money and lost their boy, though their intentions were of the noblest.

One of the saddest pictures I have seen had to do with a woman widowed when her daughter was two years old. She labored at menial tasks throughout the years to educate this child. At last she was to graduate from a university with high honors. She was to teach and take over the burden that her mother had borne so long. She had been ailing during the last months of school, but sought to finish her education before consulting a doctor. I saw her immediately after graduation. She was obviously a brilliant girl, her face anxious from suffering, a picture of a possible future madonna never dreamed of by the artists. The most cursory examination showed a cancer of the breast—in a girl of twenty-two an utterly incurable disease. The thought flashed through my mind: "Is there no God in Israel?" The mother caught the message, though I did my best to conceal my feelings. Had I the gift of a painter and could place on canvas the look on the face of that mother, I would melt the hardest heart. I did what I could for the daughter, which was nothing, and in six months she was dead.

For the mother I could produce only sleep. The memory of that prematurely aged little woman haunts me still. She had neither words nor tears in the end. She was long past all that. What a story that life would have made. Even a picture of that face as I saw it would burn itself into the memory of any one, but the silence—that was only for the doctor and the eternal stars. The newspaper notice of this young lady's death occupied just four lines: "Recently graduated from the university, the twenty-two year old daughter of Mrs. Doe who has served in many of our readers' homes, was buried yesterday in the local cemetery."

It was not my privilege to follow this mother for long, but I have had as patients many others only slightly less tragic. Most of them have full faith that somewhere, sometime, they will meet that child again. Many seek surcease from pain by incessant toil. Some engage in work for others, become mothers to other children.

The tragedy of this high school girl was no one's fault, unless possibly the doctor's. Despite endless effort, many forms of cancer are beyond our skill. All society can offer is just what we doctors have to offer, understanding sympathy. Tragedies which cannot be prevented may be in part alleviated by a helping hand.

What has society to offer in such instances? Those who have no knowledge of the real problems of life know just how they should be met. Facts are constantly obscured by those who have never seen tragedy at work, but who attempt to base the rules of conduct on the pratings of a bygone age in a civilization that never was.

It always aggravates me when ministers feel that it is their function to console such persons. Many years ago in such a situation a minister delivered himself of the following: "Sister Doe, God just couldn't run heaven anymore without your angel daughter so he called her home." After he turned away, "The skunk!" was the bereaved mother's comment. The mother's mind was occupied with the same thing that has filled mine. Would some other line of treatment have prevented the tragedy? If that child had had, those forty years ago, the treatment available today she need not have died. It was not God's fault at all. Medical science had not yet reached out its conquering hand to subdue that disease. But the hand of man can do it now.

Doctors are faced by immutable laws that do not deviate to meet the wishes of a bygone teaching. I heard the intoned "Pray, sister, pray and everything will be all right," in situations such as faced the washerwoman. The disease progresses to an inevitable end. Prayers never halted the growth of a single malignant cell. Why not face the truth? Indeed, the great human heart cries out in time of distress and gives courage to the individual who bears the burden, but it is inarticulate, knows no clock nor calendar, brooks no audience, and cannot be hired by so much an hour. Such prayers help the individual bear the burden, but they are without words. Prayers, as I have observed, are the cry of a distressed soul for a loved one. They have nothing to do with the weather, the crops or even world peace.

The real tragedy comes in teaching the ignorant to believe that prayer can combat disease. Because of this belief, the help medicine is able to give is denied them. The tragedy does not touch the false teachers, nor even the hapless who needlessly sacrifices his life. It is those left behind who suffer.

Nor is it only the major tragedies that concern us; more often it is little things that threaten or worry people, and they seek the doctor's advice. What makes doctors mad is the uselessness of it. If society would do as we doctors must, search for the truth, the atmosphere would be cleared at once. What is the basis of belief? Beliefs are what people have been fighting about since the beginning of time. Truth never started a fight, unless of course it ran up against belief —like a flat earth. It would be a great thing if all the beliefs could be treated as medical problems. Go back to original sources and find out who said what. That would deflate a lot of beliefs that have wrecked human lives for centuries. For instance, we are told God created man in his own image. Did the person who said that know what he talking about? I have never known of but one painter who had the temerity to paint God. And of all things, the artist presented Him in the come-on pose. If there is such a thing as unadulterated sacrilege, that artist certainly committed it.

Suppose some one sees a divine creator, incomprehensible and infinite, all about him, in the little babe, in the vast celestial system, what difference would it make? Professor Carruth once wrote a beautiful little poem entitled "Each in His Own Tongue." The prevailing sentiment is expressed in the line "Some call it nature, others call it God." Yet he was chased out—of all places—Kansas, a state where all sorts of ideas are tolerated. Yet that was my father's belief, and he died as he lived, without fear.

We doctors see funny things. Sometimes difficulties arise because of unwise or false teaching. Sometimes a pregnancy is represented as a mystery, couldn't possibly be any such thing, must be a case of immaculate conception. After being confronted by such an instance, I asked a clerical friend of mine what he thought of immaculate conception. He solved the question for himself rather neatly. He said he believed that immaculate conception did happen once, but will never again. That remark is evidence of his great faith and tact. It satisfies both the clergy and the biologists. But teach the young folks that it will never occur again, and thus save us doctors some embarrassing moments.

Sometimes beliefs come home to roost. I saw this happen once in high places. A stately matron, followed by a stunning daughter, came into my office. I sensed at once that here was dynamite in real life. The daughter was unduly florid and well nourished. The history revealed the fact that the young lady was an only child, had been properly raised, had just graduated from an exclusive school for young ladies, and had at no time been exposed to debasing social contact with males. It was evident, even at first glance, that the young lady had been unfortunate. When I sorrowfully announced my diagnosis, the mother shot me a look of venom, as though she had her suspicions that somehow I was responsible, and then looked at the daughter and burst forth, exploded almost: "Why, daughter!" The daughter gave her mother a hard, cold look in return and calmly replied: "Well, if there is anything like that it is a case of immaculate conception." The mother replied in crescendo or fortissimo, whichever represents the maximum in tonal qualities: "That's ridiculous." The daughter replied with a touch of sarcasm: "Well you have taught me all my life that it is possible." They sat glaring at each other. It seemed I was no longer needed, so I arose and announced: "Well, since this has ascended or descended into an ecclesiastical problem you will excuse me —since I cannot qualify." I saw them no more. That girl had learned to hate her early training. She hated her mother because she had been deprived of the contacts between boy and girl in her childhood.

Let no one presume that this is an isolated instance, but they are interesting only when they are exceptional. I was consulted by a woman who said she had a tumor. It had been diagnosed as an ovarian cyst and its removal advised. I could hear the heart beat, and there was no doubt but that she would be spontaneously relieved in a few months. "Impossible," said the lady, because she and her husband never had had sexual relations. The lady was very mad at her husband, because they had been married less than a year, and no highbred woman would have a baby so soon after marriage. The husband was mad at me because I told the truth. Though that household was a chilly place when I had to wait on what actually proved to be a mother, I have never quite been able to regard it as a tragedy.

Nowhere has there been a greater change in the past fifty years than in the American family. When I began practice in the wide open spaces, large families were the rule. Economically this was expedient. Limitless fertile acres made large families not only possible but profitable. Each child could be started out with a farm of his own when he attained maturity. Everybody worked, and there was no time to quarrel. Father was the law and the gospel. Social problems did not exist. Mother was too busy with the last child and the next to have strange ideas, and father was above suspicion because his shape and features and lack of opportunities made it impossible for him to fall from grace, even had he had any inclinations. I always get a chuckle when I see some one spraying himself with incense for not doing what he could not do if he tried. So there is no call to place these old fellows on a moral pedestal. The modern man is morally his equal, and a much better mathematician.

Few large families escaped the consequences of overproduction. Many years ago I was called to attend a member of a large family. The primary business attended to, the mother led me to a little back room. There lay a boy aged eighteen, a complete idiot. He could not feed himself and he wore a diaper, as helpless as the day he was born. I asked the mother why the boy was not sent to the state institution. The mother replied that it was a visitation on them for their sins and they must bear the burden. "What sin did you commit?" I asked. With a startled look she replied that she did not know. Evidently she had never thought about that. "Listen," I said, "you have seen instances in which too many stalks of corn had been planted in one hill. There is a little shriveled stalk about a foot high sticking out somewhere between the healthy stalks?" Incidentally, I was called in a few months later to attend this woman in labor. Despite every care, she had a terrific postpartum hemorrhage and nearly died. In a year or two the family prepared to move to a distant state. She came to tell me goodbye. "Doctor, I hate to leave. You are the only man who understands." She represented the tragedy of heredity, which was bad enough, but the tragedy of self-accusation caused even greater suffering. She was guilty of marrying a moron.

The commonest tragedies in large families resulted from similar causes. A member of the family may be far from normal. Some develop a mental aberration and spend the remainder of their days in an asylum. The community forgets, but the parents remember where the child has gone. The fathers could point to themselves with pride because they had large families, with the approval of a former President, the Church, and presumably of Providence. That just about made it unanimous.

I recall many years ago I was consulted about a member of a very large family. I announced that the patient was hopelessly insane and it would be necessary to send him to an asylum forthwith. The father looked at the mother and asked the patient's age. The mother told the date of his birth. The father made a calculation and discovered that the patient was three months over twenty-one years of age. He jumped up, clapped his thigh, and gleefully exclaimed: "He is over age. I don't have to pay." Later, after the boy had been sent away, the father remarked to me that he certainly got a break.

Had the boy been under age the father would have had to pay the State for the son's keep. But to the mother it was tragedy.

In the study of the modern trend of smaller families, it is interesting to inquire how and why the large families gained the unanimous sanction of the triumvirate of clergy, war lords, and heads of state. I sought to find the answer by reading, but found nothing. I appealed to three of my friends, all noted biblical scholars. The first replied positively that there was none. The second, a teacher of biblical literature in one of our large theological seminaries, replied that he also had never found anything. The third opined that it was just the same as when the saloon men cited the Bible to bolster the moral basis of the liquor business. It says in the Bible that wine is good for the stomach, but in the opinion of my friend it was rather a long stretch to interpret this into a justification for papa to get pie-eyed in the saloon and then go home and beat up mama. So far as my researches have revealed, the large family idea came in after the concubine supply ran out. I have long been disappointed that some candidate for a degree in sociology has not selected for the subject of his thesis: "The rise and fall of the concubine." It would make interesting reading.

If one searches for the underlying reasons for large families, one finds a number, chiefly ecclesiastic and military, but not one based on any noble sentiment. This unlimited coinage of morons, it may be mentioned in passing, has its serious public aspect because many of the numerous progeny become public charges. Only on election day are they more than ciphers, a fact that moves me to add "politics" to the two causes mentioned above. That escaped me for the moment.

When one inquires into the cause of the modern small families, the dominant reason is possibly a commendable one. To say the modern mother desires a small family because of laziness is not true. Many of them devote as much time and care to their few children as other mothers did to their large families. That is to say, they devote their whole lives to their children. Each child just gets more care. It is easier to hoe corn when there are only three stalks in a hill than when there are a dozen and one avoids the nubbins. To me that is no figure of speech.

Under our present economic conditions, it is possible for but few families to raise a dozen children. The new element is the children. They dominate the picture, and too often the home, but if they do, no harm is done if they are not apprised of the fact. But it is the desire to raise and educate them properly that concerns the parent. The children are no longer chattels but the occupants of the family throne, or at least junior partners. It would sound funny for an old doctor to say that the new sense of parental responsibility was due to a spiritual awakening. I presume I use the term spiritual as one of my distinguished friends uses it, that is, as a confession of awe at an unexplainable situation. It seems an old doctor comes to spend half his time in saying: "I don't know."

One may say with confidence that, with the lessened number on the family register, the tragedies which beset families have grown distinctly fewer, and the variety of causes much smaller. The doctor is made fully conscious of the changed point of view about the child. He is consulted before arrival of the child, greets him on his arrival, and is called on to inspect him at intervals during his childhood, particularly if his weight and height do not correspond to the figures given in the tables sent out by the baby food companies. No matter what the size and shape of the parents, they worry if the child does not meet the figures. The doctor can usually calm this worry by observing that a pup is a pup but what sort of a dog it will become depends very largely on the mama and papa dog rather than on the kind of food given. This low comedy often causes the parent to lose confidence in the infallibility of the weight charts.

The solicitude of the parents sometimes presents scenes that are impressive. One mother brought her daughter a long distance to me because the child was underweight. I asked this mother how much she herself weighed. She replied rather sheepishly: "Eighty pounds." "Little dogs, little pups," I remarked. She had not thought of that before. Nevertheless, so firmly was the possibility of disaster fixed in her mind that I had to examine the child painstakingly on two separate days—and then she still had her doubts. These little things loom large in the eyes of an anxious mother and the doctor should appreciate the situation or else he is going to hurt a little lady's feelings. The charts sent out to schools represent the average arrived at by weighing a large number of children of a given age. These charts are all right theoretically, but being based on averages, fall down when applied to a particular child. Unless this fact is recognized, distress is caused. Now the school report cards say: "Pat's weight is seventy pounds, average for her age, ninety pounds." That is less frightening than to say she is twenty pounds under weight.

There is much in this new order we doctors like and have played a leading part in bringing about. It is a lot more fun to deal with well born, well fed children. We could remove a lot more tragedy if we could assure them, as I have said elsewhere, that their small family would remain numerically small. I wonder if the still small voice that first told mothers to quit breeding large families and start raising children might be whispering to us doctors to do something about it. If so, that still small voice is just going to be obliged to keep on whispering.

On the other hand, one-child families are supposed to be tragic. The "hen with one chick" gives mothers with numerous progeny a laugh. Not so the doctor. This situation is supposed to be serious. The idea is that a single child becomes selfish, but that depends entirely on the parents. Instead of having no companions, the child should have at least two: his father and mother, and many do have these. The difficulty is that so few parents have the knowledge or desire to be playmates to their child. There are so many things to do. Of course, in a measure, a one-child family is a great misfortune to the parents because they miss the play of the children, just as one pup is less interesting than several.

The chief misfortune of the single child is that he is likely to be constantly nagged by his parents. Every mouthful of food is inspected; play is regulated until he has no more liberties than his papa. The chief tragedy the one-child families meet is the creation of a couple of fool parents.

There are two kinds of one-child families, the involuntary and the voluntary. The involuntary are those who, through no fault of their own, have but the one child. Desiring more children, they live with one child and a hope that others will follow. The failure to produce a playmate for their lone child has its tragic angle. If sterility follows the birth of one child, it may be because of an incompletely cured infection that the father had acquired in his gayer days. Of course the doctor does not tell the mother. In one case I met, the one child, a little girl, died. Knowing the facts, the bereavement was to me an additional tragedy.

The voluntary one-child family is quite a different matter. The mother says one is enough. For example, I once sat out seventy-two hours in a difficult labor. The patient cussed the husband throughout all that time. She knew she was going to die and it was all his fault. The daughter then born was the only child, but the mother never ceased to berate that husband. He was an able business man and his friends could not understand why he did not take a ball bat and settle things before breakfast. The facts are really simple: She convinced him that he was a low down skunk, and he submitted to her vituperations.

Of course, the daughter's life likewise was ruined. Strangely enough, she married a fine young business man who, after a few years, committed suicide. What the connection was, I never learned. Any attempt to learn the details was vigorously rebuffed, which in itself was sufficient evidence that there was some connection. A superficial public pointed to this as the result of a one-child marriage.

How husbands can be given a permanently guilty complex is illustrated by a method quack doctors sometimes use to insure themselves of permanent business. If a father brings a defective child to one of these fiends, he will ma-

neuver around and make a diagnosis of congenital syphilis.
Of course everybody assumes the father is the guilty party.
In his remorse, he will spend his last dollar in the attempt to
cure that child. If the child is a congenital defective, of
course, a cure is out of the question. I knew one man who
spent more than thirty thousand dollars in seeking a cure,
and died all too early, a bankrupt. To add to the sad picture,
the wife heaped on her vituperations. The truth of the matter
was that the father never had an infection he could transmit.
That seems to me to be the cruelest form of blackmail. The
child had a birth palsy, the fault of no one.

Childless wives present a variety of pictures. Many wives
blame their husbands for their childless state. Many are not
really happy if their husbands are enjoying themselves, and
never so content as when they are obviously uncomfortable.
There are many ways to bring about this situation. Every
house-broke husband can take his pencil and add to this
meager list. Perhaps the most common is to have friends,
preferably old ones, strangers to the husband, visit the household. The conversation runs along lines wholly mysterious
to him. As a sample, Aunt Lizzie relates how she made over
her last year's pants into the cutest little hat. Just seeing
Aunt Lizzie, it is difficult to imagine that any part of her
raiment that once encircled her could ever be made into
anything cute. Next in line are the more formal dinners to
which one wears a coat in August. The clothes the ladies
wear are chiefly concealed by the table. About all there is for
the male to gaze at makes him sad, because it reminds him of
the scenes of his babyhood. Of course he does not remember
them, but now he can imagine what a fine time he once had.
This reminds me that it was once related that a noted bishop,
when asked as he viewed a fashionable ball if he had ever
seen anything like it, replied, "Not since I was weaned."

On the other hand most childless couples are very devoted
to each other. They call each other "papa" and "mama" and
treat each other as children. Only occasionally are serious
domestic broils the result of sterility. That is one custom of

ancient times that we have not dragged down to date. In the old days, barren women were shown the gate.

Obviously, whether many of the plays in domestic life are tragedies or comedies, depends largely on the point of view. Often people come to the doctor with some indifferent complaint whose real cause is a maladjustment in the domestic machinery. The complaint would instantly disappear if the cause could be removed, which usually means if one could convince them that there is nothing to their delusions.

I have mentioned elsewhere that women get funny notions and suddenly explode for no very good reason, but men are not immune either. A man whom I had known for a long time came to me in a state of great agitation and stated that his wife was deliberately preventing herself from becoming pregnant. I had operated on the wife some years before and could positively assure him that pregnancy was impossible, but he was not convinced. So I concluded to try a little strategy. I got him to tell me about his hobby—raising calves. He replied he had been too busy recently to give them much attention. "Been working too hard, losing weight, I see," I told him. He was surprised and declared he did not think so. I weighed him. He could not see the figures on the scale. I told him he had lost fifteen pounds and that a weight loss of that magnitude meant something. So I examined him with great care and then pronounced a big diagnosis and gave him a sedative and everything was lovely. What set him off I never did find out. Perhaps it was thinking about the calves. He declared when he first came into my office that he would secure a divorce, but my strategy worked and he never suspected that I was making merry with him.

I met a contrary situation once. A man whom I had known for a number of years came into my office and at once angrily declared his wife had just had a baby which was not his. Sometimes such ideas are the first evidence of incipient insanity, based on a sense of persecution for boyhood indiscretions. That, it seemed, could be ruled out. I next tried to convince him that his notion of his impotency was all in his mind, but it seemed he established a good case for himself. I knew he was a man who believed his Bible "from kiver to kiver" so I tried the immaculate conception idea on him, but to my surprise he categorically rejected it, declaring that he knew that I, too, knew better. As a final effort, I reminded him the people catch diseases in public closets and they might catch pregnancy the same way. This possibility appealed to him. As he arose to go he remarked: "Do you reckon it could have been one of the New Deal fellers?" I assured him not, because that bunch were too impotent for any good. The word evidently went over his head but he was satisfied. The point is, I talked him out of his anger, and since nothing disturbed the domestic routine he evidently was impressed with some part of my argument.

More often it is the wife who gets peeved by some rather sudden event. One patient who had lost a baby from scarlet fever wanted a new baby to replace it. She got the idea that her husband purposely was refraining from impregnating her, and she was of a mind to leave him. I asked: "Just how do you figure that leaving your husband would increase your chance of becoming pregnant?" She had not thought of that. I heard nothing further about it.

In days gone by, when husbands went to a city to attend a grand lodge meeting, some of them brought something back to their wives. In that event, all the sisters of the lodge knew about it, and I could figure on several of them consulting me to see if possibly they also were recipients. Occasionally one was, but she never found it out. I always found some respectable lesion to account for her complaints.

This is a real problem for the doctor. Shall he tell the wife what is wrong with the husband? She is already infected, and to tell her will but disrupt the family, with attendant hurt to the children. Curing the wife and saving the family seems the best thing to do. Changing the point of view of the public would be a large job for a lone doctor; besides it would do nothing to remedy the injury of the past.

I cite these cases to show that when these little domestic rifts come to the doctor's notice, he can if he has wit and is a good liar and will take the time, in most instances argue them out of their troubles. Anything to avert tragedy. There is hope of being able to do this as long as no other woman appears in the picture. Once another woman appears, argument is futile, and the case belongs in a later chapter.

Besides the marriages of infants there are also the marriages of the physically unfit. Why under-developed girls secure husbands with such ease while the neighborhood is teeming with normal girls, surpasses understanding. In most instances these girls marry at a very immature age which adds another complication. Nevertheless, these substandard girls succeed in getting the pick of the young men, and the men stick faithfully to their unfortunate choice of a wife. Usually they never wake up to the fact that their lot represents tragedy. If any one deserves a new deal, these men do.

A single case serves to illustrate the countless ones I have seen. Mother aged seventeen, child two years old. Frail, utterly exhausted beyond any help. I turned to the grandmother and inquired none too kindly: "I suppose this baby married with your consent." "What could I do?" she blubbered, "they loved each other so." Fool parents should not be allowed to pass on the welfare of yet younger fools. A heifer is not bred until she attains maturity. To breed her sooner would ruin a good cow.

Society can be very cruel. Some young couples find it necessary to marry a little earlier than they had planned. A high school girl was unfortunate, but her boy friend, considerably older than she, came forward like a man and married her. The local newspaper featured this story, dragging out all the details to the extent of nearly a column. The editor was mistaken. He assumed that his readers wanted all the possible sordid details. I knew the town and am reliably informed that a majority of the readers resented such a reflection on their character. One of the citizens expressed the situation thusly: "It is only the nasty-nice people who want young people so exposed." I used to meet such cases more frequently than I do now. In those cases in which father and the shotgun did not play a part, they ended happily. The explanation is that these people usually have known each other for a long time and were truly in love, but things just got to moving too fast. The doctor, when he finds a girl in distress, can in some cases bring about a happy solution by inducing the young people to marry, and make some miscalculations in order to deceive the public. Small town stuff of course. The gabby public makes the tragedy in such cases.

Finally, having put it off as long as possible, I must mention a situation happily growing less common, but still a discerning doctor's problem.

A lovely high school student just before graduation married a very desirable young man. It was discovered that she possessed some anatomic defect that made consummation impossible. I record with the greatest humiliation that they consulted the family physician. He, in his incomprehensible stupidity, advised waiting two years; suggested that maybe things would right themselves. Not a chance in a million. The groom demurred at the prospect of so long a wait, applied for a new deal, and got it, leaving the distraught young woman behind. For fifteen years she has borne the mental anguish so initiated. Now she has a suitor, and is still in the bloom of womanhood. She is the problem of the clinic. Sure, we can correct the trouble in a few minutes. But here is the restraining hand: She was married once and must not marry again, her parents say. They say this because of some fool notion they got into their heads seventy years ago. They are cheating the grave every day yet the future good of their daughter does not weigh against the old teaching. What, I ask, does religion gain by increasing the sum total of human suffering? This is not history; it is a clinical problem facing us now. Will she disregard the ravings of a pair of senile fools, allow us to operate on her? Tragedy home grown.

Many years ago there lived in a country community a gentle lovely girl. She early adopted the tenets of Christianity and lived them. Growing into young womanhood, she proved a capable seamstress and knew how to dress her slender form. The minister protested. Such clothes would attract males, which was carnal; so she was compelled to make and wear unbecoming clothes.

In the course of time she arrived at the age of thirty, apparently forgotten. A minister in an adjoining congregation discovered an unattached male. He told the young man that he knew a daughter of a rich farmer, available for the asking. They went and looked over the young lady with the approving eye of a cow buyer, which the young man was. A subsequent visit resulted in the application of the holy bonds.

The groom discovered that his recently acquired father-in-law was not rich but only well-to-do. He flew into a drunken rage. As partial compensation he took into his home a confirmed alcoholic for his wife to take care of. He had many cute notions, this new boarder. One was to take his horse into his room, pull out the bureau drawer, place therein the required number of ears of corn for the horse to eat. The extra house-cleaning thus entailed depended naturally on the horse's disposition at the time. The bride had to clean up.

Life dragged on endlessly, attended by drunken sprees and abuse. All was borne by the wife uncomplainingly. In the meantime, the money which was hers was gradually dissipated.

After some thirty-odd years the husband's alcoholic brain became apoplectic. His wife had in the meantime acquired an ununited fracture of the hip and could get about only with the aid of a crutch. But this brute demanded that only she care for him. If she was not beside his bed, he yammered like the coward he was. They were destitute, and she sought to raise a garden but could work at it only when he was asleep. After a time he died. Anxiously waiting outside hands paid the funeral expenses with great delight. She lived a number of years in cheerful resigned widowhood. The fates, relenting, had given her a lovely daughter and an honorable son-in-law. Two weeks ago she died, aged 81 years, one of the great horde that have passed before my view where it does verily seem God forgot.

This woman was my sister, the only mother I ever knew. Hers was the only hand I did not fear in childhood. During all those long years I begged her to allow me to take charge of things, send him to a hospital, an old folks home, a soap factory, anywhere. I received only the soft simple answer: "You don't understand; it is my task." Who made it such? She believed that the matrimonial bonds were sacred. When she was sixty years of age she startled me one day, while I was imploring her to give me a chance, by saying simply: "Art, you know that I have always done my best to live the religion of my church. There is nothing to it." She said no more and naturally I asked no questions. During these many years as boy and as doctor I have been trying to figure out whereby is religion benefited by the infinite increase of human suffering its tenets encourage. Tragedy of ecclesiastic manufacture.

Take a look in review. Lovely girl, suppressed lest she become attractive. Spinsterhood reached, a goodly sum was given a drunken brute, who at some time in his youth had expressed church allegiance, for taking her to wife. This gentle woman endured a life such as Milton never dreamed of, faithful to her early religious teachings. Sure, this case is now history; she is two weeks dead. Yet this whole panorama burned itself into my soul until I hate with a consuming hatred those who deliberately produce human suffering, because of a creed.

These cases are rapidly growing less common. There can be no doubt of it. But why? Our American mother has seen visioned the Mother Mary, with the Christ in her arms, and has taken this for a cue, and is changing the face of things in a way we doctors are delighted to see. How she achieved this position is beyond my ken, but none save a fool can help but see it. It is she who is ordering the changes today and the ecclesiastics are following grudgingly after. I know what it is the underprivileged need, but money will not buy it.

I may end this chapter as I began it. It has to do with incidents in a doctor's life, things that have happened. They certainly do not belong in the picture of a happy home; they are not the product of human cussedness, at least not of the cussedness of those who suffer most, nor do they lead to divorce. The tragedies may be temporary from the point of view of the public, but their effect on the lives of the actors is permanent. They are doubly tragic because many could be prevented if the teachings of the past might be replaced by what we now know to be true. Even if not preventable, the suffering might be lessened if those about them would extend the victims a helping hand instead of leaving it all to the doctor.

IX

Paradise in Turmoil (Hell with the Lid On)

THE great American home, discussed in a preceding chapter, may be described as that institution in which it is possible for the child to grow to maturity under the best conditions. It does not demand absolute parental harmony, but such disharmony as exists must not reach the child and create in it hostility to either parent or to the world in general. It demands that parents share equally in the responsibility of the family, or that one be completely submerged and accept his or her lot uncomplainingly, so that to the child all is harmony.

In this chapter we have to do with those discordant domestic states in which the setup affects the child but stops short of the severance of marital bonds. The events in this chapter are chronic in character, and in that respect they differ from the events discussed in the last chapter. They also differ in that the difficulties are of the family's own creation. The disharmony may find expression in anything from constant verbal backbiting to physical combat. Even though hate may be camouflaged with endearing terms at intervals, the effect on the child is disastrous, since he is robbed of the influence which the home should provide for him. Perhaps I am all wrong, but when I find myself where husband and wife constantly repeat in the presence of company "dear" this and "dear" that it seems to me the fine words are just icing on a cake that has fallen flat.

States of domestic turmoil may furnish the doctor with his most perplexing problems in regard to either the children or the parents. The consequences of disharmony come to him often under the guise of physical complaints. The doctor usually is not taken into full confidence but he is expected to understand. Usually he does understand to a certain extent, but the causes of the complaint lie in the distant past quite beyond recall. Often there is sex disharmony, disagreement about the children, differences in economic ideas, or irreconcilable notions of social obligations, behind the scenes.

The doctor must be constantly on the lookout for domestic causes of seemingly organic diseases. I have before me a letter from a patient who came to the clinic. She was, it seemed to me, a suitable case for the neurologist and I sent her to that department. This letter says petulantly: "I went to you for understanding and you gave me science." Now I understand what is wrong, in an indefinite way, but there was no inkling of it while she was in the clinic. She was obviously pitying herself, and expected the doctor to lend a hand. Certainly there was a domestic brawl, about the nature of which I am still ignorant, but a more careful history might have given me the lead. That type of person is always anxious to talk, but the difficulty from the doctor's point of view is that talk is so time consuming, that it is easy to overlook the actual facts in the case. As I recall now how she was rigged out, any of the above general causes, perhaps all four, may have been present. The hurry of the clinic prevented me from noting that she was not only nervous but also angry. Her case is a reproach to me because I made no attempt to find out why she was neurotic and angry.

The quarrels of the parents are the least of the problem. It is the effect on the child that is of importance to the doctor and to society. The ordinary, more or less genteel family disagreements, revolving around whether mother gets a new coat or father does some duck hunting, are part of a happy home and, I believe, do not affect the child. He is hurt only when a difference develops sufficiently to warrant both in becoming permanently angry, and one of them, usually the wife, retires into a state of self-pity. The male equivalent is a belief that his wife does not understand him and a consequent readiness to listen to the sirens around him. There is in such cases a break in the domestic relationship that is permanent, even though the state of disharmony may escape the notice of friends. It is with them as with denominational enthusiasts. They are fully imbued with the idea that their church is the only one, yet when innocently asked, as I have often asked them, exactly in what way their church differs from those for which they feel sorry, they cannot make a sound. So family bickerings continue after the cause has been forgotten.

But it is futile to try to fool the child. Even mild, permanent disagreements cause the parents to place their difficulties above the interest of the child. He understands that he is forgotten in the selfish squabbles of the parents. I doubt very much if it is possible for parents to hate each other and either one have a real love for the child. They are so busy pitying themselves that the child is forgotten in the shuffle. When such a parent devotes any love to the child, he does so in order to use him as a weapon against the other parent. At any rate the child is a reflection of his lot, a fusion not only of the blood of his parents, but also their moods, a picture of the environment in which they grow up. The child's after life will be made up of scenes of his childhood, influences active in years that antedate his memory but which appear as impressions that will follow him throughout his life, and that will in turn be reflected in his children. A fighting family is a detriment to the community in which they live.

This chapter, therefore, has to do with those homes in which the spiritual life is lost yet which somehow are not "broken" in the legal sense. But the child is robbed of the atmosphere of parental respect and love which should be every child's birthright. I recall numerous families in which the parental fights were respectable but the children showed early antisocial tendencies. When I read of a boy raised in a respectable family, who has gone astray, I feel an urge to learn some details, which of course are never given. One is confined to the range of his own personal experience in his efforts to ferret out the cause of the difficulty.

In such families, usually the chief bond is sex, and sex without love is lust, ever the handmaiden of hate. There may be a violent quarrel at the breakfast table, but when the evening comes there is a mental agreement that after all they are not such a bad match. They need each other. It is not love that keeps them together.

This may seem to be an overstatement, but strange things happen which one may be able to trace if he observes the family throughout a period of years. In fighting couples sometimes lust dies with the passing years and love, long ignored, returns. It is proof that the cause of dissension was sex, because when sex declines with the years, the bickerings become modified, and may perhaps finally cease. A love that has once really existed never fully dies. It is eternal, even though obscured with baser things. This may be interpreted as a reason why parents should stick it out, even though they live in a state of constant turmoil, hoping, like a patient with the migraine, that the change of life may bring relief from the affliction.

But the growing child exposed to disharmony in his formative years will retain the imprint of it in his adult years. If the parents later cease their bickerings and live in harmony, he will by that time have left home, and carrying his scars with him, may engender a conflict all his own. Therefore I say a family row may extend to future generations. Parents, in such cases, in their declining years wring their hands wondering why the children are as they are. Soldiers who died before the armistice stay dead; that is the tragedy. The terms of peace in any war do not include a resurrection of the dead.

In the foregoing type, the parents have a like sex need sufficient to hold them together. Though the doctor feels there is a sex element he must approach the problem cautiously. The causes of discord in the home resting on this basis are of an endless variety, defying classification. One wonders why the union endures amid endless dissension. It seems the parents continue to tolerate each other because of the children, because of the fear of notoriety or scandal which would ensue if the lid came off their domestic box, or because of religious convictions, or perhaps because of a combination of these causes. In such cases, even if the sex relationship is not satisfactory, the union endures because of fear of the associated complications which would ensue if a rupture were allowed to become public.

In many respects, some of these unions are more sordid, because of sex differences, than those which do end in divorce. Most commonly in such cases the children are the binding influence. "I stand it because of the children," the doctor hears times without end. This conclusion seems in the main correct. Almost any travail that can be kept from the public is better for the child than an open break, for public scorn brings him new problems. Yet when the children hear from the mother what a reprobate their father is, it is a question if the children are better off in that state. I can think of nothing more tragic than the wide open eyes of a child as he listens to a parent vilified for whom he has a child's love. Certainly if the mother tolerates a union for the sake of the children, this concern should seal her lips against the offending sire.

In such cases one often finds definite bones of contention which in the beginning are trivial. Perhaps the father refuses to dress the children as the mother feels they should be dressed. Often the contention has a more selfish basis. The wife is mad because her raiment is not what she would like it to be. What the facts are makes no difference, but in many instances she is right. Strange to say, if the wife suffers innocently she accepts her lot uncomplainingly. But such women, through necessity, develop an amazing ingenuity in making things for their children. For instance, a very small miss exhibited a new dress to me. With a beaming face she said, "Mama made it." The prideful little miss was decked out with something money could not buy; "Mama made it." A greater reward than this can come to no mother.

Too often complaints are based on imagined wrongs. These have the debasing element of self pity, which is usually the spark that starts the conflagration. The mother sees, or thinks she sees, her children develop an inferiority complex because they are not dressed as their playmates are. There may be more or less mother love associated with a varying degree of father hate which is really the fundamental thing.

It is the hate which comes from satiety. As a matter of fact, the father may be hard working and an exemplary provider within his feeble talents. Perhaps the mother gads about to this or that, dissipating funds which if applied to the good of the children would leave no cause for complaint. One look at the mother, or her big toe nail, is sufficient to form a judgment. The children are forgotten and hence neglected. Sometimes one sees children dressed like little queens, and yet the mother demands yet more and more. It seems to me this is evidence of the existence of a mania just to spend money; the object is secondary. Many women cannot head the car toward home so long as they have a dime in their pockets. Her concern for the children in such cases is only a vicarious manifestation of her own selfishness. The important thing is that papa is in bad at home.

Sometimes the mother spends her time seeking her own glory or decking herself out in fine raiment. In these cases there is a hired girl left to provide a base of supplies for the children, and in many instances she supplies the affection a mother should give. I recall one family which I saw often in which two wonderful little girls in deep affection called the hired girl "little mother." The affection was definite and strong, and was returned to them in kind. But the mother was not there; she was gadding about in company which made the judicious grieve. I chanced to be in that home on another mission one evening and heard the "little mother" tell the girls that their mother would be in on the nine o'clock train. "What do we care," was the chorus as they headed for bed. The mother had forfeited something that was gone for good.

When parents forget that the keystone of the home is the child, trouble brews. Regard the child in the manger as real or allegorical, or deny it entirely if you will, the only ray of light apparent today is the emergence of the child. Why not sit at the feet of the child and find out, if we can, what it tries to tell us. What does the child think of us as parents, and of our collective conduct which has as an end product our domestic atmosphere and our civilization? In order to elimi-

P

nate hate from the world it must first be eliminated from the home. Parents cannot quarrel while one or both are playing with the baby. The little rascals eliminate all fight from any grouch. We will learn more sitting on the floor building block palaces with the baby than adding our vocal gymnastics to the Pharisee's on the corner.

How long are we going to be content to raise common cannon fodder and lose what little sense we ever had, as soon as the loud mouths shout and the drums of hate begin to beat? To put it bluntly, the child is more or less a byproduct of our way of life instead of being the end and object of our existence. When the love of the child becomes intense enough and universal enough, the blah-blahs, who kept us out of war while pushing us in will hear a noise that will startle them. Figure out what a difference it would have made in our national life if we had paused to consider how much cannon fodder we would have to contribute before we ran after the sirens who extolled the virtues of fighting a war to end wars.

Sociologists, with a great show of scientific acumen, spend much time in the study of the great American home. They send out many questionnaires to be filled out. These questions have to do with the most intimate affairs of family life, and on the face of it, might seem to produce valuable information. But things are not so simple as that. The questionnaires reflect the individual's mind at the moment the card is being filled out, or as much as he at the moment feels like writing down, but they do not reflect the real reaction to life. The difficulty is, the individuals filling out the card do not know themselves what ails them. The answer calls for a conclusion which is not admissible in any court of record, being incompetent, irrelevant and immaterial besides being cockeyed, nutty and silly. For instance, it is startling to note that in the answer to the question: "If you had it to do over again, would you marry?" fifty per cent answered: "No." Yet it is safe to say if the door was suddenly opened to freedom, they would dart to a dark corner like a scared calf, or make frantic efforts to get themselves into the same situation they just got out of. When asked the cause of domestic disharmony, they write down that the husband is stingy, pays too much attention to business, plays too much golf, has lost the finer sentiment he used to show, and so on. Good gosh! Consider what he has to kiss when he starts to work, compared with what he had in years gone by before "love" found its satiety.

The husband, confronted by a card, will write that the home bogged down because the wife is slovenly, gads about, is a poor housekeeper, and an endless number of other silly replies. He should stop to think that he married her because he was attracted by a pretty face and a fetching shape, both of which any fool should know are as unstable as a snowball in Hades. He should recall that when she promised to obey he had something else in mind besides the future fate of her features and shape. Nothing was said or implied that guaranteed the retention of these attractive features.

Perhaps the transverse diameters of both have increased to such a degree that osculation over the garden gate would be impossible except to those who are built like a giraffe. And the lady may be put to a test when she sees something spread over the landscape of the sitting room, shoeless, coatless, ashes all over the floor, a poor presentment of what she promised to "love, honor and obey." Yet if carefully studied, his neglected clothes, his apparent disregard of the landscape about him, reveal that he likes his home, that it is a haven of rest to him. He thereby constantly tells his mate that his affections for her have endured. Peeved women, when they come calmly to inspect the partner, remember that after all he represents a good meal ticket, which as a matter of fact was the reason for marrying him in the first place. Too many women are peeved because the blue-prints they drew setting forth the alterations they intended to make in their husbands fail to materialize. The essentials of a good partner are congenital things and are as unchangeable as the shape of his face. We often hear young ladies declare that they will marry some one, pointed out to them as tainted goods, with the purpose of reforming him. Such instances appear to me like cranking the old Model-T. One never knew if the engine would start or whether it would back-fire and break one's wrist.

On the other hand, when the wife loses her streamlined form she declares to her husband that she is the mother of his children, and that she is content to remain the captain of her home. Women do not starve themselves in order to retain a willowy form just to please their husbands.

Social reformers, to be at all consistent, should have the questionnaires filled out by the children, but the spirit of the home, meaning that intangible something the child feels, cannot be written down. It can only be felt, as we doctors feel it when we make a visit and the armor is off the belligerents and we see them as they are. Take a look at mama after she has sat at the bedside all night with a sick child and then take another look when she is dolled up to go forth to conquer an imaginary world, long lost to her because of the handicap of the other half of the team. Listen to papa's solicitations for the welfare of the child. Nothing is too good. I have witnessed a reconsecration of parents over the bed of a desperately sick or a dead child so often that I am sure their differences were due to the fact the child was forgotten.

Yet the people who make up these surveys are nice people with large heads shaped like a pear. They discover that the great causes of domestic discord are wives who gad and serve half baked biscuits and get plump, and husbands who lie about their earning capacity, are lousy and smell. That is social science; the procedure is scientific investigation. But the child, and his potential influence, does not appear on their cards. Elemental logic teaches us that the conclusion bogs down if the minor premise is wrong. The reformers have suggestions as to how to increase the income, delouse and deodorize the husband, how to make the biscuits bake in the middle, or put the lady on a diet. They put them down as underprivileged people because their foreheads do not bulge, and because they grow fat and smell. The conclusion naturally is that they should be streamlined and equipped with electric lights and bath tubs. Doctors know that it is difficult to reform a person who is satisfied with himself. Just try putting an unwilling person on a diet, or inducing papa to take a bath in winter-time. The fact is children love their parents in spite of their shape, be they fat or thin, and that is all there is to it. The only person I know of who ever boldly attacked these complicated problems was a negro preacher who announced the subject of his discourse was to prove the "inevitableness of the inevitable."

I recall with pleasure that, in the days gone by when I had the time to devote to such pursuits, and when I had a lady who was not having much luck in remodeling her husband, I would recall some contact with him at a hunt, or a meeting somewhere, and extol his fundamental good qualities. Usually too it was not all lies. One can lead the lady's mind to a point where she is willing to go back and reinspect her catch.

I remember with great glee that once I had a little red-headed school teacher whose wife was getting on his nerves terribly. After the examination was finished and the consultation ended, I casually remarked that I had been much impressed by the stately personality of his wife. His face brightened, he never had thought of her in such lofty terms. She was an arrogant old hen whom I dreaded to meet socially, but I believe I helped my patient. No highbrows with their delicately scented cards can get under the hide as can a little personal attention.

Much more intricate and more difficult to fathom are those cases in which nobody understands what is wrong. When we seek for more revealing facts we find some very confusing phenomena. One of the most common is the aversion the mother has for the father, once children are born. It would seem to be hate, but it is not quite that. Some female bugs, after they have been impregnated, kill the males, because they don't need them any more. The Fates are not so merciful to humans. The strange thing here is

that the mother will show her aversion openly to the father
but not to the doctor. Others feel it but do not show it to
any one except the doctor, and to him only inadvertently.
The exact cause may be difficult to find. Some women bear
children in complete frigidity, the cause of which is frequently a mystery. Often, however, it dates back to a lack of
adjustment in the early months or days of married life.
Some women bear large families without ever experiencing
a particle of sex sense. They hate their mates every day of
their lives, and the home suffers, of course.

Two typical instances come to mind. I was asked by a
husband to find a cause for his wife's hostility. I found
nothing relevant. She moved to another town taking the
children with her. The husband made no complaint and continued in his business. I talked the matter over with him.
He knew no cause. I am sure if he had known he would
have told me, for he was one of my most intimate friends
and one of the noblest men I have ever known. He died; and
strange to say, after his death the widow mourned deeply,
bitterly complaining of the doctors who attended him in his
last illness, a condition which medical science was utterly
helpless to cure from the beginning. One might think her
attitude after his death indicated a surviving or a revived
love. It looked like hate for her husband first and then
the doctor. But to assume this would be unkind. They were
victims of a peculiar sex state impossible to define. One
would need to know all the facts from childhood on to
arrive at a conclusion, and then might fail because past
generations were not consulted. If we knew all the facts I
suspect we would find a deep and abiding love, but a type of
affection which refused to mix with sex. Whether that in
itself was the cause, or the fear of having more children, one
does not find out.

In the other instance, the husband and wife continued to
live in the same house; to their friends they were in apparent
harmony, but as man and wife they were utter strangers.
I suspect that in this case the wife figured that her two
lovely daughters were all she wanted, but I never knew for

sure. The husband was a good soldier, and thus they remained, to all but themselves and their doctor, a model
family. The argument against my theory is that after the
menopause they retained their distant cordiality. If it was a
fear of pregnancy that kept them apart, they should have
been spiritually united in their old age, which they were
not. It was this family that first suggested the title for this
chapter, but it was not the most striking example I have
met for the children grew up apparently unconscious of the
tragedy that surrounded them.

Unfortunately many cases do not run such a smooth
course. In one that came to my attention, the whole fault
lay in the fact that the husband was wont to walk about
from room to room imitating as best he could the great
Caruso. Either he was no Caruso or the wife was no judge
of music. It makes no difference because she got to dread
the sound of the voice which in all sincerity was attempting
to reveal the nobleness of its soul. The trouble was that he
applied the common bathroom technic to other parts of the
house.

The sad part of this is that often nobody knows what
it is that irritates the other partner. Something happened
to develop this mental attitude which was beyond the control
of the sufferer, perhaps even beyond his memory. How
would people solve such cases with their questionnaires?
People avoid the truth, even if they know it. Perhaps the
wife of the unappreciated Caruso had a sick calf as a child
and the sound of her husband's voice brought up painful
memories, even though they may have been subconscious.
All this may sound facetious, but the truth too often is not
nice and people refuse to recognize it, although to disregard it brings a living hell. Of course in this specific instance the reformers could do something about it by starting a movement to discourage singing while in the bath,
for artistic reasons as well as sociological. That would have
nipped the difficulty in the bud by preventing singing in
any house in which any one lives.

It is strange that husbands in such cases of wifely frigidity usually remain faithful. They know something is wrong but do not know what it is. They ask the doctor and, if he expresses his ignorance, accept their lot. Unfortunately these mothers ofttimes seek to transmit their queer biologic aversion or hate to their children. Fortunately it is mild, lacking the fury of the jealous woman. Usually the relationship is not 'mentioned to any one, even the children. They sometimes shower their children with a cold love, minus understanding. It is a problem of love that never existed, a dead sex, if sex ever existed, and such does not engender hate, usually not even self pity. Some such women whom I have seen fulfill my idea of human cabbages, and I say this only in deep pity.

Cases like these are sometimes the result of an event long past, perhaps forgotten. Sometimes it is fright at the advent of menstruation, the sudden acquaintance with some phase of sex, or something of that sort. One woman after her husband died, said that the cause of her frigidity was that once, as a child, she chanced to see her father stark naked while bathing. It was in the days when the wash tub served not only in its classical capacity, but also for mixing sausages, and on Saturday night in the kitchen served the whole family as a substitute for the more conventional article. From that moment she hated males not fully dressed. I asked her why, with such an attitude toward men, she ever married. "Mother wanted me to," was her reply. Looking back on the fine qualities of her husband, his enduring faithfulness and the fine lady he never knew, he lingers in my memory though he is long dead. I know of nothing more tragic than to see two fine people living in the same house as total strangers throughout a lifetime.

I recall here, not without a grin, a couple I once reckoned among my best friends. The lady was teaching English drama when she married my friend. She was a tiny vision, as frigid as ice. Her favorite subject, of course, was literature. She inquired of me at dinner once what I was reading. I replied that on the train I had read the life of Billy the Kid, but that my favorite author was George Ade. She gave me a withering look of incredulity. Being tiny, she served meals that might have satisfied a dyspeptic canary, but for full sized males, such as her husband and his guest, they were only an aggravation. After the first visit, I took the precaution of eating a full sized meal before I accepted another invitation to dine there. I wondered how her husband subsisted. I visited his laboratory one day at three in the afternoon. Sensing my presence he called out: "Have an egg." He had boiled four of them. To compensate for his domestic frigidity and small meals, he drove himself to the limit in his science, and wrote his name big in the history of the nation. Here is one case in which the husband could truthfully have said: "My wife made me what I am."

When a patient whose difficulty may have a domestic phase appears before a doctor, he tries to go as far back in the history as he is able. This is possible in many cases when the doctor has long been resident in the community, as I have been in mine, now more than forty-six years. The local residents in fact are already known to me. If one knows the family antecedents one can write the history on the wedding day. The doctor asks why did this woman marry? Obedience to parental wishes is sometimes the answer, or the obvious necessity of securing a permanent meal ticket, or social position. Mother tells them love will come after marriage. I have heard that often when wives declare that theirs was a loveless marriage. Love just did not come.

Some girls never reach puberty, yet they marry. Sometimes unpreparedness for the events of the wedding night, or timidity, or a thousand other things, may play a part in bringing about frigidity, as I have pointed out elsewhere. Perhaps the chance to observe males in track meets or in basketball games will permit future brides to see what an ungainly animal the nude male is before the closer contact on the wedding night, for let it be admitted that the human male undressed vies with the giraffe in being the least lovely of all the animal kingdom to look at.

However the real problems of this chapter have to do not with frigidity but with heat. It requires the cooperation of sex and hate really to start the fireworks. One might think these are affairs that should be confined to the private battle grounds of the parents, and in many instances they are, for years without end. But hate takes no vacations and is the one thing not controlled by union hours; it is nearly always vocal and it does not confine itself to bathroom melodies. However I have seen excellent families grow up under such conditions. The point is, a roof will stay in place so long as the sounds beneath stick to one key, thus avoiding discordant notes.

Usually there are discordant notes and the roof trembles. Therefore in most instances the entire family suffers because of the disharmony. Almost inevitably the real tragedies come when the children are made a part of the family discord. Often the children are made a bone of contention. The mother wants this, the father wants that. Most commonly the father corrects the son for taking the family car, or wants him to work. The mother defends the son. What's the car for? Why work? Let father do that. Sure, the doctor gets in on this. The mother, in order to justify her position, concludes the easiest way out would be to find some physical reason as to why the son should not work and should enjoy the breezes the car would stir into motion, so she appeals to the doctor to find something. I have been consulted so often in such cases that when a mother comes in with set features pushing a young yokel before her I know the answer. Of course one is obliged to make a pretense of examining the alleged patient. Very likely he has pimples on his face and his heart may be beating faster from the effects of incipient love. The doctor explains that he has pimples because he is a young male, and the heart beats because of the nerves going to it. The doctor knows that the mother does not know what he is talking about, but she does get the idea that papa is not responsible for any of those things, which but increases the mystery.

If or when papa finds the son was brought to the doctor by his mother, he wants to know what was found. What shall the doctor say—"Just growing too fast, in the adoles-

cent stage?" When parents come separately to ask about a
boy's health, the doctor knows there is serious trouble at
home. Funny thing: daughters are never the cause of these
difficulties in families. Most girls brought to the doctor are
the mothers' problems only. Usually the mother tries to
make the daughter a neurotic like herself. The important
thing for the doctor to do is to extricate the child from the
pincers of the family quarrel. Fight they will, because the
real cause of trouble dates a long way back; but if the son
can be got away it may save him from acting the part of a
buffer. The most effective measure a doctor can employ is
to give the lad a change of scenery. The most extreme
measure I ever employed was to send a boy to an uncle in
Texas under a diagnosis of "suspected tuberculosis."

Usually when the mother acts contrary to the wishes of
the father, relative to the conduct of a son, it is an expression of the aversion or sex disharmony between the parents.
A discord arises which does not reach the dignity of hate.
Women just get tired of that old idea of "obey." The kind
and degree of reaction are endless. It is odd that one should
develop a belated aversion to something he never had to
do. It is purely theoretical, like the objection to the tax
on tea, but, like the tax on tea, it may be enough to start
a war. Very often the husband may be ignorant of the fact
that even though the word in the contract carried no limitation, human endurance does. Too often he is wholly indifferent to the rights of the other party. Concubines, like
the Model-T Fords, went out of circulation before their
usefulness had ended.

However, abused women seldom complain. An attempt to
limit the act is much more apt to bring hate, because it
means unsatisfied sex. When the element of hate enters,
things become more serious. The mother is not satisfied with
hating the father. She wants the children to assume the
same attitude and help her hate him. Hate is quite a different matter from the simple disobedience mentioned in a
preceding chapter. Sons are coached to do those things

which will annoy father or cause him grief, the more the better.

Such instances have repeatedly come up to hit me in the face when I had not expected such a thing. A fine boy suddenly goes amuck. A good start is for the son to take the family car out against the wishes of the father. Perhaps father in defense carries the switch key with him. In retaliation the son drives away the wrong car. Then come the police. The tearful mother seeks out the doctor and explains to him that when Johnnie was a baby he bumped his head against a pillow, and she wants to know if there is not some sort of operation one could perform. It is interesting to observe how vividly trivial accidents are remembered when filial shortcomings need explaining. The doctor is supposed to explain the effects of the accident to the judge.

When confronted by these cases I feel like asking the woman why she married her husband in the first place. It is a great help if the doctor already knows, but in consulting practice it is seldom possible to obtain documentary evidence; still, a doctor becomes, with the passing years, a good guesser.

How well concealed such cases may be, was revealed to me by one of the most tragic instances that I have had to witness. It was as follows: Years ago I had as a patient, one of the most magnificent men I ever knew. He was loved and respected by everybody, except his wife, as it turned out much to my surprise. The home seemed to be ideal to outsiders. After I had treated him for some months for what I knew was to be his final illness, he said to me one day: "Just how long do I *have* to live?" The form of his question, not how long could he live but how long must he live, and the peculiar look in his eye, told me he really wanted to know. I told him the best estimate I could make was that he would live from about three to six months—he lived five. His reply staggered me. He went on calmly to say that he was glad of it because it would be a release from "mama." "I would never have stood it except that I thought it would be best for the children, but I don't know. She taught them to hate me," was his simple observation.

I have thought of this occurrence many times and still I have not arrived at a conclusion. The mother had done all she could to turn the children against the father and he felt helpless. The parents never had had a quarrel but the mother thought that in order to have the love of her children in the fullest measure they must needs hate their father. There was apparently no sex element involved— just selfishness on the part of the mother, a desire to corner for herself the sum total of the children's affections. He tolerated this situation because he felt that it was best for their children. The result naturally was that the children disobeyed him and disregarded his wise counsel, much to the everlasting misfortune of all of them and the ultimate disaster of one of them.

I was able to follow more or less closely most of the members of this family for many years. The mother lived to a ripe old age, and in the last twenty years was almost completely ignored by her children and had to be dependent for her care on strangers. Yet she was an exceptionally intelligent, noble woman. I learned from a brother that she grew up under a tyrannical stepmother, and from the dawn of memory until she married knew nothing but hate. Her marriage was actuated merely by the desire to escape from intolerable home conditions, and I am sure she never achieved more than mere toleration for her husband. Twenty years of hate because of home conditions, and marriage to a man who was virtually a stranger when she married him and whom she never learned to know!

I sometimes wonder how many such instances there are which come to the notice of no one. All one sees to excite speculation are the unexplained criminal tendencies of some members of families in which there is no obvious hereditary taint. Such cases often involve a son, usually the mother's pet, if he is an only son. If father tries to guide him in the way he should go, he will have but little luck. Father takes his slight as a matter of course. Most often I believe it is

because father has forgotten his courtship days and the
mother seeks consolation in her love for her son. Feeding
and clothing a woman is not enough.

That broken homes, meaning homes which have resulted
in divorce, furnish an undue number of wayward children
is recognized by criminologists. That homes in which there
is a constant bickering between parents are in many cases
as widely, perhaps more widely, broken than those which
do end in divorce is not usually recognized in our statistics,
because it is not obvious. Such children, let it be repeated,
are physically legitimate, but spiritually they are bastards.

Frequently, childless couples are involved. Having no
children, the wife seeks to baby her husband and he doesn't
care to be babied. Every childless woman should have a dog,
or a cat, whichever she prefers. Happily, more often than
not, the husband is quite willing to be babied. He calls
her mama, perhaps to the suppressed derision of their friends.
It seems to be a matter of technic. If my observations have
been accurate, it is the big man who folds up and purrs
when "mama" calls him "baby." To view one of these large
persons carefully balancing a hot water bottle on his stomach to please his wife when there is nothing under the sun
wrong with him is certainly something.

A husband likewise has his way of nagging, too. He may
want to know what his wife did with fifty cents he gave her
a year ago. Why a new hat—here there is some excuse because the latest creation is certainly worse than the one
before—and so on endlessly. Unfortunately the husband's
technic is such that it cannot be designated by such a gentle
word as nagging. It is just overbearing selfishness even if it
stops short of brutality.

Ofttimes, where one would most expect domestic discord
in cases of nagging it is not there. The hen-pecked husband
does not complain. The wife is boss constantly and in every
respect. He may loom large in the business world, but at
home he is a worm. He may be so adroitly handled by some
sweet thing that he does not recognize his state. I once
saw a famous man, at a dinner given in his honor, lay his

hand gently on his wife's shoulder as he made response to the encomiums in his honor, and say his wife was a silent partner of his success. Yet I knew she was anything but silent —a constant nagger who made his home life miserable. Though successful, from the world's view-point, at home he was a minus.

Perhaps viewed broadly, an ornery wife may really be a mainspring in her husband's success. She may drive him more intensely into his business or profession, and this may result in achievement which he would have missed had he had a habitable home. Because of the domestic atmosphere he works longer hours, and being mad everything goes at a higher speed. However, in justice to the wife, one must admit that it is often difficult to decide which is cause and which is effect. Is the wife a nagger because of the neglect of an over ambitious husband, or does the husband seek to forget the activities of the pestering cootie by increased labor? After years of careful study, I would suggest that as a compromise we regard it as a vicious circle.

Perhaps most men who amount to anything are more or less hen-pecked, if not by their wives, then by their children. Most often they attack in unison. Then add to father's burdens the endless solicitors who want money for this and that. Not being able to locate the bush on which money grows, they go to one who is supposed to have located one.

Usually, such a home seems happy because everyone, except father, gets what he wants. Perhaps this might be regarded as the normal state of a happy home. The fly in the ointment here is that there is no limit. Something more is constantly demanded, and since a balance satisfactory to all is impossible, somebody is constantly mad at papa. The doctor does not enter until some complication arises.

Most men, I dare say, are in a measure the authors of their own difficulties. They spare their wives and their children. It is fun at first to please them, but it becomes more difficult as time goes on. A child will be pleased with a nickel, and it will bring a greater expression of appreciation than the gift of an automobile later on. If every man could expand his income to meet the increased demands all would be well, but there is not that much money in the world.

The one cheering thing is that so long as a man is not cognizant of the fact that he is hen-pecked, it does no harm. A man is really not hen-pecked until everybody notices it except himself, and no really hen-pecked man realizes that he is. Even if the man knows he is being imposed upon, he does not know how to escape. Everybody knows or thinks he knows, what he can afford, and if he pulls back he is accused of having no affection for his family since he refuses to provide for them the things other children have. The accusation of a lack of affection, particularly from a child, strikes the father where the skin is the thinnest. He has heard it from the wife for so long that it has become accepted as the truth. Sooner or later father gets a pain in the stomach and the doctor x-rays him and finds nothing. One day he drops dead with a heart attack. This the doctor understands; it was not his stomach at all but a beginning heart block. At home all is confusion. When the probate court gets through with them, they discover that father was a noble person. It is worth noting that the outlay for a monument in such cases is not very great.

The chief difficulty may come in the next generation. Papa is dead, in fact, as he had long been dead so far as his influence over his family was concerned. Daughter, having worked on papa all her life, tries her technic on her newly acquired husband and he promptly throws a fit. Daughter comes home and requires the services of the old family doctor. Having seen the workings of the family for years, he just renigs. "Incompatibility," the judge is told, and surely the truth was never more accurately inscribed in the court book of records.

This hen-pecking business is an art and is open to further elucidation. The wise woman selects the technic suitable to her physique and mentality. She does not let the family in on this technic.

One type of woman is not strong and requires all kind of care from the husband, which of course is delivered as ordered. I once knew such a man. His wife and daughters were all sickly. He got up early and carried their breakfasts to their beds before going to work. He was the finest example of a devoted father and husband I have ever seen. He did not know he was being imposed upon. When I called at the home to see the "invalids" it was at once apparent that they were a lot of contemptible malingerers. His affection was such that he regarded my every movement with pitiable anxiety. Did I want a spoon, a glass of water? Was the room the right temperature? Was the ventilation adequate? The only implement I really wanted was a barrel-stave, but so deeply was he imbued with the conviction that they were really sick that it would have been futile to have tried to convince him that they were playing him for a sucker.

My problem was soon solved, for one day without warning he up and died, a most inconsiderate thing to do. This made it necessary for the lady members of the family to earn their own living, because they had so carefully anticipated the arrival of the pay check that all he left was a memory. Their recovery was instantaneous, without benefit of a physician, and they all got jobs. And, pleasing to state, they were much happier engaged in gainful occupations than while they were sharpening new pins to stick into papa. Love sometimes hasn't any sense. Good intentions are noble but often they do not pay dividends, and in the end defeat their own purpose.

This leaning type is very common and is an eternal trial to the doctor. Fortunately, a single glance is usually sufficient to assure a diagnosis. The husband believes the wife is sick and jumps at every whim. She suddenly becomes short of breath and he hastens to fan her as she rolls appealing eyes at him. All this show is put on for the doctor as occasion demands. The doctor innocently asks: "Did you ever have an attack at a bridge game?" The answer is: "No."

The domineering type of hen-pecker is more difficult to manage. She must needs be large and the husband small in order to meet the demands of the comic strip artists, and they are usually just that in real life. Also he must be meek.

Q

Here again, if the doctor suggests that the best remedy would be a barrel-stave applied judiciously, the answer is: "Oh no, doctor, you must be mistaken. I know she suffers terribly." Nothing will convince him that the degree of suffering cannot be gaged by the volume of vocal effect. If, in a moment of petulance, the doctor observes that she does not look exactly delicate he will be met with the assertion that it takes all her strength to keep her looking well, that the doctor should have seen her when she was in good health. Of course the husband cannot understand that the further the skin capillaries are from the base of supplies, the more difficulty they have in keeping up a pink complexion.

Your large lady usually does not resort to the subterfuge of being sick. She is the big stick kind. I knew one of these ladies who lay in bed for years so that she could have her husband cook and bring her meals to her in bed. She had a large cane which she used to strike at him with as soon as he had deposited the tray of food on her bed. He was nimble and usually escaped injury. He tolerated this for endless years until, through the act of an inscrutable Providence, one day she really became ill. I was called. As I detected the unmistakable signs of pneumonia I couldn't help but feel like shouting for joy. And she did actually die, from natural causes. To fit the domestic picture, of course the husband should have died first. But so unfeeling was he that the lines left his face immediately after the funeral, and he enjoyed life for a number of years.

But this is not the end of the story. The children of this happy home learned to hate their father through the coaching of the mother. This hatred was transferred to their husbands as soon as they married, with the result that one became an excellent cook in a small restaurant while the other found employment in a laundry; victims of a mean mother. The sons left home while still quite young.

In many cases, let me hasten to add, the wife is superior to her husband in intellect and ambition. Finding her husband unresponsive to her high aims, she seeks to see her ambitions realized in her son. Many sons of obscure, self-sacrificing mothers have rewarded their efforts by making an enviable place in the world. We hear that he was the son of poor parents. All wrong; his mother was the richest kind of mother in the world. Just what mama thinks about papa in such cases does not become a matter of court record, but the record is written on her face. The I.Q. experts write down that the son of ignorant parents ranked ahead of the son of the professor of philosophy. We doctors record many things in our memories which we do not write down in our case-books. The statisticians make the mistake of rating the intelligence of the parents according to the earning capacity of the father.

If one seeks for the common cohesive factor in family discords tolerated throughout the years, one will discover that as long as the sex life remains satisfactory almost anything else is tolerated. One might liken it to chronic rheumatism. The victims come to take a philosophic view of their affliction. This attitude usually appears after the family has grown. A virtue may be made of necessity. The old rheumatic learns to predict weather changes by the degree of pain in his joints. He toddles down to the post-office telling all and sundry of the impending changes in the weather. If some tactful friend will inquire: "Grandpa, how is your rheumatiz this morning?" it brings him great joy. I knew an old fellow who always responded to this question with: "Poorly, thank God, poorly." I presume he meant to imply that he was glad to be alive despite his afflictions. He was as proud of his rheumatism as most men are of achievement. Likewise, a member of a domestic team may learn to take pride in his particular affliction, and grandma is as proud of grandpa's rheumatism as he is. The moral to be drawn from these situations is that in case of family discord, concentrate on some neutral problem, like rheumatism.

Too often domestic disharmony may become more voluble even if not more painful. This is true if sex enters; the voice finds itself. The most devastating element in the home is jealousy. It is apt to come when nagging has brought neglect. The wife, instead of investigating herself honestly, concludes that her husband has found some other outlet for his affection. It is always amusing to me to observe a wife searching for the other angle of a triangle, which she just knows must exist—for how else could he overlook her charms. I once heard such a person express her suspicions to a none too sympathetic friend. This friend burst forth with the following gem: "Absolutely nothing to it. Besides don't you know women have some sense? Who would have designs on an insignificant little shrimp like your husband?" That speech really did a lot of good.

One of the hardest things to understand is why or how husbands will tolerate jealousy as they do. The husband, as a matter of course, must account for all of his time. He must say where he is going, or where he has been. If he is going to a given place, the wife manages to find some pretext to phone—to see if he actually did go there. Most men just tolerate it, but some have a sense of humor and play tricks on the lady, thereby showing her how groundless are her suspicions. One of my friends played a mean trick. He phoned that he was going to Excelsior Springs on business. The wife's detective followed. There was Mr. Business Man big as life feeding a lady. The detective discreetly got a picture of the pair seated at the dining table and in great triumph took the picture to his client. The lady beheld her husband, sure enough, peacefully dining with his sister. But this did not bring any notable amelioration, as one might expect. She remained mad, but it did reduce the range of her voice, and that was something. I was their neighbor. Of course no nice man would play a trick like that.

I would like to interpolate this advice to any wife who feels an urge to have the movements of her husband watched: That she hire a detective who is a friend of the husband. Detective and husband can then decide on a schedule for the day. This arrangement makes it possible to get better pictures in case a photograph is needed, as in the above case; but of course in this instance the wife did not know her detective was a friend of the husband.

A husband with a jealous wife has small chance ever to go anywhere unless his watchful wife is along. I knew a doctor whose wife was in his office every day for twenty years, just to be near him because she loved him so. He was a specialist, hence had fixed hours. It annoyed him, naturally, because his friends made remarks, but he tolerated it. There were no children, so she had nothing else to do but make life miserable for him. He died in midlife of heart block. The fates found a means of relief which he himself could not provide.

One should always remember that the greatest cause of family discord is living together. There should be a law compelling each married pair to travel for two weeks once a year, one east, the other west. Once a month, even every two weeks in some cases, would be preferable, but we reformers must be moderate in our demands, at least at the start. We doctors have an expression which we write on our prescriptions that could be used here. It is *ad ibitum*. The druggist writes on the box: "Take as often as necessary." It has been my privilege to prevent several family disasters by advising a long vacation, in one case for six months. Time to think things over sometimes works wonders. The fundamental factor in these mild jealousies, often camouflaged as love, is an entire lack of trust, and trust is one of the essential factors in anything resembling affection: no trust, no love.

Happily, changing conditions have lessened the number of jealous women. There isn't time for them to worry about their husbands because their various activities absorb their time. Of course no prudent person would suggest that a chance to exercise their tonsils may play a part, the salutary result contributing to a salubrious domestic atmosphere. The husband is more concerned about finding the lady at mealtime than she is about his whereabouts. A little miss not long ago expressed exasperation at the effort it took to keep track of her mother. I have never known a husband to develop a very violent headache in trying to locate his spouse. They probably learned in their childhood the little nursery yarn about little BoPeep. It will be remembered that this little miss was sure the lost sheep would return without the loss of any appendages.

As a matter of completeness, it is necessary to admit that there are jealous husbands. One reads of them in the papers. I have never seen one, even in this day when wives roam widely. Of course doctors see young swains sick with jealousy, but they recover quickly when they gain the object of their affections. I once witnessed an amusing incident. Two young friends of mine had a real fist fight over a girl. The winner lost because he won, and long bemoaned the fact that he had won the girl. The vanquished lad did not fail to gloat when he observed how many relatives the girl he lost had concealed in the background.

Jealousies of the mild type above described sometimes go on as private affairs for years without end. Jealousy cannot function well in the abstract. The children know nothing about it; are aware only of the chilliness of the home. The tragedy comes when jealousy becomes vocal, which it does when directed against a specific person. All and sundry, including the children, learn about the perfidy of the father. Such cases as these, though they have their beginning in this chapter, inevitably move over into the next.

Once jealousy has reached this stage, it finds a siren whispering: "I just wouldn't stand for it." All well regulated duels have seconds. A careful study of most cases of "other woman trouble" would demonstrate that the real triangle has for its angles, husband, wife and female friend of the wife. A female friend forms the third part of the geometric figure more often than the proverbial blonde secretary. I use the designation "female friend" advisedly for she is just that. Too often it is the wife's mother who plays this part. Many mothers, strange as it may seem, never quite forgive a man for marrying her daughter, no matter how badly he may have been stung in the transaction, and even though she may have moved heaven and earth to land him in the first place. The mother is jealous, apparently, that a mere man has taken her daughter's love.

Funny thing appears here constantly, as I have noticed it. If the sympathizing friend must be secured from the environment, one may predict in advance her general shape; mentally they are all alike. If the aggrieved person is small her second is likely to be a large truculent woman; if large, the second is pretty sure to be small and feisty. This association is so constant that I call it to the attention of the judges. If a large and a small woman appear before him, it is a certainty that there is no innocent party facing him. I have learned to take heed when I see a large and a small woman who are boon companions. The row is about to move into the next chapter. In such cases, if papa comes complaining of stomach trouble, I do not put him to the expense of undergoing x-ray examinations.

That family rows are in many instances the result of physical causes is not sufficiently appreciated, and the investigation of this possibility should always be made when there is discord. They may be so obscure that the persons interested may not be conscious of being sick. But the subject phenomena may lead the doctor to find a remedial physical cause. At least give him a chance.

Early in my practice, when I thought I was a surgeon, I had a patient who required an operation, a very rare event in those days. She had a lesion which I knew my inexperienced hands could remedy. I did so and secured an interesting specimen. I was so pleased with myself that in the afternoon I attended a ball game. The big Blues catcher parked one in the lot far beyond the centerfield fence, three on, and a ball game. That was the end of a perfect day. But how perfect only subsequent events showed me.

The morning after the operation I received a letter. This was all it contained, scribbled on tablet paper with a lead pencil: "Do what you can for my wife. Spare nothing. She is a good woman." The name was the same as the woman's on whom I practiced my surgery, but the address was a different town from that given by her as her home. In a hazy sort of way I realized that here was something interesting. When it came time to dismiss the patient from the hospital, she told me she would like to stay in the hospital a week or two longer. At the end of the stay she said very quietly and simply: "You have found the cause, I am going home to my family."

Now most assuredly here was something interesting. I located a sister of the husband. She told me: "Mary left Ed and five children; just walked out without saying anything. Ed has kept the children with what help I could give them. He has always felt sure that some day she would come back."

I kept in touch with this family for more than twenty years, the contact being made possible by the sister. After the children all left home this couple settled down to a serene old age. "Mary never said why she left him and Ed never asked her," the sister told me. The simple fact was that Mary had a pain and instead of telling Ed and going to the doctor in her embarrassment she elected to leave her family. How or why after a number of years she decided to consult a doctor I do not know. I modestly ascribed it to the fact that she heard of my fame. In those days I seldom lost a patient, or had one.

I never met Ed. He did not make the headlines, and Mary never was described as an attractive blonde. The reason is plain to see: Only the parties concerned and myself ever heard of it, and besides, it had no news value. If Ed had bitten a dog it would have been different. If Mary had shot Ed in the back she would have had a chance to show her attractive legs to the jury. The practice of medicine is such a prosy job. A little head work on the part of the doctor may deprive the public of an interesting "human story."

This is still my prize case; it excited my interest, disclosing the possibilities of a surgical practice in relation to domestic difficulties. One seldom sees so clearly the results of his handiwork. Usually one has to be content with little side lights, like the lessened tension in the face of patient. Perhaps years after, the husband may drop in to say that he will always be grateful for service rendered his wife, and that she is a different woman since the operation. I have never had the courage to ask in what way is she different. These are scenes too sacred for a scientific analysis; besides, usually one already knows. Here again one sees that for the most profound things in life there is no language. The only means of communication is human understanding. One does not need to inquire. One has relieved a pain and restored harmony.

Having said this much, I must add a little more. The complaints, remediable by surgical measures, which come between man and wife usually have to do with displacements of the uterus, old lacerations, adhesions, definite physical lesions. The responsibility of the surgeon is great. That the patient has these lesions is no assurance that their correction by operation will end her complaints. The real trouble may be chiefly one of disharmony not due to an organic lesion, and of course an operation then is worse than useless. There is no class of case requiring more judgment on the part of the surgeon. Sometimes I wonder what would happen to us surgeons if the papers would publish wild pitches and passed balls on us.

It has always been a source of interest to me that when a physical affliction comes between a couple there is no hate; on the contrary a very impressive tolerance. This sometimes gives the observant doctor a clue. Physical defects discovered in the course of his examination, and a fine solicitude on the part of the husband, give him a line on how far reaching the difficulty may be.

Family rows are often bid in just as one buys a piece of antique furniture. The husband has gained a certain degree of opulence and the wife can afford a vacation, even if he cannot. The wife takes a prolonged vacation seeking deliberately, it would seem, to find disaster. The husband is left at home to earn the expenses of the trip. If he is a male, perhaps he takes his stenographer to lunch some fine day. The wife has friends, less fortunate than herself, who must stay at home and nurse an envy. This slight indiscretion on the part of her husband is promptly reported to the vacationist. Of course I understand everybody else understands that husbands are prone to become lonesome on slight provocation, but there is no need for one to heap vituperation on a belief everybody has and intends to retain. Even so any husband alone at home is guilty unless he has evidence to prove his innocence. His most common mistake is to fail to look under the icebox for stray bottle caps. Wives taking these long vacations are selfish; being selfish they are introspective, and introspection is the forerunner of jealousy. Most jealous women have their own private tipster. Women friends, so-called, tell the disgruntled one that they would not stand for such goings on. Apparently it is impossible to get really jealous without a willing audience. Then things start. The long, hot summer on the job has not improved the husband's temper, and he is grouchy when his wife returns. Unappeased sex on the part of both is ready to turn to hate at any slight provocation, as for instance the discovery of the aforesaid bottle caps.

For a long time I thought jealous women were strongly sexed, their jealousy being due to a belief they were missing something; sort of the tail end of the concubine idea. Certainly this is not always the case. For instance a nice lady kicks her husband out, and after a time acquires a new one. This new one may really be strongly sexed, and then wife lets out a wail which, if it were not a professional matter, would be exceedingly funny.

A very close friend of mine once experienced a variation of this. His wife started on a prolonged vacation which the husband obviously could not afford. Incidentally, I knew it took his savings of an entire year to finance his wife's trip. To make sure he kept in the straight and narrow path during her absence, she hired a detective to observe his doings. This detective, by chance, was a friend of the husband as well as of myself. After he had received a letter from the wife soliciting his services, he came to see me. He remarked to me that he believed our mutual friend was the soul of honor, and asked my opinion. I assured him that our friend was in ill health, in fact he had tuberculosis, and was scarcely able to meet the demands of his large practice. Even if inclined, he had not the physical ability to be naughty. "Just another fool trying to separate herself from her meal ticket —I will have just nothing to do with her," was the detective's remark.

It turned out to be so in the end, though strangely enough, through uncommon tact and charm this lady retained her husband. It was not until years after, and at her own bidding, that a separation followed. One can hardly imagine anything more contemptible than that. Can a woman be cold as steel, money-mad, and love at the same time? Boy, page Solomon! Besides being inspired, he had a lot of experience. He should know the answer. The uninvited thought comes to mind: What if all of Solomon's seven hundred wives had become jealous at the same time?

One strange case came to my attention. It had to do with a musician, at least he played a bass violin in an orchestra the leader of which was a good friend of mine. He loved that big fiddle and sought to write music for it. This was interesting to me, for it had not occurred to me that there was any music written for that instrument! I had the idea, expressed by Mr. Perlmutter, that the instrument was played with the knees, that the player just took a poke at it when the spirit moved him or the director pointed toward him with his little stick. At any rate, he became so engrossed in the writing of music that sometimes he did not leave his studio for days at a time. One day his wife visited him at his studio and shot him in the back, of course because she loved him so. Now it chanced that this lady, save for the neck, resembled that bass violin in general outline, although the big fiddle had a constriction in the middle. The strange part of it was, let it be repeated, that she shot him for love without going to the trouble of first finding a paramour to become jealous of.

The facts are, of course, that sex hunger had turned at once into hate, giving no time for the customary byplay of finding the other angle of the triangle; and in this case, being a fiddle, it would not have impressed the judge. The jury apparently appreciated her noble sentiment and acquitted her. I suspected this was only the apparent cause of the acquittal, because it was evident that if she had been committed to jail, and a jailor had had to fit her into a jail cot, he would have required the services of a hoisting engineer. The jury just sympathized with the jailor, I opine. The puzzling thing about this case is that she should become jealous of her musical prototype, a bass violin. Had he been a clarinet player it would have been easy to understand. A fat woman prefers a petite woman as the other angle of the triangle, and of course vice versa. Such cases stop in this chapter; no time to allow it to make the next one.

It cannot be too much stressed that a doctor sees a lot of things in the boiling domestic pot that can be fixed. If sense and intelligence instead of sentiment and roses were dispensed at the marriage ceremony, it would make for a better beginning. If the officiating minister were compelled to give post-marital care as we surgeons give postoperative care, he would be less disposed to take offense when we doctors question the holiness of his handiwork. Recently a prominent minister implied that his kind and the sociologists were the proper parties to handle domestic relations. Maybe so, but they talk in general terms and never get down to cases. After the clergy have fixed up a mess, it is up to us doctors to see if we can find out what is wrong. If or when a pot boils over, it doesn't mean that there is necessarily any reason for throwing the whole mess into the alley. Perhaps turning down the fire may help.

To the doctor nothing is so complicated as domestic disharmony. Once it exists, it is difficult to discover the cause. A mean husband may be the innocent party, just as a nagging wife may have been forced into becoming one. To actually get at the facts one needs to find first causes, a thing difficult to do because one finds two irreconcilable opinions. It is only when one has first hand knowledge that the facts can be known from the beginning. I see no way out of it except to allow us doctors to issue the marriage license, marry the couple, and then take charge of the after-course. That would make sense.

But that is a dream. Laws were made by ecclesiastics to

serve ecclesiastic purposes. We were born too soon. How much too soon it is impossible to say. In two thousand years the back wheels spin a few times, the engine back-fires and all is still. But that is enough; there is life in the old cart yet. Following the old inspired prophets got us nowhere, but now people vision the mother and her babe and we are on the way toward a Christian civilization. If we can but get the idea that the highest things in life are exemplified by a child, and that sex, a necessary thing, is inimical to the highest sentiments which the human being is capable of reaching, we will see a new civilization. Then a child will lead us, lead us past the multitude of causes of domestic discord which, small in the beginning, will, if neglected, make a mockery of the home.

X

Paradise Lost (Hell with the Lid Off)

THERE are so many instances in life when a little sense of humor, or the sense of the proportion of things, would save a situation. When a farmer introduces a gentleman and lady cow, at the invitation of the lady, and afterwards the gentleman goes off and eats grass quite disdainful of the lady's charms, the farmer makes a record in his book and calls it a day. The farmer does not say when he introduces the two that the meeting will be for better or worse. He doesn't need to. Having carefully selected his blood lines he knows that it is going to be for the better. Just because Ferdinand goes off into the south pasture in a pout the farmer does not have a moral fit and call it a divorce. He knows he will be back for the same reason that he was present in the first place.

The human race varies this procedure in several ways. The most veritable scrubs are allowed to come together, no matter how impossible the combination; and it is believed that by a certain ceremony it is possible that something "better" may result, even though such a hope has not a particle of fact to sustain it. In the second place, when the male goes off to eat grass, society records a divorce despite the fact that he would be back if given time. Despite the closeness of the two problems, nobody laughs. It is regarded as a moral affair when humans are involved and hence to be deplored. The real difference is that the stock breeder uses intelligence in his proceedings because he knows he must. If he did not, his dairy cows would be producing about two quarts of milk a day. The humans receive no attention whatever from persons of intelligence. All they get is an assurance that it is now all right. The study of the truth is unpleasant business, unless of course one is trained in the dealing with it—and no one dealing with the divorce problem is.

Most people are careless in the use of words. Generally speaking, by divorce is meant the breaking of the marriage vows, which in turn means that husband and wife become again legally single. The word may represent a variety of concepts. Suppose a patient comes to a doctor and complains that he has an eruption. That is quite specific in the mind of the patient—he thinks he has made a diagnosis—but to the doctor, until he has inspected the lesion, it may mean anything between a sunburn and the dreaded pemphigus.

Likewise, when you say "divorce" to a doctor, he thinks that possibly two persons attended a night club, and awakening with a headache in the morning, concluded that they did not like it. Whether or not a little mumbled ceremony preceded the honeymoon does not alter in the least the biological nature of the transaction. If a doctor looks at his case-book he finds every gradation of biological conflict, but it is a biologic problem from beginning to end just the same. Many degrees of preliminary disturbance follow, but they form an unending set of curves of sex urge and sex satiety. The fundamental factors have been discussed in a previous chapter but a repetition, at least a restatement, in this place is unavoidable.

A learned judge tells me that nine-tenths of the divorces which appear in his court are simple problems in biology, that the doings of the parties are hardly to be considered those of serious human beings with a moral sense. As previously noted, dissension in well regulated homes may continue for years without an explosion, chiefly because there is a sense of moral obligation somewhere in the background. Because the fireworks are not set off by diverse and sundry relatives and friends, the integrity of the union is somehow preserved on the surface. Only in rare instances does the idea of divorce originate in one mind. Some accessory before the act must act as detonator. These persons are called friends of the plaintiff.

However not all marriages are primarily biologic. Real tragedies come when a noble sentiment has once existed between the parties but through some misadventure has gone on the rocks. Here one may be free to admit that what God has joined together somebody has mussed up. But to apply this view to the great majority of divorce cases would clearly be a waste of sentiment. If we gave more heed to what constitutes marriage before the act is committed, many would pause before taking the fatal step. If people considered carefully what it means to live together, what it implies, what must follow in the way of give and take, they would be more careful to consider the rights of each other.

It cannot be too strongly emphasized that even though we look on marriage as a sentimental affair, divorce is anything but sentimental. If marriage ceased to be regarded as a face-licking journey, and people thought their way through before facing the license clerk, there would be less need for divorce. Imagine what would happen if the three learned professions could get together before a license is granted, and make it mandatory that the couple look at the facts in the case. Much could be accomplished. It would be discovered that marriage, and equally divorce, is very much a biological process, and that saying it is not, does not change the facts in the least.

First of all, it would be discovered that what the officiating person may say cuts small ice in the end. Unless the young pair bring some spiritual understanding to the altar, all the clergy in the world cannot put any there. Strange that that profession allegedly most concerned in our spiritual welfare seems wholly to ignore that phase when approached by persons with a marriage license. Also, if the legal profession would see to it that laws are made looking to the ultimate good of the parties, and made moron proof, much might be accomplished. Perhaps if the other two professions associated with doctors they might discover: a) that we view the situation as what it is, biological; and b) that we gather facts and follow them according to the rules of scientific thinking. Honest consideration of the problem in all its phases would prevent most of our divorces. I said honest consideration.

But instead of giving careful consideration to the facts,

we tear our hair out by the handfuls and wail that our high divorce rate is a disgrace to our civilization. It is not the high percentage of divorces to marriages, primarily, that makes it so. The disgrace lies in our complacent, indifferent attitude toward divorce as such, as well as toward marriage. We insist on disregarding the fact that marriage is in large part and in most instances a sex transaction. Our ceremonies make it so.

Just take a look at the history of divorce. For a long time adultery was the only reason for breaking the marriage ties. In other words sex was the only factor. Some one, it was assumed, was being cheated of "its" share of something and had a right to holler. It was overlooked that when recognized concubines were wiped off the social register there was bound to be a strain on the social order. The solidity of the marriage state was dependent only on one thing: fidelity. The wife might stick pins in papa years on end, and it was all right. If he kept in contact with his pants only by the aid of shingle nails, that was all right too. On the other hand papa might beat up mama as much as he pleased so long as it did not disturb the neighbors, and it also was all right.

Now of course we have gone to the other extreme, and the meaningless word "incompatibility" makes it possible for one or the other to call for a new deal without the necessity of bothering about facts. The old doctor, when he was unable to make a diagnosis, which was generally, stated that the patient suffered from a complication of diseases, and everybody was satisfied. No one thought of asking him what it was a complication of. The same thing is true in the case of "incompatibility" in divorce cases. No one inquires about the factors which go to make up the allegedly aggrieved state.

We will never get any place until we classify divorces as we do skin eruptions. I deny any attempt to be facetious when I propose that a division of the types of marriages into groups might be of help. In clinical medicine it is common to divide the degrees of severity of a disease into groups of one to four. For instance a pathologist says to a

R

surgeon: "Cancer type iv," and they have a common understanding; even though it lacks exactness it is a help to the
surgeon in making his prognosis, that is in helping him to
predict the future course of the disease.

Group one, we may classify as cases of love at first sight.
Met at a night club, public dance, both slightly inebriated.
These should not be classified as marriages and will not be
as soon as an attempt is made to find out the difference
between marriage and the doings of the red light district.

Group two: parties sober but met as strangers and just
automatically liked each other's shape. For instance, a young
lady has lost her taste for toil. She deliberately sallies forth
bent on finding a meal ticket. Such matches succeed in a sur-
prising number of instances, because young ladies clever
enough to make such conquests know that a fish, even when
caught, must be kept in a domestic tub of water and occasionally fed worms, or whatever the original bait consisted
of—maybe just tin flies, gorgeously painted.

In group three, we may include the young people of high
moral standards, who have met often enough at social gatherings to develop mutual affection. But if the parties concerned are of such hopelessly different types, ethically and
economically, that a happy married life would need to be
recorded as a great moral achievement, some sort of fence
needs to be built about them until they can work out an
economic and social adjustment—that is, until they discover
which is the boss. Of course, usually this works out so that
the lady is the boss but the gentleman thinks he is, and in
this relationship they may do very well. If some one, during
this period of adjustment, drops a monkey wrench into the
machinery, it calls for the services of a mechanic, and not
for a wrecker.

Group four comprises young people of like tastes and like
breeding, who through contact with each other in church
basements, schools or business, have learned to respect the
rights of others in general and of their future mates in particular. In other words, they instinctively have learned the
fundamental factor in a happy wedded life is to treat the

mate after the wedding with the same respect as before. With this background they discuss the problems of life together, particularly the economic and sexual phases. These people have a good chance to have an enduring marriage because they recognize that, despite the spiritual side, it is still a biologic problem that must be solved as such.

Any intelligent person could group couples as they approach the marriage clerk with a great deal of accuracy according to this scheme. With such a basis of classification, it would be possible to develop a divorce percentage that would have some sense. A percentage could be worked out for each group.

Those who howl for adequate medical care belong to the same category as those who now cry out against the divorce evil. The reformers overlook the fact that the purpose of medical care is achieved when the patient gets what he needs. This may require the single glance of a good doctor, or a prolonged study by a group of specialists. So with divorce. Let it be repeated, that despite the wailing and gnashing of teeth over the divorce problem no one has ever really studied either its beginning, end result, or after-course. A single glance at a domestic row may disclose the whole situation, or the most profound study may leave us puzzled. The great trouble is that in order to lift up, it is necessary to get underneath any social ill. Like lifting an injured person from a wrecked automobile, or raising a drunk from the gutter, it is such messy business. The solution of the divorce problem requires personal contact, understanding, and above all an abiding wish to help, all things which do not lend themselves to remote control.

Warring couples are but children floating down the stream of life. They are angry with each other, and one can do little with an angry child. A cooling off process is the first requisite. Perhaps all that is needed is that, as previously indicated, Ferdinand needs a little time to think things over down in the south pasture. The point is that a warring couple are incapable of helping themselves. That is society's job; yet nobody does anything about it.

I remarked above that one of the two fundamental causes of divorce is marriage. Even this would not be so bad if the parties did not try to live together. This at first blush may sound silly, but it is not. It cannot be emphasized too often that marriage is not a private affair between two persons; it is a matter of public concern. Impecunious persons marry and become public charges the next day. Anyone with half an eye can see that we are rapidly becoming a nation of dependent morons, with only sense enough to make trouble if adequately led. This being the case, the public has a right to know before a couple marries what the outcome is likely to be. A little exercise of common sense here would work wonders. Not a chance. Here comes the archaic idea of a "right." Of what that right consists, I have discussed elsewhere. However nobody has a right to do anything that is going to wreck our social order. If a man wants to build a woodshed costing thirty dollars, he must secure a building permit; but to be married requires nothing. Nothing but a slip of paper costing two dollars. All else can be done on credit.

The necessary corollary to marriage as a fundamental cause of divorce is the possibility of securing a divorce. Young people marry knowing that if they do not like it they can call for a new deal. People starting with that idea in mind most certainly will need it. The desire for domestic relief is one thing, but the possibility of securing it is quite another factor. Those of us who knew the old pioneers and how they struggled uncomplainingly against adversity, have a suspicion that the reason so many people are now on "relief" is the possibility of getting on, nay more, the invitation to get on and stay on, at least until after the next election. This statement does not imply a breach of confidence because everybody admits it.

In the old day there was no relief from poverty, even starvation, and being none, no one wasted time seeking it. In those days the old saw of "Root hog or die" was no figure of speech. If no such thing as divorce were possible, there would be less thought of it, less thought of recourse to it, naturally. That of course sounds silly. Just play everything underneath is lovely and it will be so, that is the idea. If one cannot get out he stays in, and he spends little time considering ways and means of escape. I once heard an ex-army man give advice to some newly enlisted men as to how to get along in the army. "The only way," he said, "is to obey orders and to conclude you like it." This attitude he opined was dictated by the fact that you cannot get out and you had the choice of obeying orders or going to the guardhouse. There are no such rigid rules applying to married persons. Anyone who concludes that for the moment he does not like it can get out. Suppose every soldier, when he at some time or other considers his environment not to his liking, could get out of our army just by saying it was "incompatible to him." As it is said of the Mexican army, it would be made up of a few morons and the officers.

This reminds me that my foster grandparents were killed by a young man aged only twenty-three. The officers found the stolen money, and some cartridges that fitted the murder weapon, in a young man's pocket. His shoes fitted the tracks the murderer made, and he admitted the deed. The crude justice of that day was brief. The judge believed what the prisoner told him, in view of the supporting evidence, and just pointed his thumb toward the penitentiary on the hill and said: "From now on."

This institution is located in my home town, and I was curious enough to go out once in a while to see how he liked it. The prisoner lived there almost exactly fifty years. I concluded that he accepted conditions as he found them because he could not get out. I saw him last when he was nearly seventy years of age, a serene old man with a faraway look, indicating that things were not ideal. Although apparently it did not suit his taste, evidently he had made up his mind to like it, even though his fingers were crossed when he thought of it.

The point, of course, is that that man should have done a little thinking before he shot the old folks. We doctors learn to recognize that far-away look I saw in the old prisoner's eyes whenever we see it in our patients, which we do many times; but nobody mentions it. I have seen that unmistakable far-away look in hundreds of women's eyes and in many men's. There is something that just is tolerated because it never occurs to them that it is intolerable.

It is well to look at all phases of the divorce problem. A number of religious denominations, including the one in which I grew up, do not permit divorce. In order to enforce this dictum it is necessary to instill thoroughly in the very young mind that such is the law. This means that the children, as infants, learn that they will be required to marry within the church. The obligations should apply to both. If our young people are under obligation to the church, the church should be under obligation to the young people. Therefore the church attending to the ceremony should feel some responsibility for the nature of the union, and refuse to perform it when it is obvious to anyone, at least to any doctor, that the outcome is bound to be unhappy. People forget that we must live on this earth before we achieve heaven, and our concern should be with things in that order.

The unhappy phase is that religion and intelligence may be divergent, that the most ignorant and those economically the poorest are not subject to any law. All they remembered of the old dictum was that it was their duty to raise as many children as possible. We must admit that this did much to prevent obvious domestic discord. I have never yet known a woman with ten or more children to seek a divorce. The reasons are many, and all obvious.

However the fact must be recognized that things do change. The more independently minded may figure out things differently. The most notable change is found in the matter of the number of offspring. The church says, or at least did until recently, "Produce a-plenty." Like it or not, denominational lines give way before the changing notions of women. This reminds me of the expression used by an old neighbor when I was a boy, anent a different problem: "When Ma has spoke, she has spoke." That just about explains everything, at least so far as we poor males are concerned.

To make it impossible for married couples to escape is of course not the ideal answer. Marriage then is likely to settle down to the simple routine of the barnyard. For a marriage, even to approximate the idea, the partners must regard their state as an ideal one. I pointed out that on the farm, those animals which had no desire to wander about required the least fencing.

An egg not exactly prime might seem better than no breakfast at all. There might be food for thought in the idea of not permitting remarriage in cases in which separation is inevitable. The judge, emulating the one who sentenced the murderer of the old couple, might say: "If I grant you a pardon it will be a large package, large enough to last from now on, meaning that henceforth you do not shoot any other single party." We are told, when this scheme is suggested, that this would lead to immorality or promiscuity on the part of the separated person or persons.

Well, what of it? Immorality is no less immorality because it is covered by fine linen and tinctured with the essence of orange blossoms. Would it not be just too bad if "liberated" persons should be naughty. We may spare ourselves a too close examination into the meaning of words. Those denominations which allow only the "innocent" party to remarry penalize one party. I have been confronted by some cheerful liars when an innocent party is seeking to prove his right to remarry. Slipping a handful of cockleburrs under a saddle blanket of a pony is the work of no "innocent" party. We lose sight of this little playful act when the broncho bucks and throws the rider into the next county. He obviously is the guilty party. Sure, he is the guilty party —that is until the unseated rider finds out who slipped over the cockleburrs. Still, one never can tell; perhaps somewhere, some time there was an innocent party; how else would the idea that there is have originated?

In a previous chapter I discussed the various wranglings which go to make up the average home, and in another chapter the more pronounced differences which still are compatible with the retention of the married state. One or the other of the couple must have seasons of more or less sanity if such states are to endure. I once heard an old codger present a solution of the divorce problem by saying that if only one party at a time got mad there would be no divorces. But once hate and anger move in, of course both are mad which causes reason to fly out the window; then there is danger ahead. Even at this stage when the union is threatened, or separation is actually sought, the exercise of intelligence applied from without might result in much good. The judicious use of bromides or ice caps applied to where they would do the most good would help, if only as a play for time.

Imagine where surgery would be if we operated on a patient just because he says he is sick, without any inquiry as to whether he really is sick, or as to how he came to be sick, and then forgot him as soon as the wound was sutured. Suppose the surgeon should point to his crown and say: "I am a holy guy, so whenever I do anything or whatever I do it is all right." Nothing like it; the surgeon inquires daily as to whether or not the wound he made is healing, and furthermore he inquires how the patient got along after the wound had apparently healed. The reason the surgeon is self-critical is because if he does not criticize himself his patient will, and besides may sue him for malpractice.

If those who "operate" on the future of young people were subject to criticism and suits for malpractice, they would do as we doctors do, spend long hours in the study of the process of wound healing before reaching for the knife.

If the results are not satisfactory to the young couple they call for a new deal. But do not blame the judge who gives it to them. The laws he must follow are made by a bunch of track laborers facetiously called legislators. If a man or woman conclude they do not like their marriage, the judge hears that he and she are "incompatible." More loose talk. When the big word is used it is supposed that they do not check with each other. Quite as often, I am sure, they are simply mad at themselves, and each other, and the other partner is only the accessory after the act, and was innocent before the fight started. Of course the contending pair cannot remember such a big word, so one or the other goes to a properly qualified person, designated as attorney for the plaintiff, who writes it down on a piece of paper and takes it to the judge. No one, contending parties, attorney for the plaintiff, or the judge, know the meaning of the word as applied to any particular instance, but that makes no difference. The law says it is all that is needed.

Even if judges do not make the laws they might do as we doctors do, and stop to ask, when confronted by someone suffering from "incompatibility": "Who said that? Who caused what we are about to operate on and why?" But the judge, being trained in the law, is not supposed to know anything and so the legislature puts a number of words into a specific attorney's mouth. The judge must start with the assumption that in the first place some vulgar persons have committed a great sin or there would be no need for his service. What is presented he sees as a reeking ulcer. What caused it? Did someone deliberately plaster a cancer paste onto someone else? What seems to be an ulcer may be only dirt under the bandage, which soap and water will remove. Said sin, or cancer, denuded of all dressing, may not look so bad. The judge, representing the legislature, assumes that the holy bonds have been kicked into the discard. The doctor would ask: "Who said holy?" He may have been only a conceited old liar, his holy state being just an idea of his own; some self-appointed guardian of the fates, in other words. Suppose he had to take an examination before the National Board to prove that he is qualified to do a holy operation. Maybe he does, but he is not required by the state to take an examination before an impartial board as we doctors do.

But suppose the ceremony to have been honest, if anyone can imagine that. The person officiating would have said something like this: "Children, I am about to commit a questionable piece of business. Forget what I say and when or if you recover your sanity, just remember this: A precious

thing is handed you for better or worse, get those words, and
it is for you to say which. It will be a lifetime job requiring
all the intelligence and forbearance both of you can command. It will be a foot race between the gods and the devil
from now on. The rights of this pagan stuff I handed you is a
delusion and a snare. Of all things, do not forget that little
peck over the garden gate; that is and always will be, the
most eloquent word the fates speak to man. In comparison
with that, the words I have just mumbled are incompetent,
irrelevant and immaterial and tend to fog the issue."

But I do not blame the officiating person. He has been
handed a set of instructions, as the judge is, formulated by
persons probably long since returned to clay. Not long ago
one of my best friends lamented the fact that he had officiated
in uniting a sweet little girl to a young man whose family
history caused one to believe he belonged to the human race;
she died trying to emulate the cats—nine children in ten
years. The clergyman asked: "What could I have done?"
evidently as a rhetorical question, but I took the cue. I replied that nothing could be done because the woman was
dead. But his profession could do much if they collectively
brought it about so that we doctors would be given a chance.
We know what killed the woman.

It would seem to me that the commandments are not
specific enough. It should say: "Thou shalt not kill, neither
slowly nor rapidly." The civil legislators might take the cue
and legislate likewise, with perhaps an added codicil, or
whatever it is legislators hang on as an afterthought, making
mandatory in such cases a public execution, if not of the
entire man at least of a part of him. This idea is my own. I
am sure no one but a smart doctor would ever have thought
of it, and he only because he has been compelled so often to
sit in on the kill.

Think of the wailing and gnashing of teeth the modern
inspired persons indulge in over the situation in which society finds itself. Yet they put forth but little or no effort to
assemble facts, always the forerunners of efficient prevention.
Sure, societies are busily engaged in solving the problem.

They send out silly cards, as noted in a previous chapter, and delude themselves into the belief that they are finding out something.

They remind me of the old time surgeon who, when he approached an operation, just put his high hat on the table and proceeded with his work. He did not trouble even to take off his long coat. Of course all wounds suppurated and most patients died. He was doing things according to the rules and he was not disturbed when the disasters of suppuration continued. He was perfectly complacent in his ignorance. Comes Pasteur, saying the suppuration is caused by bacteria, and Lister, showing surgeons how to keep the little pests out of the wound. Did the surgeons hail the new idea with delight? They did not. They declared most vehemently that it was all nonsense. It is human nature to be attached to the fool things we do. Is society likely to look upon marriage and divorce as a public problem? Not until the women get through working on the clergy and the legislators.

We doctors, if handed the responsibility of solving the divorce problem, would not send out cards. We would follow the histories of a lot of divorced persons in our case-books and establish concrete facts, in order to try to determine first the cause, then the aftercourse. Starting with persons who had taken the step toward better or worse, we would inquire into the premonitory signs. By this means, disturbances which occurred before the patient himself recognized that he was sick would be discovered. "When did you first feel that you were in love? Were there any digestive disturbances or loss of sleep? What did you first notice in the object of your affection—was it some cleverness on her part, or was it her cute shape? Did you have any preliminary fights while you were adjusting yourself before or after marriage? When did you first get the idea that she was the one and only? Did you at that time make a mental calculation comparing her shape with her mother's?" The girl I would ask only one question, to wit: "How high did the water splash when you fell in?"

When divorce impends, one would inquire who first verbally kicked the other in the face. "When did you get the idea that you would be better off if the thing had never happened in the first place? When did you first hear the word 'incompatibility,' and when did you first suspect it was affecting your stomach?" and a lot of other pertinent questions. "In the second place," one would need to inquire, "have you seen an incompatibility pill, which you will be required to take, and calculated its diameter and compared the diameter of your esophagus with that of the pill? Suppose it should get stuck and you could not quite get it down, or up? Suppose it should stick and taste worse than you expected?"

Then we would hand them a list of previous cases, indicating what happened to them after they got the incompatibility pill down. Did they feel as free and easy as they expected? Have they had moments when they wished they had less freedom and more of the incompatible companionship? Careful inquiry would show that all they got was freedom according to the law in the Judge's book. What the judge hands out is not guarantee to blot out the memory of the past. If people spent more time in preliminary consideration of these things, there would be less wailing in retrospect after the pill is swallowed.

Careful perusal of a series of reports of this sort would cause those looking over the brink to pause for a second, and would do more good than all the weeping and arm-waving of those who know nothing about it and haven't the remotest intention of soiling their hands in order to find out what the facts may be. But no one would study such things voluntarily. It would be necessary to confine them until they studied the cases, and to make them take an examination before they were released in order to determine if they had really studied them.

Suppose, if such a thing were possible, that the men who make the laws should assume that judges, being versed in the law, and being courageous, honest men, were capable of handling cases before them according to their merits, untrammeled by rigid rules. It is easy to suppose that such a judge would ask himself when a person came to him for an operation for relief from the marital bonds: "What will be the ultimate outcome of the operation?" Suppose he would pull out the record and say: "Here, you poor deluded fool, is the end result of the last thousand cases I have operated on. Look here—what I wrote down as a new freedom turned out to be only a delusion. They burned up the highway in their haste to do an even more foolish thing." A new alliance. Quite likely the prospective "patient" would say: "Gosh, they are about all failures, the last sometimes worse than the preceding one. It looks as if once one takes the plunge there is no turning back, law or no law. It looks as if even though marriage is a failure, divorce is an even greater one. I believe I will try bromides a while longer."

Thus, if judge and doctor would collaborate in assembling the statistics, a set of facts could be gathered so it would be possible to say in which cases bromides should be given and in which six months' separation should be prescribed. Such careful study would allow doctor and judge, collaborating, to cure nearly all cases of incompatibility without the use of drastic "incompatible" pills. Divorce is a problem in civil and biologic law. The clergy slip the cockleburrs under the saddle blanket, perfume themselves, and depart. Even if we assume marriages are made in heaven, divorces, and those which break down but do not end in divorce, should be put down as wrong diagnoses on the part of those who acted as intermediaries, and they should shoulder the responsibility. They would discover that when they assume that all marriages are made in heaven they are taking in too much territory.

I am not indulging in a figure of speech when I say I can go to my case records and bring out concrete examples. I cannot, as the newspapers do, escape responsibility by saying, "It is alleged." The law specifically states that the doctor may say nothing about his patient to any one whatsoever without a written consent; whether it is true or not true makes no difference. Therefore I must indulge in fiction. Suppose John Doe found that he was free, tore down the alley and fell over a grass widow and bumped his head. When he recovers consciousness he complains of his stomach, because brain concussion usually produces nausea. So I operate on him for a stomach ulcer. The operation does no good because there is no ulcer there.

Or say Mrs. Doe got the wrong number and kicks out Mr. Doe; then thinks it over and concludes that he was better than none. When she thinks of these things she often gets a backache. I do a nice repair job and shorten the ligaments. Nice operation, but it does no good, because the trouble was a pain in the head owing to the fact that she was thinking that perhaps Mr. Doe was not such a bad sort of person after all. The operation was successful, but the patient remains sick.

Unfortunately, even to a doctor, the whole picture of a daily ruckus is seldom set before him ready labeled. But he meets many things in a professional capacity which are connected in one way or another with the past history of the patients. What he lacks in evidence in a concrete case, he may possibly piece together from previous experiences, and then come to an accurate conclusion.

He might remember for instance, that the aggrieved person's mother had an awful time getting a halter on daughter's young man in the first place. And he, when he found out about the joker the mother-in-law pulled on him, was peeved. Yet the doctor might discover on closer inspection that the patient isn't a bad sort, just a fool like her mother. Perhaps also the husband, after due deliberation, will come to the conclusion that women are peculiar, especially some of them, but that you can't get along without them and that, after all, he had held still while the halter was being adjusted. Perhaps if the doctor will apply a little ointment on the spot where he thinks the halter rubs the worst he will gradually forget about it, and perhaps at some social gathering he will burst forth with a confidential account of what a hard time he had winning his wife and how she made him. So perhaps a spinal brace, to be worn for twenty or thirty years, may help him a lot. But if the doctor operates on his patient for an imaginary ill, he will collapse from softening of the spine, which was his trouble in the first place, and will be worse off than before.

As a corollary, we may suppose he beats up his darling, verbally or otherwise, because she nags him. Even so one must remember how much a tin can tied to the tail of a dog accelerates his speed. That many wives "make" their husbands is no idle joke. When a man gets so mad he can't sleep, if he will put in the wakeful moments in gainful toil he may achieve something, and having reached the heights he may point to his wife, as I said before, and say: "She made me" and there will be loud cheering by the multitude. He does not liken her to the can on the dog's tail. Men are so gallant, or dumb, or liars.

That is just a concrete example, slightly facetious of course, of how a doctor would go about solving a given problem. Few domestic situations are as bad as the interested pair think when they are mad. If some one will distract their attention until they cool off, a lot of trouble can be averted; sometimes it takes only a little tactful lying. The direction strained domestic relations will take sometimes depends on surprisingly trivial matters, as often as not on a misinterpretation of facts.

A doctor does not kill his patients just because they are sick. A tactful doctor sometimes senses the cause of a strain between a pair, and maybe by a little judicious lying places a different light on the whole trend of affairs without their even suspicioning that he knows there is trouble at home. He pretends to pay no attention to what the husband says about the pain in his neck, nor to the lady when she implies that papa is not the burden-bearer he once was. She tells the doctor this by simply mentioning that she finds the housework so much more burdensome to do than formerly, whereupon he suggests some electric equipment to lessen the labor.

The point is that while we doctors often see an ailment which we know cannot be cured, we can do something to make life more bearable until somebody dies, of his own accord of course, or until both forget about their complaint. I would hate very much for any one to know how many

women have taken my pills simply and solely because they
do not like the shape of papa's face. I save a family break and
save human suffering thereby, and that after all is the doctor's chief job. One always has the assurance, when treating
such cases, that family squabbles, like rheumatism, tend to
reach a chronic form when the suffering lessens, and may
even, as noted elsewhere, be really a source of diversion or
enjoyment.

How little the public understands family relationships is
easily appreciated when we note that to everyone divorce
means the breaking of domestic relations. But once children
have been born to the pair separation is no longer possible
in a spiritual sense. The children represent a part of the
marriage contract which cannot be terminated by the judge
or anyone else. This being the important factor, the question
of divorce should begin with their welfare. No divorce should
be granted until it has been determined that it will react to
their good, which it must be admitted is sometimes the case.

In order to decide what is best for the children, a close
examination of all the factors is imperative. If a jury trial is
more apt to result in a just verdict than trial before a judge,
that should be the method of procedure. But I believe a
judge trained in the law is better able to arrive at a just conclusion than is a jury. I think this because in another case
where technical knowledge is desirable, that is in trials for
sanity, a specialist in mental diseases is better able to arrive
at a just decision than any number of persons with no knowledge of mental diseases.

It sometimes takes a week or two to try a person accused
of murder, even after the criminal has confessed all the
sordid details, but has changed his mind on advice of counsel. The attorney for the defendant resorts to every means
possible to prove to the accused that he was somewhere else
at the time of the murder. To one ignorant of the law this
maneuver looks like an attempt to defeat justice. Why this
zeal to prove to the accused—who has confessed his guilt—
that he was wrong? A few sometimes—forbid the thought—
may see a fee. Sometimes possibly it is professional pride, if

one can call it that, like wagering one's shirt in a poker game. Too often we see an inexperienced county attorney pitted against the ablest criminal lawyers, an altogether unequal contest. Even when twelve tried men and true have declared the defendant guilty, the battle continues to free the defendant, seemingly only because he does not like being in prison. All else failing there is the pardon board, the enemy of all law enforcement agencies, and the governor, to turn the prisoner loose on society again. An honest criminal it seems cannot convict himself, so long as he has money.

Contrast this with the three minutes required to dispose of a divorce action. A few tears by the wronged party, the ever present weeping female friend, a little corroborating evidence of domestic malfeasance, and the wronged party is freed. In most instances it would properly take a battery of wise men representing several professions to determine which is the innocent party, if there be such, and in most instances there is not.

The public is wholly indifferent to individual cases of divorce. The statistics are viewed with horror. If we doctors shut our eyes against the truth just because doing autopsies is a messy business and the specimens we handle stink, we would still be wailing in the wilderness of ignorance facetiously labeled "belief." But society closes its eyes and we doctors hold the sack.

We know that if love ever has been present it may hibernate endless years, but it does not die; it lives to haunt the memory of those who have once felt it. Hate may chase it away while anger lasts, but it comes back. Long divorced persons develop a peculiar facial expression which a doctor can identify as grief. I once heard a woman wail that if she had done her part as well as George did in the early years there would have been no trouble, and yet she used to go home and tell the children what a reprobate their father was. After the children are grown up and gone these women become a problem for the doctor.

In a previous chapter I have considered instances of turmoil in the domestic set-up which might very readily have

S

resulted in divorce, save for the fact that at the time the person was not divorce-minded. In the next chapter I shall discuss more fully the regret most divorced persons feel after they have thought the matter over on the basis of the cold facts of reality. "Why did I do it?" the doctor hears.

Persons do not realize early enough that the tendency of their thoughts, if allowed to go on unhindered, will lead to divorce. Even so, in that early stage divorce spells to them freedom from what, in their anger, seems like the bonds of matrimony. Few people in the beginning, before anger replaces reason, figure through what divorce means in all its phases. As a matter of fact they have no background on which to base any reasoning, even though they had the brains to do so.

The social workers who specialize in the divorce problem are a queer lot. Many fine people are engaged in it, but a doctor may see some queer things crop out, sometimes a sort of defense reaction. Most of them are persons who for obvious reasons will never be confronted by a personal divorce problem. Perhaps their crusading is a counter irritant, a sticking out of tongues across the alley fence. There are unfortunates, cerebral hermaphrodites sprinkled in, who cannot escape the watchful eye of the doctor. We are just beginning to see that many of the reformers are themselves problems for the doctor and would be for the judge, if they could maneuver themselves into a position to have a husband to dispossess themselves of. Sour grapes.

A case in point: One of the most ardent social workers in the campaign against divorce I have ever known was a nymphomaniac and in consequence a persistent nagger, on the surface a sweet, gentle little lady; at heart a pronounced pagan greatly horrified by our divorce problem. Consciously, or most likely unconsciously, she labored to prevent her sisters, who were actually suffering, from throwing away what little sense they had in a vain attempt to remedy their troubles. At the age of fifty-two, her husband took his own life because of temporary insanity superinduced by ill health, so it was stated in the newspapers. His own doctor was, and is, the only person in the world who knew that he did not die a natural death. Of course the doctor had to lie.

I may remark as an aside that the attempt to gloss over the event by assuming that the dead person took his own life "while temporarily insane" is the bunk. If he died that way, most likely he was permanently insane. That sanity would have returned had he not committed his rash act is mere assumption, unlikely if the causative factor is confirmed. Careful study in some cases compels one to believe that the unfortunate person was the least crazy of the whole pack.

But to get on with the story: Of course he was sick. I had urged him in the name of all that was good and holy to buy himself one one-way ticket to South America. If divorce was too horrible to contemplate, just disappear, I urged. He chose the easy way out. I had fed him bromides for ten years. He would come into my office holding his head between his hands, wailing: "Doctor, I do not see how I can stand it any longer." I had no idea what he had in mind. I should have known but those are things one does not learn from books, but from experience. The scene at the garden gate never lost its hold upon him; she had never seen it. It was a good match—in the beginning. He was very well to do and a successful business man, and she remained a charming little woman, to outsiders. And he never ceased to love that refined, beautiful, nagging hag. She never batted an eye at his passing. For many years I had a strong desire to tell her the cause of her husband's death, but now I am glad I did not. There was more to the story than I understood, and no doubt more than I understand now, although I am beginning to see a light.

She was a reformer, had formed an antidivorce league, in fact, as I mentioned before. She was a slender woman and perhaps she was dieting and what was really wrong was that she was eating too little sugar in order to maintain that figure of which she was obviously proud. Perhaps she was a case of hyperinsulinism, as doctors now say. It would sound silly should I say, "If you find yourself chronically mad at your husband, go have your blood sugar determined. If more sugar is needed, eat it." Women, many of them, cling desperately to their slim figures; yet if they will look about them they can see that if they will take on a pound at a time, as they must, their husbands don't mind. There is no limit to the amount of avoirdupois a husband can continue to love. I cannot help but speculate on what would have happened if the lady in my story had doubled her weight. At any rate I am glad I did not tell her that she was the direct cause of her husband's death. Perhaps it was simply a matter of too little sugar in her diet.

It certainly will be interesting to future generations to learn how much the chemical laboratory will do toward solving the divorce problem. I have mentioned that perhaps the first step toward domestic discord is the half baked biscuit. It would be interesting if we should demonstrate that domestic tension is actually due to a deficient sugar intake. It would really be funny if it should turn out that when the young swain called the little lady "my sugar lump," he was really anticipating by centuries the revelations of chemistry.

Before contemplating divorce, the aggrieved party should consider the problem from all angles. We say divorce is a breaking of the marriage vows. Divested of flowers and fine linen, exactly what is marriage? What is it that is broken? That marriages are made in heaven, I was told, was Tennyson's idea. Did he make this observation before marriage or after? Literature is silent on that point; perhaps he believed it; perhaps he was right, just as countless husbands today will attest with enthusiasm to the same idea, even though they be wrong.

Also, the couple is united by the holy bonds of matrimony. I have been unable to find who first promulgated this idea of holiness. It would be a great joke if holiness should turn out to be a matter of physical chemistry.

Even now one may ask: Just what is it that qualifies any person to perform the holy office? How do they get that way? What first gave them the idea that they were called to the holy office? When were marriages first discovered to be holy? Unfortunately Solomon is silent on that point. Perhaps not

all cases turned out alike so even he was a bit uncertain.
Divested of hokum it may prove to be merely an excuse for
the continuation of paganism.

Don't get me wrong. I am not a sacrilegious person but a
scientist, and as such must look at facts, like it or not. God
made facts. Scientists only try to discover more of them and
then to put them together and see what they spell. I believe
it is time for scientists to recognize that they must ignore
civil and ecclesiastic law and tackle the problem of divorce
in an unbiased manner, just as we do any other cause of
suffering. I have been fearful throughout the writing of this
book lest I blurt out that religion has caused more human
hurts than it has ever alleviated. If I should say such a thing
I would be misunderstood, misunderstood because, being a
doctor, my life has been devoted to the alleviation of human
suffering, and no one would understand the mutterings of
such a person.

We may start with this premise: Marriage is what one
makes it. I feel about this subject as I did when I stood at a
distance looking in awe and admiration at the great Klebs,
after his achievement in discovering the cause of diphtheria.
There he was, a serene old man who had devoted his life and
great intellect to the preservation of human life and the
alleviation of suffering, and to the pursuit of truth. Perhaps
we will some day look at physical chemists and say: "Those
are the fellows who cured divorce." Then Tennyson can
say: "I told you so." Where are the laws of chemistry made?

See how simply we doctors proceed. I have mentioned
diphtheria and the man who solved it. Take another example: After it was discovered that goiters could be removed by
operation, it was easy to admit that medicines did not cure
them. For centuries there had been remedies which were
believed to be effective. Yet any one with half an eye should
have known that they were not. Yet doctors, like the rest of
the human race, believe in what they do if they know of
nothing better. On the face of it, it is ridiculous; but it is
true.

The problem of what to do about goiters arose because

medicines did no good. That being determined, the next question was: why not remove the offending thing? Of course this did not occur to us until it was discovered it could be done. But here we had another pill to swallow. When goiters were first operated on, it was believed that the whole gland must not be removed or dire consequences would result. Old man belief stayed the hand of the surgeon. Came a time when a surgeon inquired: "Who said something terrible would happen if the whole gland were removed?" It became evident it was all just belief, since no one had tried it to see, which is equivalent to saying that it was just a rank assumption. As a consequence, one day a surgeon concluded that those dire predictions rested only on belief. He then proceeded to remove the entire gland. Nothing dire happened, nothing except that the patient was cured. The old boys of large reputations and vigorous tonsils were proved wrong, simply because some one inquired what, if anything, supported the opinions of the old high hats, and finding nothing, proceeded to act. The removal of the entire gland was found to be feasible and advisable in most cases. Here therefore is another example which shows that nothing paralyzes advancement like belief.

Belief, what is it? An excuse for doing what one wants to do, or refraining from doing what one does not want to do. Perhaps most often it is simply a state of self-hypnotism induced because it saves the need of doing anything. Our beliefs are so unstable that they are useless as scientific data. The great difficulty is that we try to make a composite picture instead of studying each event as an entity. We lose sight of the fact that not only our morals, but also our religious beliefs, have developed with the progress of the human race. Why drag an old Model-T type of religion out of the weeds and try to make it run when we can get a V-8, on the easy payment plan?

For instance, it took my grandpa two or three hours to perform a marriage ceremony. It was as painful a job as cranking a Model-T in the winter time. Now much less time is consumed, but why I am unable to find out. I suspect it is because our modern young people have weaker knees, having really never learned to walk. I got the idea early in life. Aunt Lizzie, being a properly reared Mennonite girl, stood resignedly for three hours through the marriage ceremony performed by her papa. But Uncle John, about to be, was a New England Congregationalist and fidgeted scandalously during the ceremony. The shortening of the ceremony probably does not indicate moral degeneracy, but only the advent of the machine age. Nowadays one just pushes on the self-starter according to the manner of the times all along the line.

Since our verbal perambulations have got us nowhere, we can come back to the subject at hand. The divorce rate of this country is regarded as a national disgrace. There can be no doubt of it, but before we throw a fit about it an examination of its meaning by the doctor might be in order. How did we get that way? Who is involved in the scandal of divorce? Does the disgrace devolve upon only the people on whom the light of the public is for the moment focused, or is it a disgrace to a society of which the people involved are but a very small part? Does the prevalence of divorce indicate a higher or a lower civilization? What have our laws got to do with it, what the independence of our women? Is a woman, who rebels against an intolerable beast, of a lower order than one who submits until death do them part? Each case requires a separate analysis, so let us remove the gauze that covers the eyes of the Goddess of Justice and let her take a look around. Perhaps some day the lady will go out and hire herself a chemist.

Our national rate of divorce is the greatest of any nation. Shall we weep or boast? As compared with other nations, we have a number of extenuating circumstances. Our polyglot population brings together in marriage persons wholly unmatched by race, temperament and previous experience. Our women are more intelligent and more independent, and refuse to tolerate the abuses women of more antiquated nations will endure. They prefer not to subject themselves to the slow process of murder just for the purpose of proving the "rights" were holy.

Our women are further removed from paganism than any class of persons, female or male, who have ever lived. They more 'nearly rise above sex. I will anticipate my critics by adding that even if they do not rise above sex they do more commonly refuse to be dominated by it, which amounts to the same thing. What this has to do with the problem at hand requires cautious consideration. To consider this problem may lead me into hazards, but that is nothing new. Every time a surgeon picks up his scalpel he says, in fact, here goes for "better or worse." But remember this: The odds on the better or worse depend on the skill and courage of the operator. The caps and gowns they wear are from the same pile which supplies the cub assistant, but it is what is under the cap that counts.

To solve the hurts of those who worry about divorce as a moral sore some very mundane observations are in order. The longer we boil coffee the stronger it gets, the more caffeine it contains per ounce, and the more likely it is to keep us awake. If I said that our divorce problem is primarily due to the stupidity and moral cowardice of the public in general, it would reek with caffeine; so I have chosen to serve a noncaffeine postum to make the drink less potent. But we can stay away from facts only a little longer by indulging in some more abstract statements. When a couple come to the brink of divorce, romance lies so far behind that they are occupied with very mundane things. The husband commonly has sufficient revenue to make the handling of a divorce case attractive. I was under the impression that a man on a charity roll is much safer from divorce than some one who has, through industry and ingenuity, been able to hide something from the tax collector, but I am told I am wrong. If the husband is on the charity roll, the wife can kick him out and get on the same roll. There is equality. A woman is usually not unmindful of the necessary meal ticket before she gets mad, but here is the ticket for the asking.

Therefore, generally speaking, the first essential to a divorce action is the assurance that her share of the family treasure will enable her to eat in a scenery devoid of her husband. Of course this is true only of high class divorces. It is a common observation that it is easier to get mad at a husband with lots of money, the half of which will enable the wife to buy herself a new model. But, like marrying a frugal man in the first place, there are pitfalls. Perhaps the original estimate was exaggerated, and getting hold of even what there is may offer some difficulties, after the attorney for the defendant has his say. If one wanted to state the problem in simple terms, he could say it is not so much a question of how much the husband is worth as what one can get from the judge.

A domestic grievance as I have intimated is more painful if there is a lot of money. Poverty, quite apart from attorney's fees, is a deterrent to divorce. Of course the woman is entitled to alimony; at least usually she gets it, or tries to. Unfortunately women with the largest number of children, therefore most in need of alimony, are able to get the least. The age old difficulty of getting blood out of a turnip appears here. A congenital poverty takes the added experience of marriage without rebellion. It is just more of the same. Then too, the sense of religious duty prevents many women from even thinking of divorce. Some sacrilegious person has said that the lower order of society take their religion most seriously. That is at best only partly true. The higher order take their religion just as seriously, the difference being that their acts are less influenced by it. It was said long ago that a fat pocketbook puts a heavy strain on faith, much as it creates contempt for the banker.

So long as only one party in the family row is privileged to do the lying, divorces will continue to be frequent. If it were certain that the other side would be heard from, there would be a little more hesitancy about paying money for the services of a person who can spell "incompatibility." I have remarked before, and shall again, that lies look much weaker in print, and telling them to a court stenographer is more difficult than telling them to willing ears over the alley fence, or its modern counterpart, the bridge table.

Hate is what makes the divorced state possible. But to hate is a toilsome procedure and unless it finds support, wearies. Self-pity may do much to make hate durable. But it takes jealousy to make hate reach its heights. The trouble is, jealousy implies a third party and it may take a long time to find one satisfactory to all concerned. Once hate joins jealousy, marriage is dead. Divorce is then only a public acknowledgment of it. What happens next makes little difference in so far as the people involved are concerned. But one needs to pause. Hate can be cured by time. Only two things are eternal, love and jealousy. Whether both can exist in the same person at the same time is a question. Sometimes the lady becomes confused.

Jealousy is easier to present if there is assurance that there will be no evidence in rebuttal. Technical murder is still against the law, even when committed by an attractive woman with shapely legs, and may even be outright hazardous in this day of women jurors, who, from the nature of things, are less easily impressed by scenery. The very nature of jealousy makes it necessary to proclaim it. An insanely jealous woman does not hesitate to destroy her husband, even though in doing it she destroys her children. A jealous woman has an easier job if the husband has to deal with the public. A professional career can be ruined, a business dissipated, by one blast from a jealous woman, aided and abetted of course by her solicitous lady friends. The mother has secured a decree from the public without the help of the judge, though the public does not know it. The protection of his life work, and therefore the welfare of his children, may compel the father to flee. Any one who has lived a lifetime can cite a number of instances which prove that when a jealous woman kills her children in order to kill her husband, they all stay dead, and the hand of fate is unrelenting.

The jealous woman receives greater consideration from the public than the profligate man. The public is glad to accept the lady's statement that her husband is a bad actor, doubly glad if the said husband is more successful than the husbands of the handclappers. Even the Goddess of Justice, being a lady, naturally is prejudiced. If she were not a cowardly old girl she would remove the rag from her face and take a look around.

If Lady Justice were on the job when a woman makes slanderous remarks about her husband, she would bring her automatically into court and ask her to prove her statements. Failing to do so, she should be made a guest of the jailer, for say six months. It would be a consistent act.

I have tried out this plan in a limited way. If a woman accuses her husband of adultery, as she does when she believes he brought home something, and wants proof, I ask her just what she could prove in court. "Just imagine," I say, "that you were facing a court stenographer and he was putting down every word you say. That if you did not prove your statements and the judge got mad you would be charged with perjury." She will close up like a clam, with possibly the sweeping assertion that she knows what she is talking about.

I have learned if a truculent female bluntly states that she wants a complete examination, she wants me to discover something. Six months in jail would be more effective, I think, than the pointed questioning of the doctor. Of course it does not cure her of her jealousy, but after she is released the neighbors may relay conversation with a certain degree of caution. Make lying a jailable offence, and the divorce problem will be half solved.

It is amazing how often there are divorces which the public does not anticipate. Everything has been camouflaged by respectability. Even doctors have been astonished. Then and then only do we understand why we have been unable to diagnose the complaints, supposedly due to organic causes, which have been poured forth at us. But physical causes, except as they affect sex adjustment, seldom enter. The woman will suffer the ravages of hell before she will rebel, if she suffers only physically. The reason for this is probably that suffering has been her lot from time immemorial. Ever since primitive man hit his first lady love over the head with a club in order to acquire her, he has had certain rights.

There are factors which operate before hate and jealousy become evident, and which require more complete elucidation before we can recognize them as they appear at some period of the conflagration. These are not medical problems, but the doctor must recognize their existence in order that he may get behind the ropes when the parade starts. But we doctors are not so dumb. If the lady has a certain type of backache, we may suspect that she is tired of viewing papa's face and is silently, perhaps subconsciously, searching for the other angle of the triangle. She concludes to spend the winter in Florida, but papa, despite his sojourning in a northern clime, may generate a degree of heat which may prove disastrous. At the same time it should be noted that it is not a matter of what the husband does but what the wife, basking in a warm climate, thinks he does. The husband grumbles at the expense of the trip and income taxes. Then she knows he is spending his money on some one else. If at this stage the wife were told, as I have told some of them, that the journey she is making leads but to the judge, she would strenuously deny that she had the remotest intention of separating herself from a meal ticket which includes winters in Florida.

All, or nearly all, domestic discord centers around the sex life of the individual. An infinite number of things may suggest a change of climate. As intimated above, we are beginning to understand the blood chemistry of many of the factors which puzzled the public. Endocrinology has also advanced far in the solution of many of these difficulties. Suppose one should see a sign as follows: "Dr. John Doe, Chemist; Dr. Richard Roe, Endocrinologist. Marriages performed; results guaranteed." We are much nearer to solving sex problems by chemical means than we were to conquering diphtheria fifty years ago. After sex imbalance is controlled by chemical means, high powered parties will no longer be needed to fix the holy bonds, and the reformers can find other diversions than weeping over our divorce rate. To con-

trol the human hurts surrounding sex would be the greatest
achievement one could wish for the medical profession.

In summary, one may say that among people really married, opulence beyond that achieved at the time of marriage,
not poverty, is the common cause of divorce. The best prophylactic against disaster is work, work of some kind. Nothing
else will so effectually break up the home as self-pity. Keep
your mouth shut and work. Turmoil there may be, but the
roof will stay on the domestic establishment.

XI

Purgatory (the Lid Blown Off—Gathering Up the Pieces)

HAD I the power I would paint on a board: "What price freedom? Paradise or purgatory?" and have a duplicate hang over the bench in every courtroom in the land.

In the preceding chapter, I suggested that ladies who tell the judge that they are afflicted with bad cases of "incompatibility," might find food for thought if the judge, by reference to appropriate case histories, could show them just what they will be freed of, and what they may be freed into.

I have at my elbow the histories of thousands of patients, photographs, slides and all, covering a period of more than four decades. When confronted by a patient presenting a certain type of disease, this makes it possible for me to say just what happened to other patients with like affliction in after years. Patients usually want to know the percentage of fatalities attending an operation, and even more will ask what will happen if they are not operated on. With this information at hand, the patient, theoretically at least, will be able to conclude whether or not to take the risks and inconveniences of an operation or bear the troubles they now have. That is scientific surgery.

The judges, if they were free to exercise their own judgment, could look at domestic problems in like terms of human suffering, just as we doctors do, and arrive at a definite plan to reduce misery to a minimum. So long as divorce is viewed as a moral delinquency, to be corrected by lofty condemnation and pious wishing the problem is not going to be solved. It is much more a problem of physiology than of morals.

Unlike the doctor, the judge has no complete record of what happens to the "patients" after he "operates" on them

266

on file in his office. True enough, the judge has a mental inventory of many cases, but he cannot make them available for those who need the information. Besides, he is bound by rules which compel him to do such and so.

Many patients operated on by surgeons, sad to relate, are worse after the operation than before. That means, of course, that the diagnosis was wrong. A great difficulty lies in the fact that when couples approach the judge they have less judgment even than when they approached the parson, which is near the absolute zero physicists talk about. Before a surgeon operates on a minor or a mentally irresponsible person, he must have the consent of the parents or guardian. Such consultation with responsible parties is even more important in impending divorce, because the warring parties are not the only ones the passing years will influence. This makes it much more complicated than the responsibilities the surgeon faces. He has only the patient to consider. If the patient dies, only one is dead. Besides, he can examine with the microscope the diseased tissue obtained at the operation, or autopsy, and discover fundamental details. This aids him in avoiding inoperable cases in the future.

When the judge operates he is sure to have two patients who are very much alive after the operation. Fortunately for him, he does not need, in most cases, to listen to the complaints after an unsuccessful operation. The mistakes of the surgeon leave him with a person on his hands who greets him with: "Say, Doc, I'm worse than before the operation." If the judge's patients come back to complain they criticize not the judge's work but the other half of the late domestic team. It might be well if they complained to the judge that his operation was a failure. In most instances he already understands this but the rules bind him.

Of course, the judge does have his pains in the neck. The economic distress may be the first one to appear. The judge may be asked to perform such a difficult feat as that of squeezing blood out of a turnip. In other words alimony is not forthcoming.

If there are children, the effect on them of his operation

may appear in various forms. A wayward child, the by-product of the divorce, may come to him in after years to challenge the wisdom of his procedure. The judge's lot is not exactly a happy one. The judge is bound by the law, we doctors are bound by our science, but the judge's law is more "ecclesiasticized" than our science is. Therefore, doctors are better equipped in some ways to settle family rows than judges are.

The judge's problems are greater, I will admit, than ours are. In most instances, when the plaintiff reaches the judge there has been a separation for a lesser or greater length of time and, so far as the "patients" are concerned, the verdict has already been given. One of the fundamental difficulties is the chronicity of the judge's patients. The cause dates back many years. With our present social set-up the judge's act is but confirmatory. The brawl, up to then, has been the concern of nobody. We doctors often see the quarrel in the soft biscuit stage.

A family row is the concern of nobody because until it appears in court it cannot be pictured. The fundamental elements in a home in which there is discord but no divorce, and one in which divorce results, are much the same, in so far as the parents are concerned. Divorces are bad enough but the truth may be fairly simple. A young nurse speaking of one of her divorced parents said they were both excellent parents but they were fundamentally so different that discord was inevitable. She was able to view the problem in its true light. To tell the truth, the facts involved in a divorce are not always so bad; it is the apparently inevitable lying about affairs that multiplies the tragedy a hundredfold.

The effect on the children is somewhat mitigated by the fact that, although they have already suffered the shock of discord when a divorce is inevitable, they are still protected by a veil of what society regards as respectability until there is a physical separation. The odium which society places on divorces is temporarily saved the children. The pointing fingers of the scorn of other children, the thing that cuts most deeply, is spared the child in a measure until actual divorce occurs.

The heart-rending effect of fights for the custody of the children are matters of the court at the time of divorce. The real savagery, however, comes in the post divorce period. Jealous rage finds a new high point when the passions are stimulated by unsatisfied sex, a thing intensified by the constant wailing about it. Vulgar interpretations of imagined acts of the offending partner are paraded before the children. The children must listen to the diatribes directed toward a parent to whom they still have some attachment and whom they would fain still love. These things leave an indelible impression on the child mind. This is the real tragedy of divorce. Everything is magnified by hate. Calm consideration would reduce the whole affair to relatively simple terms. This after thought can come only with time and with time it will come to the parents, and the children may salvage the truth.

After divorce one or the other or both may remarry. Commonly such an event is anticipated. This is not so bad, morally speaking, as it sounds. Nobody, not even a betrothed pair, has less sense than a couple engaged in a family quarrel. They are easy picking for the harpies looking for easy victims. That men more frequently remarry is not so much a moral indictment as a matter of circumstances. The wife, more or less anchored by children in a fixed place of abode, has relatively little temptation to make a fool of herself. The husband, on the contrary is unencumbered, has no fixed place of abode, and in spite of himself is liable to become a victim of the scenery about him.

If the husband remarries, even though there be no legal disposition of the children, they are nevertheless deprived of free access to his company. Even though he marries an angel, which isn't likely, the children will have the picture of her which the mother paints, and generally the picture the mother presents is limited only by her vocabulary. Therein lies the basis of like unhappy situations in the next generation.

The public is inclined to start something, and then fail utterly to finish it. This is seen in the silly law which says a

T

divorced person shall not remarry until six months after the granting of the decree. It is generally recognized that six months will cool off most flames but this time must be spent beyond reach of the partner of the next adventure. To expect sanity to come to a person in the company of one who "understands" him is the height of folly. To leave no curb as to associations makes of the law a poor joke. If there were really the intent to do something about it, the period should be from two to five years, depending on the age and financial standing of the male.

If the parent having custody of the children remarries, the children meet new confusions and new problems. The language of the combat remains a part of their subconscious selves and, in after life, when they have formed homes of their own, if some cause for disharmony appears, the well-worn grooves of the mind become reestablished and we find literally the sins of the fathers and the mothers extending even unto the second generation, and from then on. Or, on the contrary, having experienced the ravages of a broken home in their childhood, they recoil from a like experience and cling to a worthless mate.

A studying of the after-course of divorced persons discloses the fact that, in the vast majority of cases a separation solves nothing. The person who first pulled the old gag "out of the frying pan into the fire" evidently was a divorced person and knew it makes little difference as to the source of the heat if one is compelled to sit on it.

To discuss divorce in the abstract is difficult, and an examination of concrete cases is not always any more enlightening. Childless marriages we may dismiss without comment. Paying the clerk fifty cents for recording the fact that they have quit might be regarded as a just compensation. But this would not be the whole truth because one of the parties may have taken the obligations seriously, so even here unhealing wounds sometimes result. The doctor knows that childless divorced persons who remain unmarried present fundamental nervous problems and, knowing this, he may spare the patient a useless operation.

In following the post-divorce career of a divorced person, the judge and the doctor both have their problems. The judge dismisses the patient from his "clinic," but he is not through with him or her yet. He may only have begun. If the prospective alimony is a lure for divorce, as it often is, and the husband fails to pay the "innocent" party her alimony, the fireworks start. Unless the order of the court is obeyed, papa goes to jail. The victim tells the judge that he is so sick that he can not do his work properly. The judge tells him to go to his doctor and get a statement setting forth where or whereby he is sick. The doctor hears the story and says: "Brother, you are sick but only you and I understand, and anything I might say will be a plain lie because there is nothing physically wrong with you—but here goes, because the judge will not understand either."

If the judge's efforts fail to produce coin, the lady has a nervous breakdown and goes to a hospital, at the expense of the institution, of course. The doctor makes a visit. He realizes that she also is sick. All he can do is to bewail the fact that no one has invented a monkey wrench which can be used to tighten the bearings of a harassed soul. He gives her sedatives.

The judge does not realize that every affliction with which a doctor has to deal is different from every other disease, even of the same class. For instance, every typhoid case differs from every other, differs in the course of the disease and complications, yet one recognizes it as a case of typhoid fever.

The judge should see his patient at intervals for a period of years. As it is, he sees nothing of the patient until he or she comes before him again, perhaps several years later. Then the judge inquires of the patient: "Aren't you the guy I operated on for cancer of the 'holy bonds' a couple of years ago?" Then he proceeds to say to him: "If you had taken the freedom I handed you and kept it, you would not be here. Even if you had chosen to bump your head again if you had come to me when the growth was small perhaps it would not have taken another major operation to cure it. A little x-ray treatment, or just a little light treatment might have turned the trick. But having neglected the growth of discontent, you need operation, or at least you think you do, which is equal to the same thing; but the next time I make you free, you stay free."

When the trouble has passed the judge and reached the doctor, the "holy bonds" artist has disappeared into his sanctuary long ago and the judge has washed his hands of the whole affair and has gone to lunch. When attempting to reach a diagnosis the doctor must depend on an accurate history. Unfortunately, the patient, usually the lady, got by the judge by telling a lot of lies, and naturally she believes she can get by the doctor by the same means. There she is mistaken. Doctors deal only with the truth.

Of course, we doctors do not get all the facts, or a diagnosis would be easy; the trouble there is that often there is no way of determining them because the persons concerned do not know them. The early beginnings likely have escaped them, and they could not tell the doctor the facts even if they wished to do so. As I mentioned before, one of my patients once confided to me that if she had attended to her business in the early years as well as George did to his, there would have been no trouble. (I knew that. Too much money led her astray. George's sin was in assuming she had some sense.) Yet almost in the same breath she painted George as a hopeless moral derelict. George was my friend and I knew him to be a man of unsullied honor. I told her so and said "scat." She added that I was just as bad as George, which for the moment at least was not a point at issue.

Some cases are difficult to unravel. Perhaps the doctor knew the real trouble in the beginning was fear, a repulsion, possibly the result of sanctified rape. We surgeons every day see cancers and say to ourselves that if we had just been consulted earlier, the cure would have been easy. But time does not back up, and the disease pursues its relentless course until it has gone beyond the reach of our operative technic. The nervous complaints of divorcees are always incurable. They are spiritual hurts.

Perhaps the person who started the row in the first place

by holding the outlook up as a fifty-fifty proposition in the words "for better or worse" is really the guilty party. He should really be conducting a lottery. If he could realize the fact that his work is likely to be full of holes, he would ask for a check-up on the results of his handiwork at short intervals. He might come to realize that what he thought was an ecclesiastical problem is really a medical one. A man with a new automobile is cautioned to drive at a slow speed for the first five hundred miles. The young couple, on the contrary, are told to step on the gas. Perhaps if he saw something had gone wrong he might tell them to consult a doctor. The doctor might discover that one or the other needs a vacation, or he could pull some poetic bromide such as: "True love never ran smoothly," and put in a new bearing, change the oil and wave them on. Anything to divert their attention. Of course discussion of more intimate things is against the law. At least we doctors cannot do anything about it. Suppose a doctor should tell a patient: "You have some sort of moral infection but it is against the law for me to make a bacteriological examination in order to get at the facts and to prescribe properly for your case."

But even so there is always something else foremost in the surgeon's mind. Personal responsibility, his conscience, his professional pride, and, of all things, the judge, are what make the surgeon cautious. There is always the possibility of a suit for malpractice if the patient does not like the result of the operation. Suppose a young man returned to the preacher and said: "Parson, you promised this machine would run until death did us part. Now look at it. Bearings burned out, radiator leaks, tires all flat. I am suing you for malpractice; I want my ten dollars back." That worthy says: "I am not responsible. I was only acting for a higher authority, at least I thought I was. You go sue Him." The surgeon hasn't any one to hide behind. I once heard a pious surgeon say: "When I operate God guides my hand." The modern version is that if anything goes wrong with an operation the surgeon himself is to blame.

When the doctor is confronted by a wholly mysterious

case in which a divorce has figured the answer is easy. Such patients take their separation as lightly as they did their vows. The experiences of the past stand them in good stead and they start a new campaign. The stimulation of ever present sex hunger, is what makes grass widows so deadly. Perhaps their first attachment was the matter of securing an independent life, perhaps they were gold diggers of a more or less high degree. New adventures are not working out so well and they need a doctor because they are nervous.

Little better are those meal ticket cases who, with the connivance and aid of their mothers, "marry well." The mothers are less frank than the Indian father who holds his daughter for so many ponies, but fundamentally it amounts to the same thing. This means in civilized society that persons of different economic status are brought together. "Lack of support" is often given the judge as an excuse for separation and this reason is perhaps as valid as any. But it means to the doctor that the husband has refused to dish out the emoluments in accordance with prenuptial anticipations. Generally speaking, it appears that the prospective groom is not likely to underestimate his possessions or his possibilities. But even if the groom really has all he is supposed to have, the hopeful bride discovers that there is a vast difference between a husband having money and her getting that money to spend. The problem should have been anticipated. Any man who has come up the financial ladder got where he is by his ability to hang onto his money. Congenital thrift is not lost by a little ceremony. The wife has no holler coming. She was wrong in assuming that once in her grasp he could be made to loosen his grip on his coin.

Such cases are the forerunners of more trouble. The aggrieved wife figures her husband has an income far beyond his fondest dreams, and estimates his available assets at whatever she would like them to be. She figures that half of all that money would finance her right merrily until she could land one less cautious in the use of his assets. So she says that she has not been adequately supported, is tired of the shape of his face or that these accumulated grievances amount to "incompatibility," and so informs the judge. This is how simple the problem is. The attorney for the plaintiff often does her great harm by not informing her just what she is going to face. Being that kind of a lawyer perhaps he doesn't know anything about finance, just like the legislators who make our laws. Perish the thought, perhaps he is even honest. Presumably, if he told her the truth she would cease to be a client. Also by emotionally upsetting even a nice man, she may ruin his business and break his spirit, and what was a nice income ceases to be one. These things should be carefully figured out before getting mad. If a man hits his thumb with a hammer, he is for the moment not capable of clear thinking along any line.

One can tell an "incompatible" lady that, generally speaking, if her husband has any money it means that he has been smart enough to hide it from the tax collector, which means he is really smart. Hiding it from the judge is a simple matter in comparison. The attorney for the plaintiff is certain to make matters worse by painting too rosy a picture. That newly acquired liberty that looked so rosy may lose all its charm, because the elusive things visioned a distance away evaporate in the light of impending morning. Joshua made the sun stand still, insuring perpetual sunlight, but I have never seen a divorcee who could accomplish that astronomic feat. The whole thing is just as simple as that, if they would just take time to think the thing through. A clear presentation of the facts would be more effective as a prophylactic measure than all the pious moral wailings. Suppose surgeons should operate on a patient when he is mad at him. It is all right for the lady to get mad when "moral" issues are involved but only the facts count when the point at issue is a matter of law and finances.

The result of lack of careful consideration of the economic state is that the separation, which promised so much, fails to secure sufficient of the world's goods to allow the life of ease which the lady pictured. This class forms a large and pitiable group. We call this group the A.A.H., the Amalgamated Alimony Hunters. They are truly pitiable cases, if one has no sense of humor, or does not know the facts. Having all the hates and jealousies that lead to the decree in the first place, their constant wrangle to secure the small alimony payment which the judge allowed keeps them in a state of near frenzy. Despite all the ravings they sooner or later find themselves in the group of the A.L.W.'s., Associated Laundry Workers.

Such divorces are purely business transactions, but the disillusioned person is a problem for the doctor. He feels that exalted sympathy for them which one feels for one who has lost his fingers because he ignored the sign "danger" placed above a buzz saw. The doctor does what he can but there is no serum for vain regrets. He just gives them a sedative so they can sleep.

Sometimes the aggrieved ladies furnish the doctor a larger pain. An example: Such a person came to the hospital complaining of a number of symptoms which might mean an organic disease or just pure cussedness. Weeks were spent in proving nothing was wrong. Everything available about the hospital was demanded, including two nurses. Leaving the hospital, the woman went through bankruptcy proceedings, or whatever people do when they wish to avoid their financial responsibilities. Later she had the effrontery to demand a complete transcript of the hospital records and the treatment prescribed. If you hear a doctor break out into a loud guffaw, apparently without provocation, it does not necessarily mean that he is going silly. He is thinking of the records the patient did not get.

But these women furnish many very tragic cases. I once knew a cultivated, sensitive little lady divorcee who, one would have thought, would ornament any home, and she probably would have, had a warning hand been raised in time. She worked in a laundry for twenty years. She worked behind a window past which I had to drive daily. She was in the beginning a brunette, attractive to others besides the newspaper boys, and I was interested in observing a gradual change of her hair into a silvery white. I wish I could paint that picture and hang it over the bench of every judge and label it: "What liberty did for me." Something was taken out of the life of this unfortunate woman so that she did not seek a new alliance but remained content with her lot. Such tragedies are not enacted on any stage because it would take twenty years to depict it.

Just one more instance. I was called to see a fine lady who had taken bichloride of mercury with suicidal intent. As uremia approached she wailed for her ex-husband, George. I have never heard a more piteous crying out to Almighty God. The wails of that dying woman recounted all the virtues a husband could possess. The last words, a ceaseless repetition, were: "If I had only known," becoming less and less distinct as unconsciousness overcame her. George never came. I have never witnessed a more heart rending scene. If I could have made phonograph records of those cries, extending over several days, I would give them to the judge, and when he had a candidate he could say: "See here, Sister, I want to play you some records. It is about a man named George."

An observant doctor can see these unfortunates in many restaurants going about their work with sad fixed faces. I used to be served my noonday soup by a gracious little lady with most delicate hands. Noting her prolonged absence I inquired of the proprietor of the restaurant. He informed me that she was dead. If one has an eye for such things it is a source of interest to study the faces of some of those who serve. Sometimes they conquer their depression and become cheerful, but it is the cheerfulness of despair, which is quite a different mental state from the cheerfulness of hope.

One finds these unfortunates in all walks of life. One may see a simple card in a cottage window: "Plain sewing done." Often these women bear their ills so patiently that they ignore physical discomforts until forced to consult a doctor and he recognizes an inoperable cancer or something equally incurable. Too often even a fatal illness is joyfully greeted as an end to an intolerable life, which perhaps has missed happiness by the narrow margin of a half baked biscuit, or something equally trivial.

When trying to find an organic disease to explain the complaints of divorced persons I have often thought, that if love would just die too, it would make our problems much simpler. Even a hateful, mad, sex-driven, jealous old hag who starts out to rule or ruin finds that she has ruled nothing, certainly not inexorable fate, but that she has ruined everything. Yet when the object of their hate dies these enemies of society sometimes want to weep on the doctor's shoulder and tell him what a fine man John was. If John is still alive she may express regret at her lot, suggest a flickering love, but yet continue to hate. But John dead is something different. Then he becomes a paragon of love and virtue.

There is something strange about the divorcee. One reads on the clinical record "Miss Doe," yet knows that the "Miss" expresses something more than the single state. She certainly has "missed" but just what she did miss neither of us knows. There is that eternal silence of regret, finding its only expression in a feeling of weakness and nervousness. The doctor feels a sense of pity, of helplessness. Even cases which, as far as one can find out, were little else than sex unions leave behind a silent cloak of regret. Sometimes, after I have seen a series of these patients during the course of a day I feel bewilderment and uncertainty lest I have overlooked a certain sense of nobility in some of my patients.

There is a type of divorcee which causes neither confusion nor sympathy. She developed a habit; she did not know to what extent she had developed it until she suddenly finds herself without a means of satisfying it. Being possessed of a certain degree of respectability, her past leaves her confused and all she knows is to tell the doctor that she cannot sleep. The doctor prescribes bromides with as little emotion as he feels when he drives up to the filling station and says: "Ten gallons, George, and please check the radiator." George wipes the windshield as a part of his routine, whether it needs it or not.

There is also a group of women, rare in rural communities, who, like the doctor, do not know if they really have been married or not, despite perhaps several trips to the altar.

Usually they have all the complaints in the category, often have been operated on several times for things that never existed, involving the removal of organs that cannot be replaced. One tells them that they are like the guy in the Bible who suffered much from many physicians, and that what is left of them is beyond the help of any doctor. As they depart one watches them with a tinge of disgust which is soon replaced by the feeling that perhaps sometime in the past a noble mother has failed because she prayed for her soul but forgot all about her endocrines.

As a corollary to these is a group, the most tragic of all, about which there is little to write. These are the inexperienced, romantic girls who are married by beasts in human form with the prenuptial intention of deserting as soon as the heat wears off. These differ from the young couple who go to live with their parents after the ceremony and are taken over by mother as soon as they light. The men in these latter cases are fugitives from an intolerable situation and not wilful deserters. Others remain until a child is born. They are moral cowards and run away from their responsibilities as soon as they arise. The women so left alone seldom come under the care of the doctor.

The leniency of the law in dealing with these persons surpasses my understanding. Several years in the penitentiary may be meted out to a person stealing a few chickens. As in most sex offenses there is a peculiar indifference on the part of the public and of the law in dealing with them. This just shows how fundamentally close we still are to the old concubine age. Here, as clearly as anywhere, one sees the difference between Christianity and religion. I almost wrote it shows the utter incompatibility of the two, but that would have been an overstatement. Some people are both Christian and religious.

I have not mentioned the male member of the catastrophe of divorce. Really he doesn't count. Nobody cares what becomes of him. Because he has no home, he may be stimulated to greater efforts in his life work and reach heights in whatever pursuit he may engage in. Or he may drown his grief in alcohol and wind up in the charity ward of a hospital. Perhaps he goes back and shoots someone, usually the wife and some assorted relatives whom his befuddled mind regarded as guilty before the act. Such acts of violence are the result of the sex outlet being suddenly shut off. I have seen plenty of all kinds. However, no man can play the leading role in an emotional tragedy. There is no need to shed tears over the fool men who, having been chased from their homes, fall prey to an understanding lady friend. But even they might be extended a protecting hand if the public waited to find out the truth instead of giving them a kick at the first rumor.

When a young woman makes the welkin ring with accusations of infidelity, she nearly always has a husband who is a decent chap, doing the best he can, but who steadfastly refuses to be ruled even though in the end he may be ruined. It is a strange thing but it can be verified by an observant person. On the contrary, if one follows the real rounder to his home one will find a wife who stands by him to the last ditch, declaring to the end that he is a paragon of virtue, even after everyone else knows she is wrong. Evidence means nothing to her; she will continue to believe. She puts her protecting arms around her little brood and defies the world. Women do some funny things and this is the strangest, the noblest, the most tragic of all.

I have dealt long with the tragedies as they affect those who, in the public eye, are the parties to the divorce. I have done this to postpone as long as possible a discussion of the really tragic part of most divorce cases—the children. That the children are the all important factor in all family rows I have tried to show in previous chapters. If we could wipe from the slate all history from the birth of Christ back to the beginning of time, we would be vastly better off.

What significance has the Old Testament in the solution of our modern problem, the child? One of my staff recently, facetiously perhaps, remarked that there is a slight confusion of words. He opined that in what is called the historical account of the beginning of the alleged civilization, really the only thing remarkable is the "hysterical" tenacity with which modern civilization sticks up for the impossible accounts of the past. Be this as it may, he is a neurologist of distinction and his opinion commands respect in any circle. At any rate, the child plays a strangely small part in the historical accounts of the past, or in the hysterical beliefs of today. The children form the only tie that cannot be severed in our domestic conflicts. Nothing could be plainer than this fact. Yet even now they receive little consideration. They form the only bonds that cannot be broken. No matter how intolerable the union, how much justified separation would be, the tie that binds the parents, the children, remains unbroken, even though they hate each other and fight to the very brink of the grave.

The longer I study human beings the more I am convinced that the child is born to us for our salvation and for the saving of civilization. I believe once children are born, the parents have surrendered their rights to the rights of their children. The birthright of the child is a home. It was promised that, or should have been promised it, before it was born. It is the plight of the child after separation has been granted that concerns me here; everybody seems to think for the first time about the fate of the children after disaster has been wrought.

It is my firm belief that before the judge considers the plea of the aggrieved party, the question of the children should be settled. That is the thing that is being tried in any divorce action. Many judges realize this and do what they can, but they have certain rules that the mouthpiece for the plaintiff insists on observing. What actually happens in most of our courts, despite what the judge may be able to do, is that not until after the holy bonds have been severed are the children thought of. Even then the only question is: "Who gets the child?" He cannot be divided spiritually, any more than he can be divided anatomically, and survive. In any just court the first thing that should be asked is: "Are you mad enough at each other to be willing to give your child up forever?" That is the question that should be asked the aggrieved party. She will reply that she is to get the

custody of the children. No indeed, she is not. No judge
has the power to give anybody the custody of a child. Nobody completely gets the child; don't let the judge mislead
you. He is honest and does the best he can.

It makes me mad because we doctors are handed the
package containing the child who is in the custody of no
one except the fates. If a child is sick at heart and dwindles,
the doctor is supposed to feel his head and discover that he
had an injury when he was a baby. Sure, he got a bump from
which he has not recovered and never will, the bump he received in the courtroom. I have seen so much of this tommy-
rot it makes me mad. Twenty centuries of prayer for the
salvation of something or other and look at the state of the
world today in so far as the rights of the child are concerned! We pretend to listen to the voice in the manger but
drag the unbridled tomcat down the road of time. It cannot
be done.

If I were a holy man and had no responsibilities, being
assured that I would not need to soil my hands, I would
say, as I most sincerely wish I could, that once children are
born there should not be a divorce under any circumstances.
But that would be a cry of despair, and with reason, because
one does find impossible situations. But even in most of
them there is some better solution if we had the courage to
face the facts. But only we doctors must face the truth and
we see some cases in which it seems a separation is inescap-
able. One of the most impressive sights we doctors see is
the way a tactful woman can handle and somehow save a
situation that is apparently beyond solution. The cost is considerable—her life. Her reward: her children. It was that
strange, incomprehensible something between parent and
child, call it spirit if you will, which comes in but gives a
custody beyond the power of the most conscientious judge.

It would be easy to say any sort of home is better than
none, but it is one thing to state an abstract proposition,
and quite another matter to solve the concrete case. Any sort
of home, we may say in the abstract, is better than no home,
because once the family ties are broken, no matter what

the cause or the provocation, the children suffer. A divorce may mean only that the ulcer has been revealed to society, but the doctor knew it was there all the time. Children in such homes, let it be repeated, may be legitimate before the law, but spiritually they are bastards and as such they must face the uncomprehending scorn of the world.

If one views the concrete case, he finds doubt and difficulties. Sometimes the Spirits, by all that is just and right, have granted a decree of divorce before the judge hears about it. If a parent, by profligate living, has lost the love of his child he had best be eliminated from the environment, but the love of a child is an incomprehensible thing. Like a dog, they may continue to love those who abuse them.

If I could forget a scene I once beheld, I might hold a different opinion. At a medical school dispensary a thin, emaciated girl, nine years old, was brought to me for treatment for wounds inflicted by her father. He was present, leering, half drunk, sneering at me as I tried to soothe that child, desperately trying to restrain my tears. The child suffered less, it was obvious, from the physical hurts than she did the hurt of the spirit as she looked at the beast who fathered her. Those wonderful eyes looking through a blood-stained face at the father reflected an unmistakable appeal for love. I record here that professional dignity forsook me and that wretch departed from my presence, pronto, at once, also speedily. It may be that the only reason I did not commit murder was because I was devoid of my beloved artillery. To this moment I stand ready to travel across the continent to kick the trap for the sheriff if he ever gets his hands on that man. Sure enough, he did not actually commit murder, but only because he was too drunk. Wife beating, ten days! The plight of the child was not even mentioned in the court proceedings.

The law is a funny thing. So long as a man stays at home and kicks his family around it is all right. But if he does the only decent thing he could do except to jump into the river, that is, removes himself from the neighborhood, the law charges "child desertion" and the sheriff goes after him.

To state that any home is better than none for the child is easy, but there are gloomy exceptions. In a previous chapter I noted that in discordant families there is a blight on the children, divorce or no divorce. A home may be broken even though there be no divorce. The children do not quite understand, and the fact is still hidden from the children's playmates. But once a divorce separates the parents the children's playmates recognize it as a canker on society. That is what hurts. No one can be so cruel as one child to another. They can unerringly find the sensitive spot in the soul of another child in which to poke their exploring fingers. "Who is your papa?" or something of a kindred nature is thrown at the heart-torn child. They know the scandal of the neighborhood and they know all about the derelictions of papa. If there is divorce, it would be best for the children if they never heard of their father again, assuming the divorce was his fault. It would be too much to expect the mother to tell the truth. She isn't apt to tell them that just baking the biscuits a little more thoroughly in the beginning might have prevented all the trouble. "He is a fine man but just doesn't like half-baked biscuits." If the truth were presented, the parents, though incompatible, might preserve for themselves the love of the child.

Let us take a dispassionate look if we can. Dissipation on the part of the father in wine, women and song or the means that the children need for their well being, even for their very existence! These things, even in the absence of physical injury, make home a mockery. When the means dissipated are the earnings of the wife, the very depths it is possible for alleged humans to reach have been achieved. Just plain cussedness cannot approach such depths, when figured in terms of the children. This is pagan philosophy which our social order condones, even though it may not teach it. Of course such things are none of our business. All we can do is to pray for our sister.

Sometimes wives do not accept such situations so supinely.

Though a wife retains such a worthless reprobate as a husband on the theory that any sort of a father is better than none for the children, there is much that she can do to alleviate her position. A courageous lawyer should be consulted. Threatening such a husband with divorce, an event which he well knows will throw him penniless on the world, will do much to sober him, figuratively and literally speaking. Papers should be made out just as though it were her purpose to file them in court at once. If the lawyer has a conference with the husband and shows how things look in print, it may make an impression. However, the wife must be prepared to carry through the threat. If she doesn't, the last state will be worse than the first. If this attempt fails, then certainly the husband will be worse than no father at all for the children. Such action need not come to the eyes of the children, and the neighbors already know all about his situation.

In the most extreme cases the child in the manger sometimes shines in a clear light. Here is a familiar example: In writing to determine the after-course of an operation I had performed I got this reply from the mother: "So far as the operation was concerned May recovered but soon after, her husband left her. We with a little help from the county have managed to care for the girls. They are as you know now nine and twelve years old and such lovely girls but James just seemed no longer to care for them." That is the woman for you. Profound grief simply told. If she had torn off a whole sheet of invectives the reading of the letter would have been less moving.

Nor is the father always the offending person. Sometimes a mother may produce such conditions that the child would be better off if the union were broken, rather than that the putrid sore of hate be constantly exposed to the children's gaze. When jealous rage recounts obscenities that never happened, that home is worse than none. Neither Milton nor Dante ever dreamed of anything as horrible as a woman, in a jealous rage, bent on rule or ruin, ruin of the husband, and the children too if need be, and of herself. The soul-beating a child receives under such conditions may

U

be more lasting than the physical hurts inflicted by a drunken father. A physical hurt may heal but the moral hurt a mother can inflict, endures literally even unto the third and fourth generation.

In any mass movement there are always some members who are not ready for the change. The marvelous advance women have made in the past fifty years is remarkable, but there are some who cannot use the new liberty to their own advantage. With the increased leisure and greater financial independence many modern women are accorded, nagging jealousy seems to be left free play. The mother of a dozen children has no time to engage in the luxury of jealousy, but the mother of a few has leisure aplenty, and then there come the elements of sex and hate to aggravate matters. Thus advancement may have its perils. But on the whole, women use their increased liberty creditably. One mother writes me that she has outside interests but is always at home to greet the children when they come from school. She must prepare herself, she writes, for the inevitable time when the children will be grown and gone and she finds herself fat and alone. That is the vision of the new woman.

When one tries to trace the after-career of divorced persons he soon finds himself running around in circles. Once freedom is achieved, the parties come to realize that from now on is a long time to nurse a regret. Persons temporarily insane, as those who visit our divorce courts invariably are, should be protected from their own acts. It cannot be too often repeated that no divorce case can be decided in less than two weeks. Even after the facts are determined the whole mess should be placed in a refrigerator for at least six months. There is no case that is in a hurry. No case should be uncontested. There are at least two sides in every case and there may be a hundred. The presence of three doctors is required before a person can be legally declared insane. The wisdom of a dozen should be concentrated in one divorce case. It is less a problem of law than of the mentally sick. Pity rather than condemnation should be accorded both sides, no matter what the apparent facts may be. The pity of the Christ idea would accomplish much more than the sex right we recognize as having the right of way. In many cases no person with only a legal training is competent to make a diagnosis. It is a problem for the doctor grounded not only in the medical sciences but in the general laws of biology.

It is the purpose to emphasize in this chapter as clearly as possible the results when these mental illnesses are allowed to run their course. When the doctor sees a patient with an ulcer on his face he says: "Better have that removed or some day it will become malignant and ulcerate half your face off." About matters arising in the family, biologic from beginning to end, the doctor is not consulted. Even so, such studies would concern not primarily the welfare of a male and female. Once children have been born, they are the concern of society.

Our religions as a whole have not discovered the child. Divorce is a problem of Christianity and not of religion. We will only get at the real problem if or when our child becomes recognized as the emissary of the child in the manger. Then he will be considered first in any divorce action. The weal and woe of husband and wife will be but a secondary consideration. To the children, the family ties cannot be broken. Not until after the divorce do we inquire what is in store for the children. What a vast material this holds for study! To me nothing is sadder than legal contention on the part of the parents for the custody of the children. In that very act both parties admit that there is a tie that still binds them that cannot be broken, no matter what the judge has to say. But it is not recognized in time to avert disaster. The one parent gets the custody of the child so many months each year, says the law. The sad fact is that in such cases neither has the child for any time whatsoever. Lucky in comparison is the bastard child that is given to a home for children. The greatest service such contending parties could render their children would be for both of them to jump into the lake and thus blot themselves forever from the memory of their children. To me the most heart-rending thing is a child placed in a witness chair and asked by the judge which parent he prefers. Ask those infinitely expressive eyes which the papers show if that scene will ever be blotted from the memory of that child. I am told that no judge worthy of the name would do such a thing. Granted, but not only are such procedures recounted in the papers, but pictures of the child sitting in the witness chair are published. We might at least be spared that pain. If it is necessary to learn the wishes of the child, he could be handed over to the doctor who, without allowing the child to know what he is about, could find out the child's attitude. The memory of a pleasant half hour with a funny old doc would be vastly more salutary than the memory of being seated in a witness-chair, exposed not only to the court but to a gawking public.

It is the fate of the child that makes me sick. I have seen the human body terribly mangled by injury. Once I saw, without turning a hair, an even dozen men torn to pieces by an explosion, all crying out in agony as they gradually died. But when I have before me the picture of a child being asked by the judge to decide which parent it shall choose, I become sick, sick at heart, sick at the stomach. I have friends who are now considering a divorce and the lovely young daughter who was the object of contention wailed: "If one of them would just die I could stand it; I have a preference but I am willing to leave that to the gods." This is the cruelest scene in all human relations. There is a resulting scar which marks the child throughout life. Furthermore it lessens the morals of a public who view such scenes, and pass by on the other side.

But this is not the whole picture, perhaps in the end not even the most important part. In the broken home, the adolescent child is deprived of contacts with other young people, which may some time have a determining effect on the great adventure. Right or wrong, parents instinctively do not want their children to marry offspring of divorced persons, even though themselves maintaining homes worse than broken. On the whole, the public is right. One parent, who we are wont to say has custody of the children, cannot provide that warmth and balance of a home the two parents acting in conjunction can provide. At least that is the theory. At any rate any one can note that girls under such conditions are very apt to accept the first opportunity for alliance "for better or worse." Fleeing an intolerable scene only to repeat the tragedy in their own generation! The surviving parents view this as long as they live and they discover that there is only one Judge who can free them from that scene—and I sometimes wonder if even He can.

The boy has a wider range than his sister. He hunts up more congenial homes but even he is not free from the stigma that he carries uncongenial blood in his veins. One hears: "I cannot let my girl marry the son of a divorcee." He cannot take his prospective sweetheart to his home because he has none. Likely he never had any, nor any idea of what the word means. No wonder the mother protests against alliance of her daughter with such an unfortunate.

Criminal statisticians make note that many young derelicts are products of homes which were broken by divorce. Such figures are easy to secure but they do not say if the damage was done before the divorce was granted, or after. There is no way of saying in which cases the results would have been different if family rows had stopped short of the divorce court, or if divorce had happened years before. We do things the easy way, particularly when it comes to building up statistics we have already agreed on.

Quite aside from all this is the question of the character of the parents, whether they themselves had criminal tendencies or records. The lack of such detail makes the statistics as we see them of relatively little value when we are considering the act of divorce as a detached act. The chances are that the divorce is itself an evidence of inherent cussedness which is the main feature the broken family displays.

Yet some cases tend to cause one to come to contrary conclusions. In many cases the child is better off freed from the constant combat. One sees good families in which the parents simply get started quarrelling and can't stop. Separated from each other, they come to understand how silly it was, and show their good side to their children. The innocent wisdom of the child in many cases solves the problem his parents could not solve. He comes to see that it is possible to love both parents, thus forming a distinct tie between the separated couple. But the hands of time do not move backwards. Ugly words said in moments of passion leave their imprint.

It has occurred to me that sometime in the two weeks the divorce case is in court a brief of say a couple hundred pages should be handed the child, at some future date to aid him in determining the facts in the case. If the parents realized that the cold facts would be available to the children in their maturity, making it possible for them to sit on the judgment seat it might cause them to stop and consider. A lie never looks so plausible when written down as when spoken. This is doubly true if it represents past events on which the course of time has turned a new light.

Idle hope. Nothing can make a person hell bent for divorce, pause, or think. Yet the parent should recognize that the boundless love of a child has the power to penetrate more deeply than any court record. That judgment will become active years after freedom has been given for something or other. We doctors see the parents in this stage when they feel in their hearts that their lies brought only grief. Perhaps if we could picture such things to people who are having family rows, it would do more to lessen divorce than the combined force of all the flailing arms. But if a woman tells her doctor that in a fit of anger she cast out the best husband in the world, it is a privileged communication, and usually is not spoken until the husband is dead.

Even so I have seen many beautiful things come out of a sorry mess. I recall one case of a family of seven children, in which the mother found some one more attractive than her simple husband who was a mechanic. She had the good grace to vanish for good. Uncomplainingly, the father of the abandoned brood assumed in addition to his work as a mechanic, the task of mother to his children. A most wonderful mother he was too. The last time I saw him he intro-

duced me to his youngest daughter who had recently married a fine young mechanic. I sort of felt envious. He got
my look. "Yes, Doc, it was a hard pull but it is worth it."
Sometimes a history of a lifetime can be summarized in a
few words.

In that father the love for those children transcended all
else. He devoted every moment of his life to them, and,
viewing his handiwork, pronounced it good. There is no
approval equal to one's own estimate of his own work. One
does not always need to wait until he is dead before seeking
paradise. This simple man was twenty centuries ahead of his
time. Love triumphant over sex.

The female who bore those children removed herself permanently from her family. How much better than if she had
stayed around contending for "custody" of the children for
a part of the year. Even more important is the unselfish devotion of the father to the children. Intense love for children
is able to show mere sex where it belongs; that having done
its duty it should return to the background.

Much more commonly one sees the mother remaining the
mother, casting off sex. Frequently she becomes the wage
earner as well as mother. Love and toil are the real antidotes
to sex urge, showing once again that love and sex are separate entities. Uncomplainingly she sticks to her tasks. Children under such circumstances are better off than those
growing up in an atmosphere of strife. It takes love in its
highest form to accomplish such a task, and children always
respond when it is offered.

Looking at a doctor's case book most of the after-results
of divorce are prosy, more or less indefinite. Because they
are so, they lend themselves poorly to statistical classification. To say out of so many divorces so many children went
wrong is useless, because each child must be studied in detail, and when this is done each belongs to a class by itself.

But the doctor finds many inspiring things in records.
Often a noble person emerges from the judge's clinic, and
not so frequently there may be two. Sometimes following
the break-up of a home, one sees womanhood in its finest

form. It takes tragedy to bring out the best there is in any one, and mere man is a poor piker compared with women in times of stress. Perhaps such a statement is perilous, but it presents the nucleus of a hope for a real Christian civilization. Readiness to give one's self for the children is what it takes and that is exactly what many of these women demonstrate. I note with humiliation that it was men who put up the cross but it has taken women to interpret the meaning.

Usually family rows are clear enough to the doctor, but sometimes an unusual form presents itself. A very attractive young woman presented herself complaining of fatigue, backache, sleeplessness. It was a question of what was really wrong; which certainly was not what she complained of. It amounted to this: A woman raised in comfortable circumstances was trying to make a living for two daughters, trying "to keep the family together" by working hours that were unbelievably long, and it was too much for her frail body. Keeping the family together, the husband had been sent to prison for twenty years. "Frailty, thy name is woman"—the wise mutt that said that was no doctor. Get the situation and weep. Twenty years the hope stretched out. The father was dead so far as the girls were concerned, removed from the family, but without hate. He should have been obliterated from their lives. Even worse, in such cases the children are sometimes dragged before the Governor to excite his sympathy, when a pardon is sought for the father.

It cannot be too often repeated that boys need a father, and crime statistics proclaim the fact that wayward boys are often the result of broken homes. It should be noted however that many children are the product of parents both of whom are vicious, and grow up without the influence of any guiding hand, even though the union of the parents is technically not broken. It would take understanding toil to ferret out these cases, therefore they remain covered up. Such children are fortunate if they are deserted by both their parents and come under the efficient care of some institution. Yet no matter how efficiently conducted such institutions may be, they are a poor substitute for parental affection. However, they are far better than parental domination. There is one thing that I must record, though I would much prefer not to do so. It is that heredity shows its ugly head some time in life, as many well meaning people discover who adopt children of unknown heredity.

Thus it goes; in our present pagan state of Christian civilization we look at divorce as solely a moral issue and try to mix in the teachings of Christ—by absent treatment of course. The public is still trying to treat the "diphtheria" of domestic relations with greater and greater doses of sulphur and pious supplications, instead of honestly seeking the cause and then the remedy.

The pictures presented are plain for any one to see, if they will. When we come to trace the spiritual fate of the victims of divorce, we find a varying picture, showing sometimes clearly, most often obscurely, but they are all illuminating. There is no attempt to do anything about it, because it would mean an examination into the truth of many things we believe; and that would mean that we might need to admit that many things we have been doing are based on wholly wrong premises.

Take for instance the childless divorcee. Many of these cases have no medical aspect. Her clinic record says she is a Miss but no one needs tell the old doctor that title was restored to her by a Judge. Her facial expression indicates disillusionment. Hope gone, there remains to her only a woman's resolution to make the best of her state. There is no pouring forth of voluminous complaints. There is something silent there that even the most courageous doctor hesitates to penetrate. Quite commonly one finds old pus tubes presented to her during her brief flight into the land of disillusionment. She knows she is condemned for life to weary labor, that she must remain childless. Love gone, hope of parenthood gone. All she has acquired by divorce is freedom of body, though that freedom condemns her to a life of bondage.

I have not the courage to write out illustrative cases from my record. Thus one illustrates with a single instance the

fate of countless unfortunates. Here divorce is the lesser
of the evils. The doctor should have been consulted before
the fatal plunge was made. This state is being recognized
by society, and efforts to prevent such things are being made
by persons with large ideas but small knowledge. But it is
a beginning. These women are approachable by real honest
understanding. If women start out by organizing a society
for the care of divorced women they are sunk before they
start. Only the hand of understanding can help them. I have
seen many of them respond when companionship was offered
in the proper way.

If we are to solve our domestic problems it will be necessary to start all over again. We provide the environment and
the young girl is taught that she belongs to herself, that her
salvation in life is in her own hands, as far as it is humanly
possible for it to be, and that the pagan notion that she
must some day sell her body, under a bower of roses, and
assume the obligation of producing her kind whether she
will or not is false. But we must travel the perilous road
with her, if not always in body, always in spirit. There is
a difference of opinion as to the real value of the holy
bonds. They guarantee nothing, and too often are but a scrap
of paper. To look at facts and possibilities as we surgeons
must, would prepare the public in general to realize that
lofty pyrotechnics produce no light, just heat. Our girls
should know this before they start.

There is a more pleasing parallel to the above, even
though it be rare. Sometimes the young divorcee, escaping
infection, forms a new alliance and the fates find her a
mate worthy of her, and with him, children. In such cases
there is really an innocent party capable of rescue by proper
measures. Society laid the trap into which they fall, and society owes them full measure of restitution.

The liberated person often presents a picture not quite
so lovely: A person undaunted by previous experience,
seeking new worlds to conquer. Strongly sexed, both by
nature and experience, these persons present the type that
has given the grass widow her reputation for deadliness.

Restrained by no moral sense, she goes forth to conquer whatever she may find. Financial rating is the only criterion by which she appraises her victim. If her campaign means the destruction of a home, the orphaning of children, it makes not a particle of difference to her. In comparison to her, the woman of the street is a saint. Old man retribution will not be mocked and sooner or later he catches up with her.

But we must not condemn without a trial. Does such a person really break up a happy home? I doubt it. She does have a nose for impending fissures. She notes where rumor points to a certain desirable person and recognizes her chance. Some are even clever enough to initiate a passion, as by making needless visits to a professional man's office. Many wives in such a situation back their husbands to the limit. If, however, beneath its tranquil surface there is some festering sore, selfishness, nagging, slumbering jealousy or other maladjustment in which hate has displaced love, any hurt is eagerly seized upon and the fireworks begin. The true history of such cases is seldom written, and the real culprit is to the public the innocent party-because her gentle nagging is not part of the public picture.

An additional safeguard would be a study of facts. Suppose a record of the strongly sexed prowler should be scanned. If she were found to be a chronic campaigner, society could raise a warning hand and say: "You have had your chance plus—scat!" To catch regular fish a license is required, but angling for human suckers is unrestricted.

It is wearisome to reiterate the fact that the mad human has no sense. The capacity for doing fool things is limitless. The divorced person may leave the judge with the expressed declaration: "Never again." But memory is brief. Even if the maladjustment of sex underlay the development of the consuming hate that led to divorce, the lesson may be short. Excess, it is discovered, may not be any worse than starvation, and the basis for a new venture may become an endless plague.

The divorced woman with children starts out with a handicap, because her situation is a warning to those who are seeking a companion. Nevertheless, some happy alliances have resulted from such combinations. Some persons fond of children welcome such situations as the best chance to secure all the elements of domestic bliss at one fell swoop.

The father who has been cast off presents on the surface a different picture if, as is commonly the case, the mother is given the custody of the children. He often gets a bad reputation because of the apparent speed with which he establishes a new alliance. The period of his solitude is figured from the date of the granting of the decree. The fact that an indefinite period has elapsed from the time the home was broken until he forms his new alliance is not appreciated by the public. Perhaps he has not had a home for many years, if ever. His attendant emotional instability during this time makes him an easy object for women who "understand" him.

My father used to lament that much of what Christ said was preached and that little attention was paid to what he did. In paintings we are not confronted by parents wearing crowns because of, and according to, the number of progeny. The point to be noted here is that so far as we can learn, the child was more important in His eyes than the salvation of the souls of the parents. Seeking salvation is a selfish thing. Going about doing good is not. One looks in; the other out.

It may be of interest to speculate on why Christ's own people crucified him. It was not the money changers as so often alleged. My guess is that the teaching of love instead of sex was out of tune. Let any one wishing to learn the meaning of this find out where, in point of time reckoned in terms of centuries, our beliefs were figured out for us.

We can often learn about a machine by studying those that have broken down. When everything is running smoothly the complexity of its mechanism is not appreciated. So in a broken home the machinery of home can best be studied. The first thing we note is that the constant companionship is lost. The child was born to two parents, and belongs to both. Yet this fundamental lesson is ignored. If the child is fed and clothed it has good parents, but companionship may be denied it, most commonly is denied it. The parents have interests of their own. The love of the child is farmed out in shares to the maid, hired girl, or what not, but most often to the common herd of the neighborhood. That the common herd does so well in raising each other must remain a source of surprise. The gregarious instinct of the human animal is thus satisfied. But the intimate touch of child and parent is lost. This is the common lot in many so-called model homes.

Incalculable as the loss of companionship is to the child, it is infinitely greater to the parents. My valued heritage is the memory that wherever my father went, there I also went. This companionship even the hard teaching of the pulpit of those days could not negate. When we heard the intimation that we must beat the child to save his soul my father held up a restraining hand. He was way ahead of his time. My father lived a tragically unhappy life, but he blamed nobody, though he did know that the fundamental difficulties of home life were due to the fact that we are dragging along with us the old pagan philosophy.

There is still a sad chapter to be written. A parent who gives his whole life to achieve some ambitious end may leave a home broken. No one can cash in on good intentions. Noble ideas and endless toil may end in disaster just as certainly as a profligate life. Then it all depends. If there is a mother who seconds this ambition a lovely companionship may exist.

Taking all divorced persons above the tomcat level, I believe that the great majority regret the day when they first got the idea that freedom was possible through a court decree. I would include here even those who have not had children, doubly so those who have been blessed with children.

The fundamental problems of marriage and divorce are intimately concerned with the work of the legal profession. It would seem that if lawyers and judges were allowed to work out the cases according to the rules of their profession, unhindered by laws made by those ignorant of fundamental knowledge but possessed of the loudest voices, they could do much toward preventing some of the fool things we see.

If lawyers and ministers were actuated, as is the medical profession, with the one idea of preventing human suffering, a vast deal could be done to avoid the tragedies we see. They could supply information to those who seek to enter the married state, prevent others from rushing from the married state to a worse one of which they have no knowledge, pawning their children to secure added fireworks for their grand mad spectacle. The divorce problem will be solved only when men and women of honesty and intelligence bend their efforts in an actual attempt at its solution, approach it as a spiritual and a biologic problem, as it actually is. Now sex rules—and ruins.

XII

Paradise Earned (Twilight)

As OLD age approaches we take a renewed interest, figuratively speaking at least, in sunsets. As the sun approaches the horizon, its rays become a golden yellow and it seems much larger—seems, I say, because we know it is not—but it is a pleasant delusion. But the sun does not set that way every day for everybody. As it approaches the horizon a cloud appears, and we are deprived of the view of the final stages. It seems to set before its time. Some days end with gathering black clouds rolling menacingly toward us until we are engulfed in a storm. This being so, we can never be sure that the sunset will be beautiful. Try as we may throughout a lifetime, we cannot control the final stages; therefore we must steel ourselves to take what comes.

To the observant old doctor, among the most beautiful pictures about us are the serene old couples who have fought life's battles together, and watched the descending sun hand in hand. The sex urge has been obliterated by time, and any discords that may have existed are no more. These pictures give us some idea of what life might be if sex were held in abeyance throughout life. We realize that the conflicts of a lifetime have been useless and senseless because we have allowed ourselves to be engulfed by a false idea.

We have here in old age the last leg of the tripod which holds the hope of a new world. The first is the love of the child who knows only love, no sex; next the love of the single woman who shows us sex can be sublimated in a noble cause; and now finally the love which comes in old age after sex as such has died. These all show us that sex, a necessary thing, can be made the servant of life, that we do not need to bow to it as our master. When we get a firm hold on that spirit in the world, we will be able to dispense with the orange blossoms. Truth needs no artificial aroma.

There is an old saying: "The proof of the pudding is in the chewing of the string." I heard a fine old Scotsman make this statement when I was a boy. The chewing of the string, I was told, was a ceremony after the pudding was eaten. It meant that one could not judge of the merits of a pudding until one had eaten it. The chewing of the string was therefore a ceremony which came after the reality, the eating of the pudding. That did not seem to me to make sense because the puddings I had seen had no string; besides the string might leave a bad taste the pudding did not have. That glib statement puzzled me a long time, showing that elders, when they talk within the hearing of children, should make their meaning clear.

Looking back on life, I see the inference of the pudding and the string. Everything in life that is agreeable has a string attached to it which we must chew whether we like it or not. In fact, it may be a contrast to the pleasant taste of the pudding. For those of us who have lived life, if we liken it to a pudding, all the good may be obscured by the bitter parts of the string which linger longest in our memory, if we allow it to do so.

It seems an act of kindness on the part of the fates that in the aged, the memory of past events lives, while the memory of recent events is all but lost. Fate relents and allows the aging to remember the pudding and forget the string. If perhaps the patter of little feet forever stilled fill the memory, it is at least a memory in which regret is not tinged with bitterness. That serene old age, of which the young are wont to speak, may not be serene but speechless because of unending grief. The mind of the aged is filled with events of the past for which there is no understanding ear in the newer generation.

Just at what age parents begin to look backward is a moot question; no doubt it varies much in different people. It is of concern to a doctor when something occurs which causes the aged to seek his advice. These causes are legion, generally obscure, and the range of the doctor's usefulness limited; but even within its narrow limits it may mean much

if his services are understandingly rendered. No class of
patient appeals to the doctor so strongly as the aged. Regard-
less of whether their life has been useful, useless or even
vicious, they want to live. Is their hurt physical, due to
organic disease, or is it a reflection of the memory of the
past? That is the doctor's problem. "Doctor, I cannot sleep,"
spoken by an aged person, excites my sympathy as does no
other phrase. It is useless to ask why they cannot sleep.
They do not know and would not tell if they did. So the
smart doctor does not ask.

We may approach this problem of the aging person by an
attempt to analyze the panorama about us. The woman's
problem is different in many ways from that of the man. A
great change comes over the woman long before one dares to
class her as old. When she passes the menopause, signalizing
the fact that she can no longer reproduce her kind, she is
afflicted by a series of emotions to which she gives more or
less vocal expression to her doctor, even though she has
long ceased to want to reproduce, if she ever did. I dare say
few regret that the reproductive period is over; many hail
it gladly because it removes permanently an unending fear.
It is fate, the endocrines if you will, and not the woman
speaking. But the physical and mental changes attendant
upon that phase of her life are undesirable. The middle age
spread, which declares to the world that this stage is approaching, is unwelcome, at least to those esthetically inclined. Yet, if they can accept the inevitable and maintain
an interest in something outside themselves, the most beautiful time of life comes to many when the tears and the stress
of life have passed. They wail because all the world can
now see that they are no longer females. They suffer from
the delusions of the times because their femininity has
atrophied with the passing years, though the woman herself
may for the first time shine forth in her clearest light.

Yet every doctor's case-book bears a long list of patients
whose chief complaint is due to the stress and strain of the
past and to the fact that they maintain a rebellious attitude
against fate, which is sometimes an attitude of pure cussed-

X

ness. Those who become mean in later life do so because they have a lingering sex hate, hard to fathom, which holds on to the experiences of the past. Although sex, in a reproductive sense is a thing of the past, it yet retains all the potentialities of hate engendered during that period. It is a strange thing. What are they mad at? Whatever it is, they should lay their problem before their doctor.

Father also undergoes a change in midlife or beyond, less abrupt, it is true, than mother's but it is there. His submission to the middle age spread, though obvious to all, concerns him but little. He just buys bigger pants and lets it go at that. Having no esthetic sense, he doesn't suffer much. Most aging men give little thought to their changing state other than to note the lessened activity it entails. The sex urge lessens too, but it varies with the individual and the age limit is indefinite. It was Schopenhauer who remarked in later life (age not stated): "Thank God," (in whom he never believed) "that I am at last free from the plagues of sex." He hated his mother, which he had abundant cause to do, and all womankind, so far as we know. Yet he could not refrain from giving sex a departing curse.

Just when is a man old? There is only one infallible sign and that is when he declares, anent nothing, that he is as good as he ever was. No matter what the subject at issue may be, he thereby reveals a subconscious voice. If it concerns physical labor, he exhibits supple joints, which, except to him, creak with senility; and while exhibiting his physical prowess, shows a shortness of breath, which is due to a dilated heart that signals the coming end. I remember with pleasure a fine old man aged ninety-two who delighted to stand on one foot while he struck a match on the sole of the other shoe. He became obviously short of breath in the process but he paid no heed to that. He referred to his wife, my patient, aged eighty-eight, as "the girl." Yet, after all, since he succeeded in fooling himself, it is but a small matter that no one else shared his delusion and everybody was considerate enough not to show him his folly in assuming a vigor he did not have.

I trust this preamble presents as clearly as possible the events we doctors are apt to meet in those approaching the evening of life. We figure them as physical facts and not as evidence of moral turpitude. There is a great difference.

Not infrequently couples seek divorce after middle-life apparently without warning. In most cases this is an act long deferred. Perhaps the doctor knows it is long overdue. The mother silently submits to abuses until the children are grown and have homes of their own. In many cases one of the children, long cognizant of the state at home, adds the match to the accumulated tinder: "I just can't stand for it any longer," the mother is told. The husband may be much surprised, or pretends to be, and asks the doctor to tell him what is wrong. He may recall that she complained a lot but that he did not think she meant it seriously. It never occurred to him that the word "obey" in the original contract bore an age limit.

However, the pagan aspects of the holy bonds may extend into old age. The doctor is confronted many times by couples in which one of the pair is still plagued by sex up into old age. There seems to be no age limit. In the male, this is usually associated with inflammation or enlargement of the prostate gland, and the doctor knows his way about. He can fix all that in a pleasant quarter hour. Happily some of those who still associate that condition with the original contract develop an early cancer, whereupon the fates take charge and in a year the doctor is relieved of the responsibility. The patient dies. Sure, the plaguing prostate can be removed, thus relieving the unwelcome urge, but there may not seem to be any valid reason in the mind of the patient for accepting the doctor's proffered service. Is he not as "good as he ever was"? "Look at the bulge of my chest," he declares, though the wheezing of his respirations drowns out his voice. It reacts to his benefit, so he thinks, but to his mate, for whose comfort he has long since ceased to have any concern, it is another matter. So as a rule all the doctor can do is hope that the old devil will soon die and bring some surcease to his wife.

Sometimes the old wife develops a sex mania. For this there is no answer and no remedy. We have nothing to offer and no suggestion, except that the beleaguered husband avail himself of the benefit of the wide open spaces. This usually he is economically unable to do, and perhaps some of the old sentiment remains. And then there is the big question as to what the children and the neighbors will think. Tragic scenes these! Fortunately these pictures die with the patient and live only in the memory of the doctor.

In some cases separation takes place after all cause for strife would seem to have ended, say after forty or fifty years of allegedly wedded life. These may be due to the same old conflict, or to some actual mental aberration, but usually the old doctor himself does not know the cause unless his old case book of years back gives him a clue. Note, for instance, a woman of eighty-eight divorced by her husband because she insisted on sleeping with her cat. Understanding by some outside person and not divorce, was needed there. Crazy and mean may be separated by only a narrow margin. Such problems are left to the judge or the lunacy jury to determine. Problems too deep for neurologists to solve are simple problems for members of the spit and whittle club.

Viewed in the abstract, it would seem that aged persons who develop an aversion for each other should have the protecting arm of society about them. It would seem that any one with any sense of humor should be able to see that there really isn't anything to divorce. If they find each other's society intolerable, the simplest way would be to live separately. There is no need of cluttering up the divorce statistics, and even old folks get tired of being mad at each other. I once asked an aged woman just what it meant to her to be divorced. She admitted that really nothing had been gained, except that for once she had the chance of telling the world how mad she got at Pa at intervals for the past fifty years. Having thus unburdened herself, she regretted her rash act. I was sure she would have been quite willing to resume hostilities at close range without benefit of the wider audience the divorce court afforded. It is amazing how hate may extend beyond the grave. In one case among my patients it lasted for more than forty years. Fine people both. There is no answer.

May I present a corollary which most of us will view with varying sentiments. I mean the marriage of ancient persons. It must be admitted that this type of indiscretion is most often indulged in by the male, at least by those who think they are male. Generally, the old man's misfortune is in having sufficient coin of the realm to make him a reasonable gamble for some designing person. He is not a moral derelict; his brain is softening and he needs a guardian. When I see a picture in the papers showing a tottering old fool being united by a clergyman to a schoolgirl, I think of the story in the Bible in which it is related that Jesus wept. Thanks to the modern achievements of photography the picture gives a good idea of the wedding party, but the doctor envisages an area of softening, the size of a cantaloupe, in the brain of the hero and a decided atrophy in the brain of the officiating brother. If events should be attended by the birth of a child, for which the aged husband is generously given credit, the smile of achievement on his face shows very plainly in the next picture. So important is such an event that the discovery, say of a cancer cure, would be crowded off the first page.

No wonder we doctors get mad. Here is an office scene. A male seventy-eight years of age, who looks older, had to admit that he was having trouble. On the other side of the room sat a young woman holding on her lap two boys, two and four years of age, gazing wide-eyed at a scene they did not understand. It was easy to identify a cancer, which made me happy, for I knew that in six months the old devil would be dead. Orange blossoms! The best efforts of a regular skunk would not cover the stench of such a mess. As floral decorations at the marriage ceremony I would suggest, instead of orange blossoms, the much more expressive jimpson weed from a cow lot. It is obvious that doctor and lawyer, freed from the old pagan philosophy and imbued with a desire to prevent human suffering, could manage such cases. The fool girl deserved protection, and the scared little boys, who would shortly be left without means of support, would have a right to curse the day when they were brought into the world through the acts of a senile fool.

Sometimes in such cases it is a help to the doctor if he can stir up a little feeling of hate for all mankind.

One of the saddest sights is an old couple who together have bravely battled life's vicissitudes, but between whom in late life a long existing rift widens and becomes more in evidence. The doctor thumbs his old case book and perhaps twenty years or more back he finds the answer. One usually has only to seek a difference of opinion regarding the children, usually a son. Many mothers have a favorite boy, very likely the one who most nearly expresses her sentiments or her physical attributes. Even though it be cautiously presented, the son perceives this unexpressed favor. This very act makes him resistant to his father's advice, often positively antagonistic. The mother takes the son's part and an unhealable break between the parents begins, and endures even more persistently than one engendered by sex, lust, or jealousy, proving again that the attachment between parent and child is the most enduring of human emotions. Children all gone, they sit down to view the descending sun, uncommunicative, looking consciously or unconsciously for the day when fate may intervene. The conflict is over, but there has been so much bitterness that the wound, like an old ulcer, will not heal.

The doctor may have all the facts but there is nothing he can do except to make the declining years less sleepless, which he does without asking any questions. After one or the other dies he sees in the face of the remaining partner a confirmation of his diagnosis. The recollection of what I have seen makes me sick. A rivulet in the beginning becomes a torrent no doctor can stay, and it flows on to the end.

One such case came to my attention. A mother's boy became unmanageable and the father, at the end of his patience, handed the boy a deed to a valuable farm and proceeded then and there to give him a decided beating, ending by warning him never to show his face at home again. The pity of this was its needlessness. The parents were honorable people. The son, like his father, was of a high type, and energetic and stubborn. The boy just wanted speed, the order of the day, but the father was not yet attuned to the smell of gasoline, and not having gone along with the boy, he did not understand. Neither did the mother understand, but she had full faith that what the son did must be right, a faith which of course she had never accorded the boy's father. Any one can write the sequel. The farm was soon lost, and the boy ended in a criminal career.

The mother had full faith that he was falsely convicted and continued to live with the father in armed neutrality. The mother got indigestion and could not sleep. It was my job to cure her. Too late! They should have come to me twenty-five years before. I could have told the father that unless he whispered to mama about the garden gate, the baby boy would do so and papa would be left out in the cold.

Why criminals develop in excellent Christian families sometimes puzzles the whole community—except of course the old doctor—and has been referred to in a previous chapter. Tragic things these, but they are inevitable. We are pagans still, trying to act as Christians because no one has told us the truth. The judge tells us that ignorance of the law excuses no man. This never seemed to me to be just. The judge should imprison those who disseminate knowledge which is not true, at least no longer true. They are the guilty parties.

Seldom is the picture so clear. Usually the misunderstanding smolders and, unnoticed by both husband and wife, a division occurs. The father becomes set up as a miserly old cuss and his demise is impatiently awaited, silently by mother, vocally by the boy. Papa knows that he is in bad with his family but the cause seldom reaches the level of his consciousness. Hence he rarely becomes a problem to his doctor, except as the doctor is exasperated when he sees the look of joy on the faces of those who will soon be advised that father's end is near. I often wonder what people would think if they appreciated how much a doctor can read out of a death bed sentence.

Certainly, one sees children solicitous for the welfare of the parents to the end. The hope I dare say of most old people, as they approach the end, is that their final look at the world may encompass their children at the bedside. Every observant person knows that this is so, yet no one tells them facts in the morning of life. Fifty years ago it was the common lot of aged parents to be cared for by their children. It would have been a public disgrace, even if affection did not prompt it, if it were otherwise.

The scene is changing. With our modern set-up, old people are in the way. Their memories deal with things of the past and they may break into speech at the most inopportune times. The complexity of tools which decorate the modern dinner table is too much for the old people to solve. They attack a beefsteak or a salad with a knife with the vigor of yore, unmindful that granddaughter is delicately jiggling hers apart with the dull side of a fork. This produces an embarrassing moment for the young lady because it indicates, without possibility of a doubt, her plebeian origin, even though Grandpa's capacity for solving financial problems in years past has made it possible for granddaughter to pose as one of the elect. It isn't right that Grandpa should be chased out because of the changed situation his own industry has created; but such is fate and he is wise who will bow to fate and retire to his own seclusion. If grandchildren come, they in their first, and he in his second childhood, will find a general companionship. The sex background may separate him from his children, but as the grandchildren have never recognized it and as Grandpa is long past it, they come to be companions. Grandpa dies in this memory, and the children live in it.

In years gone by it was a matter of grave concern to all couples to provide for old age in order that they might not be dependent on their children. No single factor did more to keep up the teamwork despite intermittent jars. But

things do change. Now in this great day of enlightenment
we accept the More Abundant Life in our old age and charge
the bill in the form of added taxes to the children and the
grandchildren. I can envisage our descendants fifty years
from now working on our monuments with a sledge hammer,
because we took a joyous ride at their expense.

There is yet a beautiful picture to be presented which
is found more commonly than one would think. The madonna and child have been presented on canvas and in
song, but the other end of the line, old age, has not been
adequately presented. Cares and conflicts of life are past.
Which one of the wedding day the two have become has
been long since decided, albeit not always as it seems. Usually
papa seems the boss and pulls the wagon but mama holds
the lines. They walk again the primrose path together. We
wise doctors know that they lean again over the garden
gate. Serene old couples are an ever interesting subject for
study. We may not be able to say just what binds until one
of them dies.

Sure, the papers are filled with pictures of people who
have been married for fifty years. Well, what of it? Is there
nothing else of interest that has transpired during those
fifty years?

There is always something to make us doctors mad. I am
filled with exasperation when whole pages are devoted to the
divorce proceedings of a pair who never knew the meaning
of marriage, while somewhere in a corner one sees a little
notice that Mr. Doe died after a short illness. This takes
five lines. Following this we are informed that Mrs. Doe died
the day of Mr. Doe's funeral. The press has at least the
decency not to state the cause of death. The autopsy shows
nothing. The doctor fills out the death certificate as death
due to infirmities of old age, or hypostatic pneumonia, if
necessary to satisfy the Board of Health, which means, if it
means anything, that the heart just slowed, resulting in the
accumulation of blood in the dependent part of the lungs.
Of course, I am aware that such a statement does not make
sense but neither do the autopsies. But the doctor knows

that there was an infinitely fine love that bound them together and that when this was broken by death, they both fell. Such observations on the part of a pathologist would sound silly, but the old doctor wonders if society is not missing an infinitely fine message.

For example, a recent press despatch gives the following: "Fred Harris Steers, 79, told friends during his wife's funeral service that he wished he could join her in death. Less than an hour later, as he stood at the grave side, he collapsed and died."

How stupid of society not to see in these events a story to inspire the weary. This is not an uncommon occurrence. A biography is demanded. What if we knew the life history of both? We old doctors see much of it and can spell the rest, but there is much we must leave untold. Society sees only sex, unmindful that there is something infinitely finer which binds these old people. But it is a tie forged in the furnace of tolerance, over the period of a lifetime.

Just recently I saw a sight that nearly made me shriek with glee. We had a little old lady in the hospital, the outcome of whose illness had been in doubt. But on this day her husband, one of the unsung big men, was taking her for a walk down the hospital hall. She was taking little, short, uncertain steps, leaning heavily on her husband, himself none too certain because of advancing years. The eyes of both were beaming with an expression beyond the power of words to describe. Surely, they were going down to the garden gate again, but it was a spiritual garden gate they envisaged. It is not a silly old doctor penning these lines. These are things any one can see in infinite variety if he would but look. Neither art nor science can define them. For husband and wife to reach that state is worth a lifetime of toil, and that is just what it takes. They are tasting paradise, and it is a paradise earned.

Yet such scenes are sufficiently common to permit us to view the picture in the abstract. Laboring together for fifty years, proving first of all that matrimony can be made holy. Making serene old age possible through years of common interest, through toil and frugality. To complete the ideal picture, there should be children to see grandpa and grandma, each generation adding stature to the preceding one. A father's look at his own children is suffused more or less by the sex idea, but the grandchildren are not touched by it, and the aged look at them with a new light. Do not be annoyed at an old person for recalling these scenes; he relives them every day. A little scrawled letter perhaps is enough to bring forth an ecstasy of delight. Those things do not just come, they must be earned by the cooperation of character and intelligence.

Unhappily such serene scenes may cover painful memories. Perhaps mother has an old school book with the simple words, "Mary Doe," scribbled on the front page, which she has treasured for half a century. An endless variety of possibilities present themselves. Yet such griefs as these only bind the parents more closely together. The possibilities of such tragedies have been vastly reduced by the achievements of medical science. Neither diphtheria nor typhoid fever now threaten. Nothing tries the old doctor's composure more than to have a mother recall that forty years ago we two sat beside the little Mary of the school books. She loves that old doctor for doing his best. But the old doctor is thinking it would have been possible, with our modern advancement in medical science, to have sent Mary back to school with that little book. Recalling such things, I sometimes feel that the old rule of three score years and ten as the limit of life should be rigidly enforced against the old doctor. Such scenes blot out what little joy he might have in recalling lives saved, or professional honors attained, for after all life in the end is what one thinks it is.

When one observes old couples gradually fading into the beyond, with nothing to bind them but that fine sentiment which seems to be but a return of the love of a child, he is visualizing the highest state of which the human is capable. No wonder many noble men, observant of the translation, and ignorant of biology and physics, have preferred to think of the resurrection as wholly spiritual. My father's heaven was infinitely more vast than human conception. It was not necessary for him to think of God as somebody in the shape of man seated somewhere on a throne. Is it not far nobler to think of an all-pervading spirit, the author of all laws, laws perpetual and unchanging, and uninfluenced by the wails of humanity? Father lived without fear, firm in the belief that if he did the best he could he would receive whatever his efforts merited, and he died unafraid in that belief.

Without such faith, how could a parent find life endurable after a blood clot had taken his child in the flash of an eye? Did God fix that clot in that particular child's vein just to punish the parents for some dereliction? No. Did he think so, he would curse God and die. The laws governing the formation of clots in inflamed veins have been operative in all the human race from the beginning of time, were not fashioned as a punishment for anyone, and all the prayers ever uttered will not halt the operation of those laws. Perhaps some day, some time, some one will find the secret of imperfect clot formations and the terrible untamed thromboses will be no more. My old ears still ring with the intonation over a child dead with diphtheria: "The Lord giveth, the Lord taketh away." It was supposed to lessen the grief of the parents, but the parents grieved on. The death of a child produces a wound that time does not heal. Ministers believe, or at least teach, that faith and prayers lessen the pain of a great loss. As a doctor I do not believe it; as a father I know it is not so.

After twenty centuries of futile prayer Klebs found the diphtheria bacillus, Loeffler proved it to be the cause of diphtheria and Behring found a serum that banished the disease from the earth. My clerical friends tell me that these men were the instruments through which the prayers were answered. Maybe so. Granting all that, it was through the instruments of earnest men's minds imbued with the single desire of saving suffering that the results came about.

Considering what has been achieved, perhaps other men, by examining the causes of hate in the world, might find some point of view which will eliminate war. One would think that after twenty centuries of futile praying for the brotherhood of man, and finding all nations fighting, or busily engaged in polishing their artillery, they would be hunting for a Behring to make a serum that would cure the mess.

I have said before, and I pridefully repeat, that the mouthings sent forth in time of war, pleading for the destruction of the sons of the mothers of the opposing side, never found voice in a doctor's throat.

One of my ancestors was burned at the stake because of a difference of opinion as to the matter of baptism. It seems to me that when people are found differing over such a question, it is time to ask what difference does it make? Is not there a common factor in which everyone can agree? All peoples of all nations have children, and no one wants to see their sons butchered in the name of liberty, democracy, or menaced foreign trade, or in response to the prayers of the opposing party. To hear the mouthings of a war lord: "God is on our side" is enough to make agnostics of us all.

Everyone can agree on the fundamental fact of love for the child, if it exists. If we believe that the child at our knee was sent to save the world we can comprehend the priceless love that child offers us and cease to hate our neighbors because they entertain views, or prejudices, differing slightly from our own. I believe saying "boo" to a baby on the floor is the first step toward international peace. Take him on your lap and have him listen to the radio. Show him the stars. Tell him they are x millions of miles away, tell him there is a voice infinitely more distant which will be talking to him all his life, call it what he will. To that child my words will be unmeaning prattle, as his "da-da" is to me. Yet with all my knowledge of science and all the philosophy of the years, I still am equal to the child as far as understanding life is concerned. Of all strange scenes it seems to me most strange that a mite of a child, viewing a grandpa's visage in the fashioning of which nature has been most unkind, will unhesitatingly thrust out his arms in proffered love.

Is it too much therefore to dream that the Child in the Virgin's arms is but symbolical of the child at our knee who has come to save the world? May we not interpret the immaculate conception as meaning that the passion of the beast has been replaced by something finer? What has belief got to do with it? We must begin by admitting that all the fool things we have been doing in the name of the Lord have been futile. We have insisted on applying our own interpretation.

Be this as it may, the finer things in life are in the ascendency, in spite of our leaders. Passion as the end and aim of life has gone out of the picture. Now, in our best circles, if any one has a concubine he keeps it hidden. In years gone by he bragged about how many he had. Shame is the first step toward reform, and we should be ashamed that such things are contained in the literature we place before our children, and even tolerated when broadcast from our pulpits. As usual, civil and ecclesiastical law trails the upward trend of the human heart. It is necessary for the common people to hoist the stop sign. We doctors know the answer: Paradise lies ahead when love for the child, the smile of the child, compel the parents to hold up a warning hand against the lust of the past.

The doctor hears the first wail of the newborn babe and he hears the death rattle after consciousness has left the body forever. In between, life is the individual's, to make of it what he will. Only his own effort counts. That is what the doctor learns. There are recorded in his memory, if not in his case books, all his errors as well as his achievements. These are the facts. It would add greatly to the advancement of the human race if every one had to face his doings all put down in indelible ink.

If every one had to leave behind him, as I shall do, records of countless things done both good and bad, there would be a bowing of the soul to the inevitable. There is one large placard written before all of us: "Our best was not good enough."

May I add one quotation from Booth Tarkington: "It is love in old age, no longer blind, that is true love. For love's highest intensity doesn't necessarily mean its highest quality. Glamor and jealousy are gone; and the ardent caress, no longer needed, is valueless compared to the reassuring touch of a trembling hand. Passers-by commonly see little beauty in the embrace of young lovers on a park bench, but the understanding smile of an old wife to her husband is one of the loveliest things in the world."

I repeat the tragedy of life lies in the fact that, despite the teachings of our youth, our best is not good enough. Our best intentions fall before the inexorable laws of nature. When I was a mere boy, age fourteen to be exact, I read the following lines which I carefully copied: "What civilization has done: It has produced and protected thousands of women who from the cradle to the grave are happy; who are never insecure and never oppressed, never harassed (save perhaps by the sleep of death among the objects of love) and never to the extremity of old age unloved." Some blatant old ass, nameless here, had said these words. If he knew anything, he must have known that no one can do this for posterity. We can do our best to achieve it for our children, but things beyond our control bring grief to them and through them to us.

Whatever may have been the trials and strifes of life, everything is changed when the ferryman on the River Styx beckons. Our minds go back unbidden to the children the kind fates have given us. They are all that matter now. Success and failure in the battle of life blur into a forgotten picture, and here all men, for once equal as saint and sinner, prince and pauper, prepare to lay themselves upon the couch of death. Our best was not good enough, but in the final hour our children give us credit for having done our best. What else matters?

As I pen these lines, seated beneath the portrait of my lamented Agnes, I hear the faint strains of the radio from an unknown station: "Nearer my Girl to thee, nearer to thee—

Though like the wanderer the sun goes down, Yet in my dreams I'm nearer my Girl to thee—" And as I look out of my window and see the stars uncounted light years away, fifty years of science become as naught and I just know somewhere I shall meet my girl again.